Formal Methods for
CONCURRENCY

Dedicated to my father, Sydney Fencott (1924-1993)

Formal Methods for
CONCURRENCY

CLIVE FENCOTT

School of Computing and Mathematics
University of Teesside

INTERNATIONAL THOMSON COMPUTER PRESS
I ⓉP An International Thomson Publishing Company

London • Bonn • Boston • Johannesburg • Madrid • Melbourne • Mexico City • New York • Paris
Singapore • Tokyo • Toronto • Albany, NY • Belmont, CA • Cincinnati, OH • Detroit, MI

Formal Methods for Concurrency

Copyright © 1996 Clive Fencott

I ⓉP   A division of International Thomson Publishing Inc.
The ITP logo is a trademark under licence

British Library Cataloguing-in-Publication Data
A catalogue record for this book is available from the British Library

Library of Congress Cataloging-in-Publication Data
A catalog record for this book is available from the Library of Congress

First printed 1996

Commissioning Editor: Samantha Whittaker
Cover Designed by Button Eventures
Printed in the UK by Cambridge University Press

ISBN 1-85032-173-6

International Thomson Computer Press
Berkshire House
High Holborn
London WC1V 7AA
UK

International Thomson Computer Press
20 Park Plaza
14th Floor
Boston MA 02116
USA

http://www.thomson.com/itcp.html

Imprints of International Thomson Publishing

Contents

Preface

Aims and intended audience

The aim of this book is to provide a practical introduction to the formal specification of concurrent and real-time systems. It is intended for those with some basic knowledge or experience of computing but does not assume knowledge of the particular problems of concurrent and real-time systems or of programming languages for them. However, there is evidence to suggest that the material in this book does provide a good introduction to the field in general. The book assumes some familiarity with discrete mathematics, e.g. basic logic and set theory, gained possibly as a result of having taken an introductory course in a formal description technique such as Z or VDM [Dil94, Jon90]. The book is thus not suitable as an introductory text in formal methods. However, the formal theories involved are developed only as far as is necessary to understand and use the languages presented but not to the extent of a detailed theoretical exposition. This allows the emphasis of the book to be quite definitely practical and to concentrate on the formal modelling of concurrent and real-time systems supported by formal reasoning where appropriate and useful. For a full treatment of the theory of a particular language the reader will be directed towards appropriate further reading at the end of each chapter. The book makes no attempt to be a definitive reader in the field but rather attempts to help endow the reader with the necessary skills and knowledge to enable them to go on to develop their own appropriate skills and specialisms. It is my hope that the book will be of use both as a textbook to support Honours and MSc level courses and as an introduction for professionals wishing to expand their knowledge.

Approach

There are many formal methods available for specifying concurrent and real-time systems but I have chosen to concentrate on one group of languages based on Robin Milner's Calculus of Communicating Systems (CCS) [Mil89]. There are a variety of reasons for this:

- I have found CCS to be a very effective basis for teaching formal approaches to concurrency. Indeed, students have often commented that they *quite like* it and enjoy working with it.

- CCS has a particularly concise and intuitive syntax combined with a formal yet quite straightforward semantics which is a major contributing factor to the point made above.

- The basic language of CCS can be developed quite easily in a variety of ways so as to become applicable to a wide range of concurrent and real-time problem domains.

- There is good tool support for CCS via the Edinburgh Concurrency Workbench (CWB) [Mol92].

- Many of the skills learnt through using this book will be transferable or at least easily adaptable to other formalisms for concurrency.

The Laboratory for the Foundations of Computer Science (LFCS) at the University of Edinburgh is the home of CCS and Milner's book is generally taken to be the de facto CCS standard. I have tried to adhere to the standard as much as possible but experience has shown that it is best to work towards some aspects of it rather than start out with them. For this reason I have taken the liberty of deviating from the standard where I have found it beneficial for educational reasons. In particular I will note the following:

- The relabelling operator is introduced in chapter 4, after the other operators in the language, so as to simplify the introductory chapters.

- Indexed sums are only introduced in chapter 5 when they are unavoidable.

- I defined a version of Synchronous CCS (SCCS) which I have called SCCS* which uses bags and associated operations rather than a commutative group to define concurrent actions. I believe this approach to be more readily understandable by the expected readers of this book.

- The modal μ-calculus is very difficult for students to master and exploit and I introduce the subject of logics for CCS by way of a fairly standard branching time temporal logic whose definition makes use of notations familiar to those with a grounding in Z or VDM.

Wherever possible I have indicated which are the standard presentations of particular aspects of CCS both at the end of the appropriate chapter and in the Reference Manual in Appendix B.

Experience at Teesside in teaching formal methods, in general, has taught us that building formal specifications, using abstraction appropriately, and formal reasoning are all difficult skills to master. Trying to teach all three at the same time can be very confusing for students and this book therefore staggers their introduction in the order listed above, with most of the book devoted to the formal modelling of systems. In order to make this part of the book more effective I have also attempted to make use of larger examples of the type which are more likely to be encountered in the real world. For this reason they are often somewhat messy and do not sit so elegantly on the page as the more academic problems which so often inhabit textbooks.

For similar reasons, my approach to building specifications is a pragmatic one. I do not believe that anyone solves such problems by the simple process of top-down decomposition and stepwise refinement. I firmly believe in specification re-use, prototyping, and educated guesses, etc. along with anything else which helps to solve the problem at hand. For this reason I am also a great believer in the use of diagramming techniques and structured methods particularly as analysis techniques. Chapter 14 addresses this subject specifically.

We have found that students who use CWB as part of their studies learn far more effectively than those for whom the whole thing is very much a paper and pencil exercise. I strongly recommend that students use CWB in conjunction with this book. Chapter 13 on tool support introduces this tool and some of its uses. Wherever possible, I have used CWB to verify all the examples and analyses used in this book.

Using the book

The book is based around a number of modules on formal methods for concurrency given over a period of five years to second and final year Computer Science and Software Engineering undergraduates as well as MSc Software Engineering students. This means that, to date, some seven or eight hundred students have been given various sections of the book in various versions as course notes. The current version is presented in a way which seems to best suit students.

The book starts with a general introductory chapter which is followed by a number of larger sections of which the first is concerned with formal languages for building concurrent and real-time specifications and their application. Part One starts by introducing CCS and its semantics and in succeeding chapters goes on to discuss various extensions to the language which allow data and time in particular to be modelled explicitly. The second part of the book contains four chapters devoted to reasoning formally about the type of specifications introduced in the first part. The techniques discussed include equivalences for processes, equational reasoning, and temporal logic. The third part of the book contains three chapters which consider broader issues such as tool support, methods integration, and implementation. The final part contains solutions to many of the exercises, Appendix A, and a Reference Manual, Appendix B, where all the main sets of definitions are systematically gathered together for ease of reference.

It is possible to adopt various routes through the book. For a classic CCS course of study chapters 1–5 and 9–11 are most suitable. A practical introduction to the formal specification of concurrent and real-time systems can be found by following chapters 1–8. Software Engineering undergraduates at Teesside currently take a one semester course based around 1–6 in the second year and a further one semester course, entitled Safety and Formalism, in the final year which makes use of chapters 11 and 12 in particular. All routes should make use of Part III for student centred background study.

Acknowledgements

Of course many people have given invaluable assistance to me in writing this book. I started to learn CCS in the summer of 1989 when Robin Milner's book came out and I became fascinated by this treatment of concurrency. I find his book a continuing source of reference and discovery. I am also indebted to the team at Edinburgh who presented the week-long CCS course at the university in the autumn of that year. The team included David Walker, Colin Sterling, Kevin Mitchell, and Jo Blishen and it was their thorough and professional presentation that enabled me to begin teaching the subject for the first time in January 1990.

A number of people have read sections of the book and I am indebted to them for their time and effort. George Clelland, Glen Bruns, and a third anonymous person, all from LFCS, read versions of the book and made invaluable comments both on technical points and on matters of presentation and I am very grateful to them. Mark Woodman, of the Open University, commented with great insight on the nature of the book and its intended audience, as well as on technical matters. M. Holcombe and Dominic Stanyer, both of the University of Sheffield, also read and commented on the book. I would particularly like to thank the latter who, at the time, was a final year undergraduate. His comments were particularly useful because as a 'user' his concerns were rather different, and rather more immediate, than those of the academics. I would encourage publishers to solicit student's views on prospective text books as a matter of course in future.

Various colleagues at the University of Teesside have been of great help and I would in particular like to mention two. Andy Galloway not only read much of the book as an MSc student and later a research assistant but also debated many technical points with me over the years. Eudes Diemoz read many chapters of the book in great detail with a particular concern for consistency as well as accuracy. He now teaches the second year

Software Engineering course, mentioned above, and has made many more constructive observations as a result.

I would particularly like to thank all the students on the BSc Computer Science, BSc Software Engineering and MSc Software Engineering courses who edited and commented upon earlier versions of the book that they received as course notes. Without their help and patience I would not have learned how to teach CCS or to write this book. I would be very well satisfied if they gained as much from the courses as I did.

Of course, any remaining errors of any sort are mine and I take full responsibility for them.

Many people at Teesside have been a source of encouragement and motivation in bringing this book to fruition and I would particularly like to thank Bill Stoddart and Derek Simpson as well as all the others too numerous to mention by name.

I cannot conclude my acknowledgements without thanking my partner Anne and our son Robin for their help, patience, encouragement, senses of humour, and just generally putting up with me. Anne, in particular, spent a great deal of time constructing the index for me.

I dedicate this book to my father who would have loved to work with computers and mathematics but never got the chance.

1

Introduction to concurrency

In this chapter we will introduce some of the basic concepts of computer-based systems which involve concurrency, communication and real-time. We also identify important types of properties which we may or may not wish such systems to possess. The intention is that the reader will have a general idea of the nature of such systems and their uses and applications as well as some idea of the problems involved in specifying and reasoning about them. In addition, the aim, in this chapter, is to begin to demonstrate the role formal methods might play in the development of such systems. and thus show how formal methods can aid in the implementation of concurrent systems that meet the requirements laid down for them. We will delay the introduction of formal notations until the next chapter when we will look afresh at some of the concepts introduced in the present chapter. It will not be until the third chapter that our first full formal method for concurrency is introduced.

1.1 What is concurrency?

In the early years of digital computers almost all machines were based on the von Neumann architecture and involved a single processor executing a program which consisted of a single sequence of statements with some ability to loop back through the program. Early application areas were concerned with numerical computation or commercial data processing and all operations were in batch mode. You started a program and waited until it had finished. There was little or no interaction and no real-time considerations. Computers did not control things but performed difficult or repetitive calculations. The situation is very different now with computers and microprocessors being used to control all sorts of devices and machines in all aspects of life. In recent years there has been much interest in systems which involve multiple processors and multiple programs or processes which are to some extent autonomous yet at times need to synchronise or communicate in some manner in order to function effectively. Many of the problems associated with such systems arise through the need to share or compete for limited resources whether they be data or processing resources. Sometimes the correct operation of a system means that we must prevent certain actions occurring simultaneously. Other problems arise as a result of limitations of time on the execution of particular tasks. Such problems are not confined to computer-based systems and occur regularly in everyday life as well as in commerce and industry. Indeed, our first example has nothing to do with computers at all.

Imagine a small restaurant and what has to be done to ensure its successful and safe operation. The restaurant is

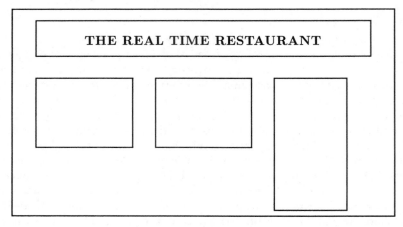

THE REAL TIME RESTAURANT

and it exhibits many of the characteristics of the type of computer-based systems we wish to study. The people that use this restaurant fall, quite naturally, into two categories: those concerned with running the restaurant and those concerned with getting a meal there.

Of course, customers are not at all concerned with the practical problems of preparing and serving their chosen meals. They are simply interested in the dishes being properly cooked and served to them in the expected order with suitable time intervals in between. In this restaurant, as in many others, customers' only way of interacting with the restaurant is by talking to the waiter allotted to their table. They cannot see the food being cooked or know anything about what is going on outside the dining area. Rather they have to give specific instructions to the waiter as to their requirements and trust that he acts on them appropriately. But waiters are not the only people who work in the restaurant, there are cooks, kitchen assistants and so on. The waiters are intermediaries, or communication channels between two separate worlds, the dining room and the kitchen. The waiter writes each table's order on a slip of paper and takes it to the kitchen where the kitchen staff prepare the required meals when they are able to. The waiter then transports the food to the customers. There is no direct contact between kitchen staff and customers, so the channels through which they communicate have to be reliable.

Some communications need not pass information but can be simple acknowledgements. For instance, suppose a customer wishes to pay his or her bill. It is often enough to catch the eye of the waiter who will understand from the situation what is required and return with the bill although no specific request has been made. Elsewhere, another example of communication purely by synchronisation occurs in athletics relay races in which each runner passes a baton to the next runner. No data passes between them but simply permission to run in terms of both synchronising on the act of passing the baton. You might wish to regard the baton as a semaphore which allows the holder to perform some action. Single-track railways are often run on a similar principle by passing a token to the driver whose engine will be the only one allowed on the line as long as the token is in his possession.

Back inside the kitchen there are more complications. It will not be possible to cook each of the dishes one at a time because there will not be enough time to complete them all if there are more than just a few customers. In any case the dishes would spoil by being kept hanging around for hours before they were required. Some things take quite a while to cook so it will be necessary to start their preparation well in advance. However, some things require ingredients from other dishes so you will have to establish some order of events which means everything is ready when it is required. Chefs should also make sure that people have time to eat and enjoy each course and have time for conversation without feeling unduly rushed or made to wait too long in order to start the next. We have to organise the cooking process so that items on the menu are ready in the right order. We should further observe that there should only be an appropriate delay between courses.

This raises various questions. First of all, who is going to be responsible for what dishes? Some sensible division of labour is required. Secondly, the resources available to cook the meal are finite. You only have a small set of cooking pots and utensils. The hob has only a finite number of burners and the oven only has two shelves. It is necessary to find some means of sharing finite resources which allows the successful preparation of all meals. Suppose two chefs need to fry something. Because of heavy business there is only one frying pan and one spatula still serviceable, but each chef needs both to fry successfully. If each chef has one of the required items then they will be stuck with no one being able to fry anything. The criteria for allocating resources may or may not be fair but must be focused on the successful and safe completion of the meal.

We have finally introduced the concept of safety. All the time we are cooking this meal we have to constantly make sure we are working safely.

If we leave the carrots boiling too long they will turn to mush and we will have another soup on the menu. If we leave them boiling even longer then the pan will boil dry and start to burn and we might have a fire. If we turn on one of the gas burners but fail to light it successfully we could eventually cause an explosion. We must not only ensure the meal is cooked to the standards demanded by our guests but we must also ensure that the whole process is carried out maintaining the safety of our guests, ourselves, the building, and the equipment. To ensure this we have to constantly monitor the state of the various things we are cooking as well as the state of the equipment we are using to cook them. We will not only be looking to see if they are cooked yet but that they are being cooked safely. If care is not taken accidents could happen to chefs or the other staff which might interrupt the successful completion of the meal. A serious accident could mean dashing someone to hospital and disrupting the smooth running of the kitchen or even evacuating the whole restaurant.

We have introduced a number of important concepts and it is worthwhile to identify them before we go any further. First of all we introduced the notion of ordering of events. Some things may be allowed to happen at the same time or *concurrently* while others must happen in a predetermined order or *sequentially*. We call such situations the *temporal ordering* of events and we will call systems with these types of properties *concurrent systems* and *sequential systems* respectively. Very often the ability to proceed with an activity will depend on some other activity being completed or having reached a suitable stage. We cannot make meringue until the eggs and sugar have been whisked and the oven is at the right temperature. We must make sure all these events *synchronise* or *communicate* appropriately. Indeed, many of the real problems in building concurrent systems are to do with maintaining correct communications between processes. Two personal computers on the same desk running at the same time are certainly concurrent but there is no problem at all unless they have to communicate with each other. Communication and concurrency are largely inseparable and many of our early examples in chapter 2 will seem more to do with communication than concurrency for this very reason.

We will not on the whole use the term 'parallel' in this book because it has a rather different connotation in computer science and refers rather to algorithms which solve a particular problem by breaking it down into a number of simpler problems and solving these simultaneously. This book does not deal with these kinds of issues.

Some events must not only happen in the correct order but must also be carefully timed. The meringue must be in the oven for a specific amount of time if it is to be properly cooked while we have far greater leeway with meat and roast potatoes although they too will be spoiled if we leave them in for too long. In some situations we will need to be specific about the passage of time while in others the correct ordering of events will be sufficient.

The staff and the customers have different views of all this activity. The latter only want to know about the finished dishes as they appear from the kitchen. Are they well cooked and are they arriving as expected? The manager may well visit the kitchen from time to time to get a status report but will not want to know everything that is going on. The cooks are concerned about the correct functioning of the whole cooking process up until the moment when the dishes are ready to be carried out to the dining room. They will obviously be interested to receive comments and criticisms, if necessary, but will not help to eat the meal nor will they even see this happening because they will be too busy getting the next courses ready. To the guests the kitchen is a closed world whose internal activities only become apparent when food is carried out to their table. The reverse is true of the two cooks. We will categorise some events as observable and some as silent or internal. These categorisations will often depend on which view of the system we are choosing to take. For instance, breaking an egg into a frying pan should not be an observable event for a customer but must be for the chef about to do the frying.

If we are not careful about the way we allocate finite resources we might slow down the task at hand or in some cases cause activity to cease altogether. Arguing about who gets the frying pan and the spatula at the same time might cause you to waste valuable time but if you do not settle the argument somehow then all useful activity will cease and the meal will never be served. We will call such situations *deadlocks*. It is possible to get round the problem by attaching the spatula to the frying pan by a piece of string and forcing chefs to pick up both or none at all. Frying thus becomes a mutually exclusive action: only one chef can fry at a time. Of course, persuading the management to invest in more frying pans and spatulas would be a better long-term solution.

In the original situation another problem may arise. Both chefs holding a single frying implement agree to swap the utensil they are holding. Now one has the frying pan instead of the spatula and the other has the spatula instead of the frying pan and we are no nearer a solution to our problem. Worse, if they continue to use this attempted solution to the problem they will no longer be in a deadlock but in a so-called *livelock* situation and doing a lot of work but never anything useful.

The task we have looked at really entails the control of a complex set of interacting activities, generally known as *process control*. Very often such systems are also subject to unexpected commands or *interrupts* from the outside world which the system has no control over. Imagine some important customers arrive earlier than they have booked and demand dinner at twelve o'clock instead of one o'clock or that they are all vegetarian and phone ahead an hour before lunch to make sure they get what they want. The reputation of the restaurant demands that staff have to find some way of responding appropriately to such external requests. We will call these systems *real-time* systems. Very often the notion of *safety* is also of great importance and we will also call such systems *safety-critical* or *safety-related* systems where a malfunctioning could cause loss of life or other catastrophes.

In this section we have introduced some of the basic concepts of concurrent systems in the context of an application with little or nothing to do with computers although the oven might have had a microprocessor-based timer which could have made our task easier. It could have made our life more difficult if we did not understand it well enough to trust it. Trust, or *assurance* as it is often referred to in this context, is an important concept that will appear more and more often in the development of computer-based systems of all types. In the next section we will look at a computer-based system which embodies many of the features we introduced in the context of cooking a meal as well as some important new concepts.

1.2 An automated transit system

We can illustrate the concepts we identified in the previous section by looking at a description of a mass transit system which embodies many of the concepts introduced just now in the kitchen. The system is a genuine example of a real-time, concurrent system which relies heavily on computers for its safe and effective operation. We will imagine the sytem is up and running and its design and documentation are available to us for study. This means that we can gain a clearer insight into the problems of designing and operating such systems before we begin the study of formal languages to enable us to model and reason about abstract models of such systems.

A fully automated monorail train operates between a number of stations in a town. The trains will be fully automated and equipped with their own control system to direct and monitor train acceleration, deceleration, stopping patterns, door opening and closing, lighting, climate control and announcements to passengers. A system manager can override the automatic control in an emergency.

There are between one and five trains operating at any one time.

Each train has 11 buttons inside, one for each station and one for the next stop. There are also emergency stop buttons inside each train.

The time interval (INTERVAL) between trains will be adjustable, as will the minimum wait time (WAITTIME) for a passenger. All times are measured in minutes.

The route forms a loop with trains running clockwise round it. A train will stop at a station if someone on the train has pressed the appropriate station number or the next-stop button. The train will also stop if a person on the station has pressed the stop button.

An automatic message system will inform passengers on the stations of the time before the next train.

Each train will have four separate braking systems:

1. phase 1: brakes for general speed regulation

2. phase 2: brakes for stopping

3. phase 3: emergency brakes

4. phase 4: safety brakes, for extra security at stations

Each train has doors on both sides controlled separately. The computer has an updatable record of each station and the relevant door or doors to open.

When the train has stopped at a station and the safety brake has been applied, the doors will open. A timer will be activated to define the minimum time before the doors will be closed. Doors will not close if obstructed or if passengers are still boarding or alighting.

If there are no passengers or outstanding requests then a train will wait at the station. If the next train approaches the station then the waiting train will depart for the next station. Only one train may wait at a station at the same time.

There are sensors on the track to signify the approaching station and to signify if there is a train waiting in the station. If there is a train already waiting then the arriving train must wait until the other has left.

Passengers may purchase five forms of tickets:

1. single journey

2. 10 journeys

3. monthly

4. quarterly

5. yearly

A journey may be of any duration. Each passenger inserts a ticket into a machine by the door of a train. The ticket will be retained if it has expired and a suitable message will be displayed by the machine. For all tickets except single journeys the system will inform the passengers when their tickets are used and about to expire.

In the event of the trains currently in use becoming very busy the system should be able to bring another train into the system from the sidings. Trains may be removed in a similar manner if the demand slackens.

For monitoring and recording purposes each day is divided into eight periods of 2 hours from 6 a.m. to 10 p.m. An updatable file should record the number of trains used in each time period, so that the scheduling of trains may automatically be optimised.

A sensor system (sensors every 20 metres) will detect obstructions on the line. A train will apply the emergency brakes if an obstruction is detected within X metres and the speed is above Y kilometres per hour, based on the calculation: emergency brakes needed if $X < 2Y$. Otherwise the phase 2 brakes should be applied. When the train has stopped the maintenance department should be informed. The system should inform passengers on the next platform and on the train and the following train.

The system should record the service records of all trains and sensors. Each train should be inspected monthly and each sensor tested automatically at the start of each day and manually each week. Inspection and fault logs should be entered into the system.

Monthly and yearly reports are required for customer usage, ticket purchases, efficiency, maintenance and servicing.

It is obvious that this system exhibits many of the features of real-time systems that we have already talked about. The concept of safety should loom large in any consideration of the system. It is certainly a real-time system which must respond quickly and appropriately to events in its environment. These events might be passengers requesting trains, faults and problems on the line, and so on. There are a number of processes running concurrently and much communication between processes. Certainly the temporal ordering of events is important and in some cases the actual time and duration of events are critical.

Resources are finite. Each station can hold only one train at a time. Sections of track can in theory hold more than one train at a time but for safety reasons must never be allowed to do so. The physical resources of the system do not prevent this situation happening, which means that the systems controlling the movement of trains must do so. Such properties are invariants of the system which must always be true whatever state the system may evolve to.

In addition there are more conventional computational aspects to the system such as the database holding timetable information and generating reports. Other aspects such as the calculation of which brakes to apply in the event of an obstruction are conventional in character but must be carried out and responded to in time for the appropriate action to be taken. Real-time systems may thus also be concerned with more conventional computational problems such as data-processing and numerical calculation.

1.3 Summary and further reading

The transit system described above is a large system and required a large and detailed specification. It is not our intention to develop this example in detail in this book but to equip the reader with notations, methods and skills to enable him or her to tackle such a problem in a formal manner. Towards the end of the book we will return to this example and illustrate how formal methods might be used in a practical way to help in its construction. As the formal languages are developed within the book you will notice exercises which focus on aspects of both the systems described in this introductory chapter.

From the various discussions in this chapter we can formulate a profile of the kinds of expressive capabilities we require of a language for abstract modelling of concurrent systems. In a programming language such as Pascal [Gar86], the organisation of the flow of control within a program is achieved by means of statements constructed from

```
A;B
IF A THEN B ELSE C
WHILE A DO B
```

Statements constructed in this manner give us the notions of sequence, choice, and repetition. What is missing and what we need to add for systems involving concurrency is the idea of two or more processes running in parallel with the possibility of their having to synchronise or cooperate at various points in their operation. One solution is to add to the language a statement of the form

```
A PAR B
```

which we take to mean that A and B are both operational at the same time. There are various ways of achieving this and an introduction to programming languages which have this capability can be found in [BW90]. That book is also a good introduction to real-time computing in general but does not cover formal methods.

In formal description languages such as Z [Dil94] and VDM [Jon90] we are particularly concerned with statements which say what is to be true about a system and not necessarily with the sequencing of individual actions. Sequencing of actions is not primitive in such languages but can be achieved by monitoring the state of the system's global variables and by the use of variables as state indicators.

Languages such as Z and VDM are particularly suited to the specification of information systems and the data they process. Many of the additional problems concerned with concurrent and distributed systems are not to do with the particular information processed by the system but with maintaining correct communications and synchronisations between processes.

Before moving on to the next chapter and starting to introduce the formal methods themselves it is worthwhile stating some of the general properties we require of a *useful* specification language.

Requirements of a concurrent specification language

- The language should allow us to focus naturally on the behavioural properties of systems.

- Such a language should have a simple yet expressive syntax. In other words there should be a small but useful set of operators and means of combining them into processes or agents which are intuitively useful to the problems at hand.

- We are interested in *formal* specification languages and hence require that our language has a precise semantics which in addition we require to be useful in the process of understanding and modelling the systems we wish to specify.

- The language should be sufficiently abstract to allow systems to be modelled without premature regard to unnecessary implementation details.

- As the requirements arise the language must also allow us to explicitly specify timing and data constraints.

- Finally, we need a language which permits formal reasoning about properties of our specifications with only a reasonable expenditure of time, brainpower, and nervous energy.

As we proceed through the book we will meet a number of formal specification languages for concurrent and real-time systems and bear these criteria in mind. In the next chapter we will begin to introduce a formal specification language capable of modelling some important aspects of real-time systems.

I

Building Specifications

A language for concurrency

In this chapter we begin the study of a basic formal language for concurrency via a series of small but practical examples such as simple buffers, semaphores, and shared resources. These examples will relate our studies to some of the concepts introduced in the previous chapter. We then investigate a method for combining simple systems into more complex ones. The language is the Calculus of Communicating Systems [Mil89], referred to as CCS hereafter, which consists of a small but expressive set of operators for choice, sequence, parallel composition, and restriction. Having introduced the language, a formal syntax is defined and a larger example is studied. Throughout the chapter, reference is made to the way in which specifications can be thought about and constructed in the hope that the reader's basic intuitions concerning the practical use of such languages will begin to develop. We will not formally define the semantics of the language in this chapter but will suggest a technique for informally investigating the behaviour of the examples introduced. Finally, we will outline some simple, but effective, development strategies for building specifications in CCS.

2.1 Calculus of Communicating Systems

We shall begin by defining a language based purely on synchronised communication, without the notions of values and value passing. Later we will see that this language is sufficient to represent value passing as well. We are thus considering only the flow of control within a system and not the data which may be passed around or operated upon. At this stage we will not consider the timed aspects of systems but will put this off until a later chapter.

First of all, we consider a simple one place buffer or semaphore which we shall represent for the moment by the diagram given by figure 2.1.

This may be interpreted as the process C which has two connections with the outside world which we have labelled in and $\overline{out}$. We will refer

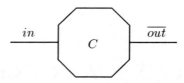

Figure 2.1. *A one-place buffer or semaphore*

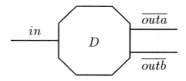

Figure 2.2. *An agent with two outputs*

to these labels as actions and by convention we regard unbarred actions as inputs and barred actions as outputs. Our required behaviour of this process should be that it waits until it receives a communication via the action *in* and then makes a communication via the action $\overline{out}$. Remember that, for the moment, we are not concerning ourselves with the actual data being communicated but simply with the patterns of communications exhibited by the process. Something else to notice about C is that we have not specified the environment in which it exists. We have not said what other process or processes C interacts with. Despite this the diagram gives a picture of the pattern of communication C is capable of.

We now try to identify the behaviour of the process described by figure 2.2. The agent D has one receiving action *in* but two transmitting actions $\overline{outa}$ and $\overline{outb}$. How are we to interpret the order of actions possible for D? Suppose we want D to do nothing until it has received a communication via its action *in* but what then should be the order of its communications via $\overline{outa}$ and $\overline{outb}$? Perhaps both actions take place at once or perhaps one at a time in either order. Or perhaps one at a time in a particular order. A further point to note here is that we have not said what C or D do once they have performed their allotted tasks. Perhaps they just stop or perhaps they return to their initial state and start all over again. It is at this stage that we decide that these diagrams alone are not powerful enough to state clearly the behaviour of particular processes.

Let us return to C and begin to build a language that will allow us to express quite clearly the behaviour we expect of processes. The language we build will consist of a set of operators that model different aspects of the behaviour of processes. Processes, which we will usually call *agents*, in our language will consist of primitive actions built up into patterns of behaviour by means of the operators we define. The simplest agent we can imagine is the agent that can do nothing and we shall represent it by the symbol '**0**'.

The first operator we introduce will allow us to build an agent which is able to perform a sequence of actions and we will use the symbol '.' to represent it. Actions will all be atomic and we shall use the set of names a, b, c, and so on to represent them. We can now represent one of the possible behaviours of the process C by means of the following definition:

$$C_1 \stackrel{\text{def}}{=} in.\overline{out}.\mathbf{0}$$

This says that the agent called C_1 is defined as ($\stackrel{\text{def}}{=}$) the expression $in.\overline{out}.\mathbf{0}$. Informally we can interpret this expression as meaning the process C_1 which waits for an input communication via its action in, after which it outputs a communication via its action $\overline{out}$ and then does nothing. Throughout this book agent names will be upper-case italic letters or strings of characters, the first of which will be an upper-case italic. Action names can be similarly extended but will always start with a lower-case italic.

Another possible interpretation for the process C would be that we wish it to perform the action in followed by the action $\overline{out}$ an unspecified number of times. The expression to represent this behaviour would be

$$C_2 \stackrel{\text{def}}{=} in.\overline{out}.C_2$$

and thus agent definitions may refer to agent constants in their right-hand sides. In this case the agent constant referred to is C_2 itself and the definition is thus a recursive one. Note, however, that each agent constant may be defined once only. In other words, C_2 can have exactly one definition, as given above, for any system in which it occurs.

We return now to the process D and look at the possible behaviours we might wish to attribute to it. Without adding to the language further we could define D by the expression

$$D_1 \stackrel{\text{def}}{=} in.\overline{outa}.\overline{outb}.D_1$$

which is the process which performs the action in followed by the action $\overline{outa}$ followed by the action $\overline{outb}$ and then becomes D_1 again ready to repeat the same sequence of actions. Of course, we could have reversed the order of the outputs. To begin to express other possible behaviours of D we have to introduce other operators. The first of the operators we will introduce will be the operator which allows a choice of next actions and we will use the symbol '+' to designate this operator. We can now define D_2 in the following way:

$$D_2 \stackrel{\text{def}}{=} in.(\overline{outa}.\mathbf{0} + \overline{outb}.\mathbf{0})$$

which defines a process which can first of all communicate via its action *in* and then has a choice of either communicating via $\overline{outa}$ or $\overline{outb}$. After either of these actions the process D_2 becomes inactive. Another possible behaviour for D might be

$$D_3 \stackrel{\text{def}}{=} in.(\overline{outa}.D_3 + \overline{outb}.D_3)$$

which defines the process which behaves initially as above but can repeat this choice of actions as many times as desired. Note that the choice is really between two agents depending on which performs an action first. The choice is not just between actions and so we cannot write

$$\dots \overline{outa} + \overline{outb}.\mathbf{0}$$

In cases such as the above it is the environment which determines which of the actions offered is actually performed.

There are other possible definitions for D which just involve sequence and choice. In the following definition a non-deterministic choice is made when the action *in* is perfomed which results in either $\overline{outa}$ or $\overline{outb}$ being offered as the next action, but not both.

$$D_4 \stackrel{\text{def}}{=} in.\overline{outa}.D_4 + in.\overline{outb}.D_4$$

In this case the environment has only the action *in* to select but this is not enough to determine the state that will be reached as a result. The agent defined as D_4 will thus be able to perform sequences of actions of the following form

$$in.\overline{outa}.in.\overline{outb}.in.\overline{outb}.in.\overline{outa} \dots$$

or

$$in.\overline{outb}.in.\overline{outb}.in.\overline{outa}.in.\overline{outb} \dots$$

or

$$in.\overline{outa}.in.\overline{outa}.in.\overline{outa}.in.\overline{outa} \dots$$

etc.

So far we have considered the behaviour of single processes or agents and have seen that a single diagram may have a number of possible expressions defining it. We would like to be able to have a number of processes running concurrently and interacting with each other. Suppose for example we wanted to have two copies of C; let us re-use the names C_1 and C_2 respectively, communicating with each other so that one copy, C_1, will tell the other, C_2, that it has received a communication. A possible diagram for the system is given in figure 2.3 where C_1 will tell C_2 that it has received a communication and wait for the next. In the meantime C_2 will now be able to communicate this fact to the environment and then return to waiting for C_1 to inform it of the next communication.

Somehow we wish to have a means of defining when two processes may communicate and then extend our language to include two or more pro-

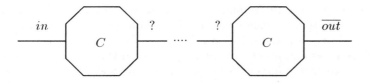

Figure 2.3. *Trying to make agents communicate*

Figure 2.4. *Agents communicating via $\overline{m}$ and m*

cesses which exist concurrently. First of all we will allow processes to communicate if they both have complementary actions available. We will say a pair of actions are complementary if both have the same identifier but one is barred and the other not. For instance, the actions $m, \overline{m}$ in figure 2.4 are complementary actions.

When C_1 has communicated via in, it is then able to communicate via its port $\overline{m}$ and C_2 is able to communicate via its port m. Thus C_1 and C_2 have complementary next actions. We define C_1 and C_2 in the following manner:

$$C_1 \stackrel{\text{def}}{=} in.\overline{m}.C_1$$
$$C_2 \stackrel{\text{def}}{=} m.\overline{out}.C_2$$

We would like both processes to perform these actions concurrently. We will use the new operator '|' to represent the composition of two processes and define the system we are after in the following manner:

$$System1 \stackrel{\text{def}}{=} C_1 \mid C_2$$

Intuitively, we wish $System1$ in its initial state to mean that C_1 and C_2 may operate independently or, if their actions permit, they may cooperate and operate concurrently. In this case, the cooperation may take place after C_1 has performed the action in and C_2 is still waiting to communicate via m.

One way of interpreting $System1$ is that it represents a possible specification of a two-place buffer that can store a maximum of two communications at any one time. However, C_2 can still communicate quite independently with the environment via m without waiting for C_1 to notify it of a communication received. Similarly C_1 does not have to synchronise with C_2 when it wants to perform $\overline{m}$. To make $System1$ behave like a true buffer we need to make sure that C_2 only communicates via m with C_1 and with no other process in the environment. To achieve this we introduce the concept of *restriction*, actions which cannot take place on their own and are hidden from an external observer. In the present example we wish that the actions $\overline{m}$ and m for processes C_1 and C_2 respectively should be restricted in the process $System1$ and thus unobservable. In essence, the effect of this on C_2 would be that it could perform no action at all until it synchronises with C_1 via the action m.

We introduce a new operator '\' which restricts the observable actions of a process. The final expression for our two-place buffer would thus be

$$Buff_2 \overset{\text{def}}{=} (C_1 \mid C_2)\backslash\{m\}$$

which means intuitively that the observable actions possible for C_1 or C_2 must not include the actions m or $\overline{m}$. However, we still wish to record that $Buff_2$ is performing not only observable but also unobservable actions. And we do this by using the symbol 'τ', tau, to record the occurrence of any unobservable actions. It will be impossible to have τ as an element of a restriction set and so τ-actions will never be affected by a restriction. Examples of possible sequences of actions for $Buff_2$ are

$$in.\tau.\overline{out}.in.\tau.in.\overline{out} \dots$$

or

$$in.\tau.in.\overline{out}.\tau.\overline{out}.in \dots$$

etc.

$Buff_2$ is thus allowed to accept up to two communications via the action in and then must make at least one communication via its action $\overline{out}$ before accepting any more incoming communications. For the same reasons each communication via $\overline{out}$ must be preceded by a communication via in.

Despite the simplicity of this example it does begin to illustrate a technique or method for building specifications of systems involving concurrent and communicating processes. We can build up complex processes from simpler ones using composition to allow processes to communicate and restriction to hide internal communications from other processes. We will use these ideas in the later examples and you should practise it in the following exercise, exercise 2.1. Exercise 2.2 gives an important insight into the relationship between sequential and concurrent systems in CCS.

EXERCISE 2.1

Earlier in this section some sequences of actions of which D_4 is capable were suggested (page 16). Suggest some of the possible sequences of actions for D_3. Is it possible to find an action sequence for either D_3 or D_4 which the other is incapable of?

EXERCISE 2.2

Specify a two-place buffer that can store two different types of values. Use action names such as $in0, \overline{out1}$, etc. to represent such values.

EXERCISE 2.3

Derive an alternative, sequential specification for $Buff_2$ that does not use parallel composition or restriction. Hint: use the agent names $B0, B1$, and $B2$ to represent the three possible states the agent can be in.

2.2 Mutual exclusion

We wish to specify a system which only allows one of two processes to perform certain critical actions at a time. In other words we want a simple system which exhibits a form of mutual exclusion, as discussed in chapter 1, where the idea of a semaphore was used to control access to critical regions of the processes' behaviour. We will once again make use of the simple process C and use it this time to represent the semaphore in our system. We will rename C as Sem to avoid confusion, and define it in the following manner:

$$Sem \stackrel{\text{def}}{=} get.put.Sem$$

Note that Sem has a very similar behaviour pattern to C, except that the action names have been changed. We wish to define two processes that are unable to perform their critical actions in parallel. We will call these processes $P1$ and $P2$ and their critical actions $c1$ and $c2$ respectively. We are not interested in the nature of these actions at present but only in making sure that they cannot both happen at the same time. Both $P1$ and $P2$ will be allowed to perform their critical actions if they can gain control of the semaphore Sem.

The semaphore will be *free* if the next action it can perform is *get* and by the same token it will be *occupied* if the next action it can perform is *put*. $P1$ and $P2$ must thus compete for control of Sem and they can achieve this by successfully communicating via its *get* port. Having gained control of Sem a process can perform its critical action and on completion it must then relinquish control for future use. Definitions of $P1$ and $P2$ are thus

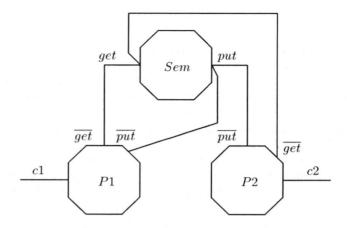

Figure 2.5. *Mutual exclusion*

simply

$$P1 \stackrel{\text{def}}{=} \overline{get}.c1.\overline{put}.P1$$
$$P2 \stackrel{\text{def}}{=} \overline{get}.c2.\overline{put}.P2$$

and a full specification of the system is defined by:

$$Mx \stackrel{\text{def}}{=} (P1 \mid P2 \mid Sem)\backslash\{get, put\}$$

with a flow graph as given in figure 2.5. An important point to notice is that we have not allowed multiple synchronisations involving the same actions. If this had not been so then we would not have the mutual exclusion property that we required. Our semantics for this language should certainly reflect this.

2.3 Informal behaviour

Before looking at some slightly larger examples we will summarise the syntax of CCS to make clear the type of agent expressions that are allowed. We will informally define the meaning of the operators we have introduced prior to their formal definition in the next chapter. Additionally, we will describe a simple game which allows specifications to be animated and tested, to a certain extent, on paper.

Agent expressions may be in the following forms:

$$\mathbf{0}, \; \alpha.E, \; E+F, \; E \mid F, \; E\backslash L, \; P, \; (E)$$

where E and F stand for agent expressions, α for any action, L for any set of observable actions and P for any agent name. In addition we assume a set of constant definitions of the form $P \overset{\text{def}}{=} E$. Such definitions constitute the means by which we are able to specify behaviours which are infinite or of indeterminate length. Really an agent name P on its own is not an expression but we will skip over this. Informally the semantics of all possible agents may be summarised in the following manner. We will present the formal semantics in the next chapter.

An informal semantics of agent expressions

0 This is the agent which has terminated or deadlocked and has no future behaviour.

$\alpha.E$ The agent E prefixed by the action α. This is the agent which can first of all perform the action α and then become the agent E.

$E + F$ The agent which can either behave as the agent E or as the agent F, but not both.

$E \mid F$ This is the agent that can behave as both E and F in parallel and, in addition, can behave synchronously when E and F communicate via complementary actions. Note that this means synchronisation takes place between exactly two agents and not three or four or more.

$E \backslash L$ The agent whose observable actions, whether barred or unbarred must *not* be in the set L. Note that τ-actions being unobservable cannot be restricted.

P For every agent name P there must be a single definition of the form $P \overset{\text{def}}{=} E$. The behaviour of P is thus exactly the behaviour of E. If E can perform the action α to become the agent E' then P can perform the same action to become E'.

(E) The behaviour of an agent expression in brackets is exactly the same as the agent expression without brackets.

The Verification Game

Specifications can be manually checked or tested by using their definitions as the basis for a simple board game. The board is constructed by first drawing a large box to represent the specification. The topmost sub-agents of the system are then placed inside their own boxes inside the outermost box. Any applicable restriction set is written above them. Keep drawing boxes within boxes until all definitions are present. A single token or arrow is placed inside each box pointing at the agent's next action. We can then *walk through* the behaviour of the specification by moving the arrows over the process definitions. Of course we need a set of rules which tell us what moves are allowed and these rules should correspond to the syntax and informal semantics we have just given:

1. Only one arrow may be moved in each move of the game unless the action is a τ resulting from the synchronisation of exactly two agents on complementary actions. In this case the two arrows concerned are moved concurrently.

2. Each move made is recorded on paper to build up a trace of the behaviour generated by the game.

3. The player represents the environment and can make choices when these are allowed, i.e. in the presence of definitions of the form $E + F$. NB: in such cases the player may change his/her mind before the action is actually made, i.e. recorded on paper.

4. Definitions of the form $\alpha.E$ offer no choice.

5. Actions may only be made if they are not affected by a relevant restriction set.

6. If an arrow ever comes to point at the null agent 0 then that arrow may not be moved again for the duration of the game.

Figure 2.6 shows the Verification Game set up to play $Buff_2$. Playing this game should demonstrate to you that there has to be an *in* before every $\overline{out}$ and that no more than two *in*s are possible before an $\overline{out}$ has to occur. Also there should be a τ between each *in*-$\overline{out}$ pair. Each game generates a particular behaviour trace some of which were started above.

In the case of $Buff_2$ this version of the game never finishes. A more systematic approach is to write down some sequences of actions which represent part of the intended behaviour of a specification and then to play the game a number of times to see if it is possible to create them. Essentially, this amounts to building a test plan and checking to see if the specification adheres to it. Of course the system might be right and your understanding of it wrong. Another way of testing specifications is to choose a possible state of the systems, i.e. a particular setting of the definitions, and then see if you can use the game to build a trace which reaches that state. Of course you can choose unwanted as well as wanted states and demonstrate that you can't reach the former while you can reach the latter.

You should use the game to test all the specifications defined in this chapter although you will find the game gets more unwieldy the deeper the sub-agent decompositions are nested. In particular, playing the game for Mx should convince you that either $P1$ or $P2$ may be active at any one time but never both at the same time. In the following sections we will look further at the way we can construct systems composed of communicating agents and the manner in which communication can affect the overall behaviour of a system.

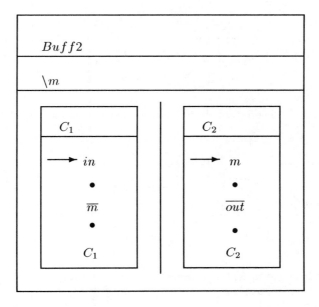

Figure 2.6. *The Verification Game for* $Buff_2$

EXERCISE 2.4

Construct the *board* for the Mx system discussed in section 2.2. Next construct a test plan which should consist of some expected action sequences and, for instance, the unwanted state where both $P1$ and $P2$ are active. Play the game on Mx to see whether or not your test plan is satisfied.

2.4 A closer look at composition

In the examples studied so far it may, perhaps, appear that composing agents in parallel is very straightforward and we can always compose simpler objects to produce more complex systems that still behave as required. This is not always the case and care needs to be taken to ensure that the desired behaviour is preserved and that additional, though unwanted, behaviours are not introduced. The aim of the next example is to illustrate the care that must be taken when using composition. It also seeks to demon-

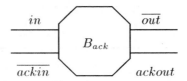

Figure 2.7. *Acknowledging communications*

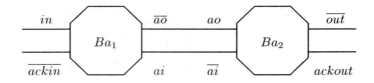

Figure 2.8. *A two-place buffer with acknowledgement*

strate, further, the need for a precise characterisation of the behaviour of
the systems we are studying.

Consider a one-place buffer that always acknowledges communications
it receives and expects acknowledgement of communications it sends. We
will call the agent B_{ack} and figure 2.7 gives a flow graph for it.

A possible definition for this agent would be

$$B_{ack} \stackrel{\text{def}}{=} in.\overline{out}.ackout.\overline{ackin}.B_{ack}$$

in which all acknowledgements are performed after the receipt and transmission of data. Suppose we now wish to construct a two-place buffer B^2_{ack}
which behaves similarly except that it can store up to two communications
at any one time. Using the same technique that we used for $Buff_2$ we
compose two copies of B_{ack} in parallel with actions suitably renamed so
that they can communicate in the desired manner. The flow graph for the
composed system is given in figure 2.8 and the definitions would be

$$Ba_1 \stackrel{\text{def}}{=} in.\overline{ao}.ai.\overline{ackin}.Ba_1$$
$$Ba_2 \stackrel{\text{def}}{=} ao.\overline{out}.ackout.\overline{ai}.Ba_2$$
$$B^2_{ack} \stackrel{\text{def}}{=} (Ba_1 \mid Ba_2)\backslash\{ai, ao\}$$

However, if you were to investigate the possible behaviours of B^2_{ack} you
would find that, far from behaving like an expanded version of $Buff_2$, it
actually behaves exactly as B_{ack} with the addition of a number of internal
τ-actions. The observable behaviours of B^2_{ack} and B_{ack} are exactly the same
in that both are capable of storing only a single communication at a time.
In fact, if you were to compose as many copies of B_{ack} as you wished in the
same manner you would still end up with a system that behaved externally

as B_{ack}.

It is a simple matter to rearrange the sequences of events and derive a new definition with the correct behaviour which will allow us to specify a true n-place buffer that acknowledges communications:

$$B'_{ack} \overset{\text{def}}{=} in.\overline{ackin}.\overline{out}.ackout.B'_{ack}$$

EXERCISE 2.5

Use B'_{ack} and figure 2.8 to specify a two-place buffer that acknowledges communications and has the correct behaviour.

EXERCISE 2.6

The following definition is meant to represent a one-place buffer that can store a pulse in two directions, both from the left and from the right:

$$Twb \overset{\text{def}}{=} inleft.\overline{outright}.Twb + inright.\overline{outleft}.Twb$$

Use Twb to specify a two-place, two-way buffer, Twb^2, in the manner of B^2_{ack} which allows up to two signals to pass in each direction at one time. Hint: it might help to draw flow graphs for Twb and Twb^2 to start with.

Play the Verification Game on Twb^2 to identify problems with its behaviour.

In what ways does Twb^2 deviate from the intended behaviour?

EXERCISE 2.7

Use a semaphore to alleviate some of the problems with Twb^2 without modifying the basic behaviour of the two sub-agents significantly.

EXERCISE 2.8

Redefine Twb so that it gives the desired behaviour when used to build the two-place version from exercise 2.6. There are both sequential and concurrent solutions to this problem and you should attempt both. Use the Verification Game to check your answer.

2.5 Producers and consumers

Our next example is a system which integrates a number of the concepts that we have discussed to date. In particular, we are interested in the ways in which we go about building a specification in CCS.

```
              --------------
              REQUIREMENTS
              --------------
```

We are required to specify a system which uses two
producers, A and B, to load items into a four-place
buffer which can store two types of values. Two further
processes, C and D, consume items from the buffer
to enable their own particular actions. The first of
these requires three 0s from the buffer and the second of
these requires four 1s from the buffer. The names of the
two critical actions are mod3 and mod4 respectively.
There is no control over the order in which items are
fed into the buffer or read from the buffer, save in the
state of the buffer itself. The only observable actions
of the system as a whole should be occurrences of the
actions mod3 and mod4.

```
              --------------
```

We will approach this problem using the method introduced in this chapter. We will specify a number of smaller agents and then combine them, using composition and restriction, to produce the complete specification. A brief study of the requirements document should convince you that there are potentially five sub-agents in this system, $A, B, Buff_4^2, C$, and D. Remember, we are talking about a specification of the system and not an implementation at this stage. For this reason we can structure the specification in any way we choose so long as it meets the requirements without thought for such things as efficiency.

From the information already gleaned from the requirements we can make the following tentative attempt at a specification:

$$PC \stackrel{\text{def}}{=} (A \mid B \mid Buff_4^2 \mid C \mid D) \backslash L$$

Notice that we have defined $\mid$ to be a binary operator in the syntax above and should really use brackets to compose PC correctly. We will discover later that in these cases where there are multiple instances of the same operator, the brackets do not affect behaviour, and we have left them out. The communications between these agents are quite simple and result in the flow graph shown in figure 2.9.

Of course we do not yet have definitions for the component sub-agents nor do we know what the restriction set L is to be, but in good top-down

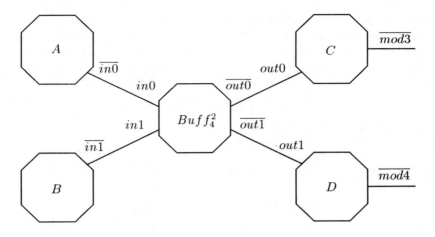

Figure 2.9. *The producer–consumer problem*

fashion we have reduced a large problem to a number of simpler ones. Let us start with the producers A and B. All they have to do is produce values to feed to the buffer. Their definitions are therefore just

$$A \stackrel{\text{def}}{=} \overline{in0}.A$$
$$B \stackrel{\text{def}}{=} \overline{in1}.B$$

and we can proceed to the other agents and consider the communications patterns later. Of the remaining agents the two consumers are the easiest as they just have to read predetermined numbers of 0s or 1s from the buffer and then output $mod3$ or $mod4$, as the case may be. Their definitions are thus just the following:

$$C \stackrel{\text{def}}{=} out0.out0.out0.\overline{mod3}.C$$
$$D \stackrel{\text{def}}{=} out1.out1.out1.out1.\overline{mod4}.D$$

and we are left with the specification of a four-place buffer that can hold two types of values. We can approach this problem by asking ourselves if we have had to solve any similar problems before and the answer to this should be yes. Earlier in this chapter we have specified a number of buffers of various types, including, in an exercise, a two-place buffer to store two types of values. We can simply expand this to a four-place buffer of the same type. To do this we will need four elements, or cells, to compose in parallel. Each cell will be in one of three states: when it is holding nothing, when it is holding a 0, or when it is holding a 1. Such a state would be defined in the following manner:

$$Cell \stackrel{\text{def}}{=} in0.\overline{out0}.Cell + in1.\overline{out1}.Cell$$

where the agent *Cell* is initially in the state where it is holding no value at all. If it communicates via *in0* then it is holding a 0 and if it communicates via *in1* then it is holding a 1. In both these cases the agent can only communicate the value it has received. If we compose four of these agents in parallel we should have the four-place buffer we are looking for. To make sure the buffer behaves in the way we wish it to we will have to rename some of the ports so that they interact and then restrict on everything except the ports $in0, in1, \overline{out0}, \overline{out1}$.

The definitions for the four cells are as follows:

$$Cell_1 \overset{\text{def}}{=} in0.\overline{z_1}.Cell_1 + in1.\overline{o_1}.Cell_1$$
$$Cell_2 \overset{\text{def}}{=} z_1.\overline{z_2}.Cell_2 + o_1.\overline{o_2}.Cell_2$$
$$Cell_3 \overset{\text{def}}{=} z_2.\overline{z_3}.Cell_3 + o_2.\overline{o_3}.Cell_3$$
$$Cell_4 \overset{\text{def}}{=} z_3.\overline{out0}.Cell_4 + o_3.\overline{out1}.Cell_4$$

The specification of the buffer will now be

$$Buff_4^2 \overset{\text{def}}{=} (Cell_1 \mid Cell_2 \mid Cell_3 \mid Cell_4)\backslash\{z_1, z_2, z_3, o_1, o_2, o_3\}$$

All that remains to be done is to compose the various agents and make sure that nothing is visible except the actions *mod3* and *mod4*, and this is accomplished in the obvious manner:

$$PC \overset{\text{def}}{=} (A \mid B \mid Buff_4^2 \mid C \mid D)\backslash\{in0, in1, out0, out1\}$$

An interesting point to note about this specification is that $Buff_4^2$ is a restricted subsystem nested inside another so we have used our method twice in this example. Notice also that we deliberately re-used an existing specification where it suited us and that we are thus using both top-down and bottom-up development techniques. CCS is particularly well suited to such an approach which the author believes is also a natural way for humans to solve problems.

EXERCISE 2.9

Amend the specification of *PC* so that *C* and *D* are now mutually exclusive on the actions $\overline{mod3}$ and $\overline{mod4}$.

EXERCISE 2.10

Amend *PC* in a different way so that *C* and *D* gain control of $Buff_4^2$ for as long as required to be able to perform $\overline{mod3}$ or $\overline{mod4}$, discarding any unwanted values as they are read from the buffer.

EXERCISE 2.11

Specify the dining room of the Real-Time Restaurant for a small number of tables and two waiters. Orders can simply be particular atomic actions associated with each table.

EXERCISE 2.12

Specify the track layout of the mass transit system for a finite number of sections of track. You do not need to specify passengers, buttons in trains or on stations, etc. but simply the means of detecting trains moving from section to section.

2.6 Summary and further reading

In this chapter we have looked at a number of specifications of varying sizes and complexities. There have been some common patterns in our approach to all these problems and our intention is now to present two checklists to help the reader structure their work in building specifications. They are not meant to be methods as such for no method can solve all the problems of a software engineer. However, some guidelines to be aware of during the course of designing and building a specification can be of great value, particularly for newcomers to the field.

We have used two basic approaches in building specifications in this chapter:

Method One

The first approach was to use parallel composition and restriction to build more complex systems from simpler ones.

1. Identify the sub-agents that appear to be required by the system and define the whole system to be the parallel composition of these with an as-yet-unknown restriction set L.

2. Establish the input–output actions of each of the sub-agents without concerning yourself about the order in which they occur at this stage.

3. Draw a flow graph to capture a general view of the possible communications of the whole system.

4. Define each node in the flow graph with an agent expression. Some

nodes may be more complex than others and will require you to re-apply Method One in order to arrive at an appropriate definition. Other nodes will be more manageable and you can proceed to Method Two.

5. At this stage you should be able to determine the actions which should be in the restriction set L.

6. Check as much of the behaviour of the system as you can to see that it is the one required.

Method Two

The second technique was to specify a whole system in terms of the possible states it can evolve to. We saw that it was possible to use both techniques to give different views of the same system. The technique above views the system as the parallel composition of a number of simpler agents while the one below gives a purely sequential view of a system. The latter is often useful in conjunction with the former when the sub-agent under consideration is relatively straightforward.

1. Make a list of all the possible states a system can evolve to.

2. Draw up a relation which shows the ordering on the evolution of the system from state to state.

3. Define expressions which implement the state transitions listed in 1 and 2.

These are obviously very rough guides to specifying systems in the language of CCS and it should be emphasised that slavishly following them will not guarantee a correct system. They are given simply to help readers structure their attempts to solve specification building exercises, such as those given earlier in this chapter. In chapter 14 we will return to this question of methods for building specifications of systems and in particular we will look at methods to aid in the specification of large systems.

In this chapter we have introduced our concurrent language by means of a variety of examples which demonstrate the roles of the various operators and the ways they can be used to construct more complex systems. In addition, we have given some consideration to how users of the language might go about building specifications for themselves. All languages, whether specification languages or programming languages, lend themselves to solving problems in different ways and it is as important to be aware of this as it is to know the language itself. The particular techniques we looked at were the specification of complex systems by the parallel composition of simpler ones, using restriction where necessary to constrain the observable behaviour of the system as a whole, and the specification of systems in terms of their general state transitions.

If we are to live up to the title of the book we must give formal definitions for semantics of the language as well as for its syntax. Furthermore, we want the formal definitions to be of use to us in modelling and reasoning about systems and not just necessary but cumbersome extras.

The standard reference for CCS is [Mil89] from which the basic presentation of the language is derived. Indeed, wherever possible that book has been taken as the de facto CCS standard; it is also an excellent book for those wishing to delve deeper into the theory of CCS and concurrency theory in general. The simple buffer used extensively in this book is also to be found there. The mutual exclusion example is based on one used in courses given at Edinburgh. Readers might like to consult [RB92b, RB92a] for some classic concurrency problems, e.g. the Dining Philosophers, shared resources, etc., treated in CCS.

3

Formal definition

The main objective of the chapter is to establish a formal semantics for the language we introduced in chapter 2. The semantics of the language will be primarily concerned with characterising the behaviour of systems. We will look briefly at a few possible approaches to this before introducing the standard semantics for CCS. We introduce the notion of a labelled transition system as the basis for the formal definition of the language we have been using. The formal definition itself is given in terms of a simple operational semantics. Other concepts introduced are transition graphs and inference trees. As part of this development the role and value of formal semantics are also discussed in the context of the examples we used to introduce the language in the previous chapter. Finally, in this chapter, we will investigate some alternative semantics for CCS and contrast them with the standard one.

3.1 Modelling behaviour

In the specification of concurrent and communicating systems we are particularly concerned with the patterns of communications, or synchronisations, between agents in a system. As the system as a whole evolves so do the individual agents, although it is more than likely that they will evolve at different rates and in different ways relative to each other. It is important, therefore, that we find some means of modelling the evolution of a system and, in particular, its patterns of communication. Systems in this context will be agent expressions which are specifications of systems. As always, we shall have to make some decisions as to exactly what we wish to model and how we are to do it. Our semantics will formalise the informal one and the Verification Game introduced in the previous chapter. A number of possibilities offer themselves as potential models of concurrent systems.

Certainly we will want to record the possible states a system can evolve to through the actions of its various agents. At any one time there may

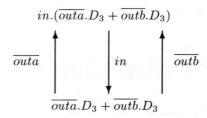

$$in.(\overline{outa}.D_3 + \overline{outb}.D_3)$$

$$\overline{outa} \qquad in \qquad \overline{outb}$$

$$\overline{outa}.D_3 + \overline{outb}.D_3$$

Figure 3.1. *Transition graph for D_3*

be a number of agents, each capable of a variety of next actions, while others may well be inactive, possibly until they are able to communicate with another process. One way to model the changes of state of a system would be to model all the changes of state that could occur as a result of any of the possible permutations of concurrent actions which the system is capable of. If we consider the very simple agent

$$Perm \stackrel{\text{def}}{=} a.\mathbf{0} \mid b.\mathbf{0} \mid c.\mathbf{0}$$

It is obvious that any permutation on the set $\{a, b, c\}$ will result in an allowable change of state. Performing all three possible actions will result in the system $\mathbf{0} \mid \mathbf{0} \mid \mathbf{0}$ while performing a and b would result in the system $\mathbf{0} \mid \mathbf{0} \mid c.\mathbf{0}$. We could carry on recording the effects of the other permutations.

Another approach results from the observation that the only actions that we can guarantee to take place in parallel are synchronisations between agents. In all other cases the order of events might well depend on the observer in relation to the system. In this case it would be possible for observers in different relative positions to the system to observe the same state change resulting from different permutations of the same set of actions. In this approach we represent the parallel occurrence of a number of possible events by the set of their possible interleavings. If we return to the little example used above we can observe that any ordering on the events a, b, c will result in the same final state. Thus, performing any of the sequences of actions $a.b.c$ or $b.a.c$ or $c.a.b$ and so on will result in the final state $\mathbf{0} \mid \mathbf{0} \mid \mathbf{0}$.

It is this interleaving approach that we will adopt for a variety of reasons, the most important of which being that it allows us to define a simple and intuitive semantics for the language. One way of capturing the possible interleavings of behaviours of agents expressed in our language is in terms of transition graphs. We will introduce transition graphs by referring to some of the very simple agents we introduced in chapter 2 and then return to the *Perm* example a little later.

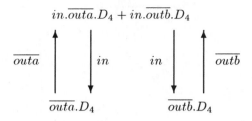

Figure 3.2. *A transiton graph for D_4*

A transition graph for the agent D_3 discussed in chapter 2 is given by figure 3.1 and we see that the graph has two states, represented by agent expressions with the actions which each agent may perform in order to evolve to a new state labelling the arcs connecting these states. A transition graph is thus a set of nodes each of which is an agent expression together with a set of arcs connecting nodes, where each arc is labelled by an action.

In chapter 2 we noted that the agent D_4 was able to perform the same sequences of actions as the agent D_3, although they had different definitions and appeared to behave in different ways. If we construct a transition graph for D_4 (fig. 3.2) we will see that they do indeed appear to have quite different behaviours.

D_4 has three states as opposed to D_3, which has only two. The choices open to the two agents in each state are also different. The graphs make clear the difference caused by the non-deterministic choice made by D_4 performing the action *in*. The transition graphs for the two agents do indeed appear to be showing up important differences that a simple listing of possible action sequences does not.

Figure 3.3 gives a transition graph for the agent $a.\mathbf{0} \mid b.\mathbf{0} \mid c.\mathbf{0}$ introduced at the beginning of this section. This clearly shows that any possible interleaving of the allowable actions produces the same final state. Notice also that the agents $\mathbf{0}$ and $\mathbf{0} \mid \mathbf{0} \mid \mathbf{0}$ would also have the same transition graphs as neither of them is capable of any action at all. In chapters 9 and 10 we will investigate ways for establishing equivalence between such expressions.

You will find some exercises below that require you to construct transition graphs for some of the systems we studied in chapter 2. You may find the following algorithm useful in the exercises:

1. Choose an agent expression with which to start. If there is one which represents an initial state of the system then choose that.

2. Find out all the possible next actions for the agent you have chosen and draw an arc labelled with the action name for each. Remember, identical actions may generate different next states, so some arcs from the same node may have the same action labelling them.

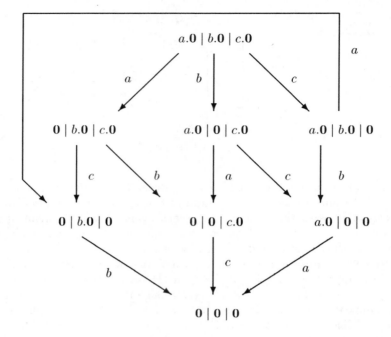

Figure 3.3. *Transition graph for* $a.\mathbf{0} \mid b.\mathbf{0} \mid c.\mathbf{0}$

3. Work out the agent expressions which should appear as next states at the end of each of the arcs and add these to the graph if necessary. This is because it is quite possible that some of the states might already exist as a node in the graph so you may not have to add new ones for every arc.

4. Check to see if any nodes have next actions unaccounted for by appropriately labelled arcs. If there are any then go back to 2 for each node for which this is true and repeat the process.

5. All nodes should now have arcs for all possible next actions. You may now find that you need to redraw the graph a number of times until you get the clearest and simplest version of it. It is often better to leave this stage until last when you have all the states and labelled arcs you need.

It is interesting to consider the transition graphs for the two versions of the two-place buffer used in chapter 2, $Buff_2$ and $B0$ (fig. 3.4). The two versions of the buffer example would appear to have different transition graphs, although they were supposed to generate the same behaviour. The difference is the presence of the arc labelled by the τ-action, which means that one agent has to perform an internal transition before it can continue, whereas the other agent does not. If we ignore the τ or internal action then

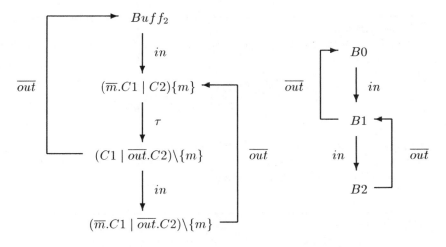

Figure 3.4. *Transition graphs for $Buff_2$ and $B0$*

the processes do indeed have the same behaviour. Transition graphs are very useful in making clear the state space of a particular specification. We will put off answering the question as to whether these two processes are equivalent in some sense until the next chapter, when we develop a theory of equivalence for CCS.

It is worthwhile comparing the transition graphs used in this chapter with the flow graphs used in the previous one. The flow graphs gave us a static view of the possible communications between agents in a specification but say nothing of the sequencing of these events. Flow graphs thus have similarities with dataflow diagrams (DFDs). A transition graph, on the other hand, gives us complete information about the ordering of the actions of a whole system but does not give us, in any obvious sense, the behaviour of individual agents in that system although you could extract that information if required. Transition graphs thus have similarities with state transition diagrams (STDs). So, once again, we see that these diagramming techniques are useful in presenting information in an easily assimilable form but selective in the information they actually give. Indeed, one might consider that such selective presentation of data is one of the strengths of a good diagram. The diagram that tells us everything we might want to know about a process or system would probably be so complex as to be virtually useless.

We have now investigated a particular characterisation of the behaviour of communicating systems, the transition graph, and our next task is to formally define this characterisation.

EXERCISE 3.1

Construct a transition graph for the agent Mx from chapter 2 and then for the following agents:

$$Spec_1 \stackrel{\text{def}}{=} c1.Spec_1 + c2.Spec_1$$
$$Spec_2 \stackrel{\text{def}}{=} \tau.c1.Spec_2 + \tau.c2.Spec_2$$
$$Spec_3 \stackrel{\text{def}}{=} \tau.c1.\tau.Spec_3 + \tau.c2.\tau.Spec_3$$

Compare these three graphs with the graph for Mx; are any identical, for instance? What conclusions do you come to concerning the relationship between Mx and the other three agents?

EXERCISE 3.2

Construct transition graphs for the following agent expressions which we also studied in chapter 2:

$$B_{ack}^2, \ B_{ack}^{2\prime}$$

How do the graphs help us to understand the difference between the two agents?

EXERCISE 3.3

Construct the transition graphs for the agents Twb^2 and $Twb^{2\prime}$, exercises 2.7 and 2.8. How do these two graphs differ?

3.2 Operational semantics

In this section we wish to define formally the transition graphs used in the previous section. First of all, however, let us list the sets we will be using and the variables we will use to range over them.

$\mathcal{A}$ An infinite set of names $a, b, c, \ldots$ range over $\mathcal{A}$; and in, get, put, etc. are examples of names.

$\overline{\mathcal{A}}$ An infinite set of co-names $\overline{a}, \overline{b}, \overline{c}, \ldots$ range over $\overline{\mathcal{A}}$; and $\overline{get}, \overline{put}, \overline{out}, \overline{mod3}$ are examples of co-names.

$\mathcal{L}$ The set of labels $\mathcal{A} \cup \overline{\mathcal{A}}$, $l, l', \ldots$ range over $\mathcal{L}$. We will use K and L to stand for subsets of $\mathcal{L}$.

Act The set of all possible actions $\mathcal{L} \cup \{\tau\}$, α and β range over **Act**.

$\mathcal{K}$ The set of agent constants $A, B, \ldots$ range over $\mathcal{K}$; and $Mx, Buff_2, B0$, etc. are examples of agent constants.

$\mathcal{E}$ The set of agent expressions, given by the following BNF:

$$
\mathcal{E} \quad ::= \quad
\begin{aligned}
& \mathbf{0} \\
& | \quad A \\
& | \quad \mathcal{E} \backslash K \\
& | \quad (\mathcal{E}) \\
& | \quad \alpha.\mathcal{E} \\
& | \quad \mathcal{E} \mid \mathcal{E} \\
& | \quad \mathcal{E} + \mathcal{E}
\end{aligned}
$$

where the operators are introduced in decending order of priority, and $E, F, G, \ldots$ range over $\mathcal{E}$.

$\mathcal{X}$ The set of agent variables $X, Y, Z, \ldots$ range over $\mathcal{X}$.

All these should be familiar except for the set $\mathcal{X}$ which we will not begin to make use of until chapter 10.

We require that there is no defining equation for $\mathbf{0}$ while for every agent constant A there is exactly *one* defining equation of the form $A \stackrel{\text{def}}{=} E$. Notice the use of K in the rule for the $\backslash$ operator. This is to ensure that τ-actions cannot be included in such restrictions. An expression of the form $E + F \mid G$ stands for $E + (F \mid G)$. Therefore, if we mean the choice to be between E and F, composed in parallel with G, then we would have to write $(E + F) \mid G$. In addition we will assume all the binary operators associate to the left and thus $E \mid F \mid G$ will actually be represented as $(E \mid F) \mid G$. The same applies to expressions of the form $E + F + G$. We will see in chapters 9 and 10 that $E + (F + G)$ is behaviourally the same as $(E + F) + G$ and similarly for parallel composition.

With these preliminaries in mind we can now go on to formally define the operators we have been using. We will do this in terms of what is known as an *operational semantics* which will formalise the behaviour which will be attributed to any CCS agent we build. In other words, it will describe precisely which transitions a CCS agent is capable of, and thus associate CCS agents with their transition graphs. The operational semantics can be thought of as defining an interpreter for CCS. The non-determinism inherent in this language means that the operational semantics does not necessarily constitute an executable interpreter.

The operational semantics for CCS consists of a set of rules for each operator. Each rule will have zero or more hypotheses and a single conclusion, with the hypotheses above a horizontal bar and the conclusions below it. In some cases an additional condition will be added, in brackets, to the right of the rule. The meaning of the condition will be obvious from the rule itself. In addition to one or more rules for each operator there will be a rule defining the meaning of constants in definitions of agent expressions.

We will introduce the rules for each operator with a little explanation.

The first rule relates to the prefixing operator and says that any agent of the form $\alpha.E$ may perform the action α to become the agent E with no constraining hypothesis:

$$\textbf{Pref}\ \frac{}{\alpha.E \xrightarrow{\alpha} E}$$

There are two rules for choice, depending on which branch of the choice expression gets evaluated, and they are slightly more complicated than the previous rule. They say that if, for instance, an agent E has a transition via α to E' then $E + F$ has the same transition giving rise to the same state E'. The second choice rule says the same for F in $E + F$:

$$\textbf{Sum}_1\ \frac{E \xrightarrow{\alpha} E'}{E + F \xrightarrow{\alpha} E'} \qquad \textbf{Sum}_2\ \frac{F \xrightarrow{\alpha} F'}{E + F \xrightarrow{\alpha} F'}$$

There are three rules for composition. The first two deal with the possible observable actions for an agent of the form $E \mid F$ where no synchronisation is involved. They follow the pattern for $\textbf{Sum}_1$ and $\textbf{Sum}_2$ except that the dormant agent in the composed pair remains after the transition has occurred:

$$\textbf{Com}_1\ \frac{E \xrightarrow{\alpha} E'}{E \mid F \xrightarrow{\alpha} E' \mid F} \qquad \textbf{Com}_2\ \frac{F \xrightarrow{\alpha} F'}{E \mid F \xrightarrow{\alpha} E \mid F'}$$

The third composition rule states the transition involved if a synchronisation does occur with the resulting action a τ. We will assume the following convention:

$$\overline{\overline{\alpha}} = \alpha$$

for doubly complemented actions:

$$\textbf{Com}_3\ \frac{E \xrightarrow{l} E'\ F \xrightarrow{\bar{l}} F'}{E \mid F \xrightarrow{\tau} E' \mid F'}$$

The single rule for restriction says that if E can perform the action α to become E' then $E \backslash L$ can do likewise only if $\alpha \notin L$:

$$\textbf{Res}\ \frac{E \xrightarrow{\alpha} E'}{E \backslash R \xrightarrow{\alpha} E' \backslash R}\ (\alpha, \overline{\alpha} \notin R)$$

The two constant rules say that constants have the same behaviour as the expressions that define them:

$$\textbf{Con}_1\ \frac{E \xrightarrow{\alpha} E'}{A \xrightarrow{\alpha} E'}\ (A \overset{\text{def}}{=} E) \qquad \textbf{Con}_2\ \frac{E \xrightarrow{\alpha} E'}{E \xrightarrow{\alpha} A}\ (A \overset{\text{def}}{=} E')$$

The final rules simply say what happens to expressions involving brackets. There are two cases depending on the structure of the bracketed expression. Basically the parallel composition of two agents retains brackets after a transition whereas choice loses them. The reason is that evaluating a choice expression results in a simplification in the sense that the + does not occur on the right hand side of the rule and the brackets are no longer needed. In the case of parallel composition, no such simplification occurs and the brackets are still required.

$$\textbf{Brac}_1 \ \frac{E \xrightarrow{\alpha} E'}{(E) \xrightarrow{\alpha} E'} \quad (E \equiv E_1 + E_2) \quad \textbf{Brac}_2 \ \frac{E \xrightarrow{\alpha} E'}{(E) \xrightarrow{\alpha} (E')} \quad (E \equiv E_1 \mid E_2)$$

We now have a set of rules for each of the operators of CCS. We have also defined how constants and brackets affect transitions. The rules should correspond closely to the intuitive understanding of the operators that we developed in chapter 2. An operational semantics of this type is not the only means of establishing a formal semantics for a language such as CCS but experience shows that it is easiest to learn and very practical. In the next section we will demonstrate the practical application of this semantics.

3.3 Inference trees

With the joint notions of transition graphs and the operational semantics for operators in the language established we can demonstrate the relationship between the two. The operational rules will allow us to prove or disprove the correctness of the arcs connecting agent expressions in any transition graphs we construct. We do this by constructing inference trees using just the rules we have stated for the operational semantics. At the root of each successful tree will be the transition we are trying to prove. Each node in the tree will consist of a transition labelled by the rule which was used to derive it. A node may only refer to transitions already proved correct higher up in the tree. For this reason all leaf nodes in an inference tree must be an instance of the use of the rule **Pref**, since this is the only rule which is true with the empty set of hypotheses. If we try to build such a proof tree for an invalid transition then we will be unable to complete the tree as just described.

To illustrate this we will prove the correctness of the following transition, shown in figure 3.5:

$$(\overline{m}.C_1 \mid \overline{out}.C_2)\backslash\{m\} \xrightarrow{\overline{out}} (\overline{m}.C_1 \mid C_2)\backslash\{m\}$$

At the root of the inference tree we have the transition we are trying to prove correct. Each node above the root node of the tree consists of an instance of one of the rules from the operational semantics. The hypothesis for each rule consists of transitions already proved correct higher up in the tree. The only leaf node of the tree introduces the subexpression which is the source of the required transition, $\overline{out}$. Notice that in this case the action comes from a subexpression which is already in prefix form. In other

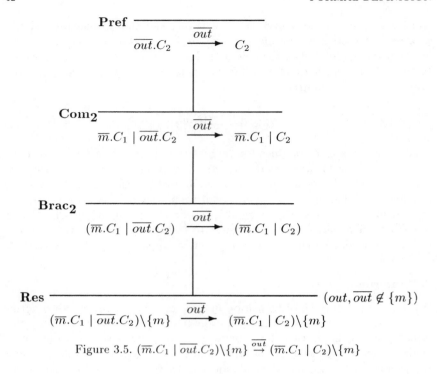

Figure 3.5. $(\overline{m}.C_1 \mid \overline{out}.C_2)\backslash\{m\} \overset{\overline{out}}{\to} (\overline{m}.C_1 \mid C_2)\backslash\{m\}$

words, in order to prove that $(\overline{m}.C_1 \mid \overline{out}.C_2)\backslash\{m\}$ can perform the action $\overline{out}$ we have to prove that $\overline{out}.C_2$ can perform that action. To find this starting point you have to first note the action labelling the transition to be proved. If it is an observable action you must look to see which expression or expressions could have generated that transition. If there is more than one then a check on the right hand side of the transition to see which particular subexpression could be responsible is required. If constants are involved then you will have to check their definitions. The proof must first establish the origin of the action involved in the transition and then build up the complete agent expressions. In the present case there is only a single branch to the inference tree because the transition is via an observable action.

If the transition in question is a τ then there are two possibilities depending on whether it is stated explicitly on the left hand side, e.g.

$$\tau.Spec_1 + \tau.Spec_1 \overset{\tau}{\to} Spec_1$$

or arises as a result of a synchronisation. In the former case, τs are treated in the same way as observable actions. The latter case means you will have to find two subexpressions with complementary next-actions and your proof tree will thus have two branches. Figure 3.6 is an example of such a proof

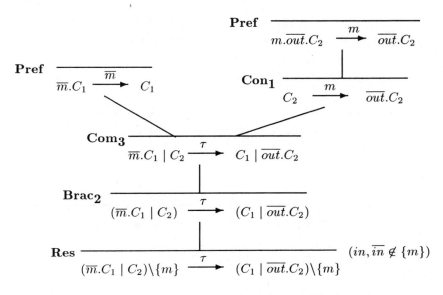

Figure 3.6. $(\overline{m}.C_1 \mid C_2)\backslash\{m\} \xrightarrow{\tau} (C_1 \mid \overline{out}.C_2)\backslash\{m\}$.

for the transition

$$(\overline{m}.C_1 \mid C_2)\backslash\{m\} \xrightarrow{\tau} (C_1 \mid \overline{out}.C_2)\backslash\{m\}$$

Thus we have proved that two arcs of the transition graph for $Buff_2$ are correct. As a final example we will attempt to prove a simplified version of the transition

$$Buff_2 \xrightarrow{m} (C_1 \mid \overline{out}.C_2)\backslash\{m\}$$

Figure 3.7 gives the attempted proof though eventually we need to use the rule **Res** which does not apply because the additional constraint used in its definition means that $(m, \overline{m} \notin \{m\})$ which is obviously false; so we are prevented from proving this transition correct for the agents concerned. This is as we would hope because we wish only the actions $in, \overline{out}$ to be visible and not m or $\overline{m}$ which should not label arcs in a transition system for $Buff_2$.

EXERCISE 3.4

Build inference trees to prove correct the remaining transitions in $Buff_2$.

EXERCISE 3.5

Prove the correctness, or otherwise, of the following transitions from the

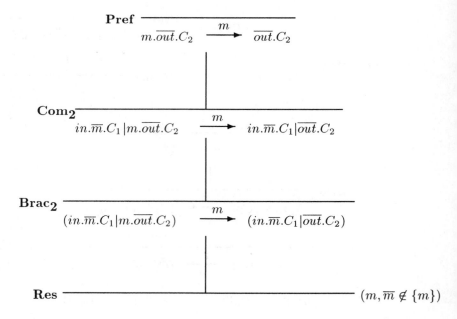

Figure 3.7. $(in.\overline{m}.C_1 \mid m.\overline{out}.C_2)\backslash\{m\} \overset{m}{\rightarrow} (in.\overline{m}.C_1 \mid \overline{out}.C_2)\backslash\{m\}$ *is not possible*

transition graph for Mx by attempting to build inference trees for each:

1. $(c1.\overline{put}.P1 \mid P2 \mid put.Sem)\backslash\{get, put\} \overset{c1}{\rightarrow} (\overline{put}.P1 \mid P2 \mid put.Sem)\backslash\{get, put\}$

2. $(c1.\overline{put}.P1 \mid P2 \mid put.Sem)\backslash\{get, put\} \overset{put}{\rightarrow} (c1.\overline{put}.P1 \mid P2 \mid Sem)\backslash\{get, put\}$

3. $Mx\backslash\{get, put\} \overset{\tau}{\rightarrow} (c1.\overline{put}.P1 \mid P2 \mid put.Sem)\backslash\{get, put\}$

EXERCISE 3.6

$$P \overset{\text{def}}{=} a.\overline{b}.c.P + \overline{b}.c.a.P + c.a.\overline{b}.P$$
$$Q \overset{\text{def}}{=} d.\overline{c}.b.Q + \overline{c}.b.d.Q + b.d.\overline{c}.Q$$
$$R \overset{\text{def}}{=} (P \mid Q)\backslash\{b, c\}$$

build inference trees to prove the following transitions:

1. $R \overset{d}{\rightarrow} (P \mid \overline{c}.b.Q)\backslash\{b, c\}$

2. $R \overset{\tau}{\rightarrow} (a.\overline{b}.P \mid b.d.Q)\backslash\{b, c\}$

3. $(c.P \mid \overline{c}.Q)\backslash\{b, c\} \overset{\tau}{\rightarrow} R$

3.4 A truly concurrent semantics

In this chapter we have adopted, what seemed to be, a compromise semantics based on the interleaving of potentially concurrent actions. Agent
synchronisations, which generate τ-actions, give us the only actual concurrency in the language. Apart from such synchronisations all concurrently
enabled observable actions are interleaved, by which we mean that they
may be performed in any order and still reach the same state. The main
reason for adopting this restriction was that the language could be defined
in terms of a very simple operational semantics. Naturally, you would expect to have to pay for such a compromise in some way, perhaps through a
loss of expressive power. Certainly a language which seeks to model concurrency by avoiding that very thing evokes some suspicions. We now return to
this decision and consider it in more detail by developing a truly concurrent
semantics for CCS and considering the advantages and disadvantages.

We will attempt to *short-cut* the interleaving of concurrent actions by
allowing transitions which consist of multiple atomic actions. If you consider
again the transition graph for $Buff_2$ and in particular the node in the graph
labelled by

$$(in.\overline{m}.C_1 \mid \overline{out}.C_2)\backslash\{m\}$$

it seems reasonable that there could be an extra transition labelled by both
in and $\overline{out}$ which takes the buffer directly to

$$(\overline{m}.C_1 \mid C_2)\backslash\{m\}$$

Of course, we don't wish to exclude the possibility that either of these
actions takes place on its own so the net result would be to produce a
transition graph with an extra arc for the *double* transition. We can't,
however, assume that we will now represent transitions by sets of atomic
actions. The agent

$$a.E \mid a.F$$

demonstrates that sets are inappropriate models for our new transitions
because a singleton $\{a\}$ would generate the three possible next states of
$E \mid a.F$, $a.E \mid F$ and $E \mid F$ even though the last of these was generated
by a double transition of two as. Things get worse if transitions involving
synchronisations are involved. To follow this line of development through
we will have to use *bags*, or *multisets* as they are also known, to model
concurrent transitions. We will use the notation $[\alpha_i, ..., \alpha_m]$ to represent
bags (where the indices $i, ..., m$ may not be distinct). Essentially, a bag
in the present context is a function from the set of observable actions, $\mathcal{L}$,
to the set of natural numbers, $\mathbf{N}$. It will turn out that we do not need to
model synchronisations by τ-actions in our new language. The bag $[in, \overline{out}]$
would be defined by the function $\{in \mapsto 1, \overline{out} \mapsto 1\}$. In the above example we will now have two possible transition labels, $[a]$ and $[a, a]$, which
make the required distinction. We will use $\cup_+, \cap_+, \backslash_+$ and $\in_+$ to represent

union, intersection, difference and element check for bags respectively. The definitions are given in Appendix B. We will also use σ, σ_i to range over bags.

Let us now build up an operational semantics for our new language which we might call CCS^+. Concurrent transitions will be built up by proving that sub-agents are capable of individual atomic actions and therefore our new prefix law will become

$$\textbf{PreP} \frac{}{\alpha.E \xrightarrow{[\alpha]} E}$$

We simply turn the atomic action α into the bag which contains just α. The choice laws follow fairly straightforwardly with the only difference being that transition labels are now bags:

$$\textbf{SumP}_1 \frac{E \xrightarrow{\sigma} E'}{E + F \xrightarrow{\sigma} E'} \qquad \textbf{SumP}_2 \frac{F \xrightarrow{\sigma} F'}{E + F \xrightarrow{\sigma} F'}$$

The first two **Com** laws are also straightforward:

$$\textbf{ComP}_1 \frac{E \xrightarrow{\sigma} E'}{E \mid F \xrightarrow{\sigma} E' \mid F} \qquad \textbf{ComP}_2 \frac{F \xrightarrow{\sigma} F'}{E \mid F \xrightarrow{\sigma} E \mid F'}$$

The third **Com** law requires rather more thought as we might now have multiple synchronisations as a result of composing two transitions. In our new calculus we do not need a specific symbol to represent τs, silent actions, as these will be represented in a very natural way by $[]$, the empty bag. The new **Com**$_3$, which we will call **ComP**$_3$, will generate a combined transition which will consist of a bag of actions which contains no complementary pairs. Basically, the rule will say that given two agents each with a concurrent transition then the resulting concurrent transition arising from their composition will be the bag union of their individual transitions less their bag intersection. We can represent this calculation by the following function:

$$
\begin{aligned}
T \qquad &: \quad bag\ \mathcal{L} \times bag\ \mathcal{L} \to bag\ \mathcal{L} \\
T(x, y) \quad &= \quad let\ z = x \cap_+ \overline{y}\ in \\
&\qquad (x \backslash_+ z)\ \cup_+ (y \backslash_+ \overline{z})
\end{aligned}
$$

Notice that if the transitions concerned were bags of single actions such as $[\overline{m}]$ and $[m]$ then the resulting concurrent transition would simply be the empty bag which, as we have noted, corresponds to the τ-action of basic CCS. In our new language we can work just with the set $\mathcal{L}$ of atomic observable actions and bags of type $\mathcal{L}$ as transition labels. The resulting rule for **Com**$_3$ becomes

$$\textbf{ComP}_3 \frac{E \xrightarrow{\sigma_1} E'\ F \xrightarrow{\sigma_2} F'}{E \mid F \xrightarrow{T(\sigma_1, \sigma_2)} E' \mid F'}$$

Thus, in our new language the agent $\overline{a}.E \mid a.F$ would have a single transition $\bar{a}.E|a.F \xrightarrow{[]} E|F$, whereas the interpretion of this agent using the operational rules of basic CCS would have generated *three* possible transitions via $\bar{a}, a$ and τ. Because of the fact that all possible synchronisations are forced by the function T we now define a new version of the restriction operator which specifies those actions which we will *allow* to be observable rather than those which we do not:

$$\mathbf{Perm} \; \frac{E \xrightarrow{\sigma} E'}{E/L \xrightarrow{\sigma} E'/L} \; (dom \; \sigma \subseteq (L \cup \overline{L}))$$

The remaining rules are straightforward and resemble their CCS counterparts:

$$\mathbf{ConP_1} \; \frac{E \xrightarrow{\sigma} E'}{A \xrightarrow{\sigma} E'} \; (A \stackrel{\text{def}}{=} E) \quad \mathbf{ConP_2} \; \frac{E \xrightarrow{\sigma} E'}{E \xrightarrow{\sigma} A} \; (A \stackrel{\text{def}}{=} E')$$

$$\mathbf{BracP_1} \; \frac{E \xrightarrow{\sigma} E'}{(E) \xrightarrow{\sigma} E'} \; (E \equiv E_1 + E_2) \quad \mathbf{BracP_2} \; \frac{E \xrightarrow{\sigma} E'}{(E) \xrightarrow{\sigma} (E')} \; (E \equiv E_1 \mid E_2)$$

If you use the CCS^+ rules to draw the transition graph for $Buff_2$ you will find that you can now add in the additional transition via $[in, \overline{out}]$. In fact all this extra effort has produced a calculus which is liable to generate extremely complex transition graphs because we have added all possible concurrent transitions and all sub-bags of all concurrent transitions. In other words, if a number of observable actions are concurrently enabled then any permutation on them may actually take place. Try working through the transition graph for $a.0|b.0|c.0$ from earlier in this chapter and see for yourself. The obvious question would seem to be: Can we model anything new apart from the extra arcs in the transition graphs? In other words, does this version of concurrency give us any genuinely new transitions? In the context of CCS this question amounts to asking: Given an expression in the syntax of CCS/CCS^+, does the new interpretation allow transitions labelled with a bag containing more than one action in a graph such that the actions cannot be separately interleaved to reach the same state? The answer to this question is simply: No! We will illustrate this by attempting to specify a system which neither CCS nor CCS^+ can model.

Three agents each have simple cyclic behaviours: A repeatedly performs 3 as, B repeatedly performs 2 bs and C repeatedly performs 1 c. At the beginning of each cycle all three agents must synchronise so that their next cycles are enabled at the same time; further, this event must be signalled to the environment by the action $\overline{start}$. Whatever you do in CCS you cannot guarantee the required synchronisation. In CCS^+ the required synchronisation is possible but not inevitable. So far we have not made the language more expressive in any real sense. The fault actually lies with our current definition of prefix rather than with the rules for composition. The situation

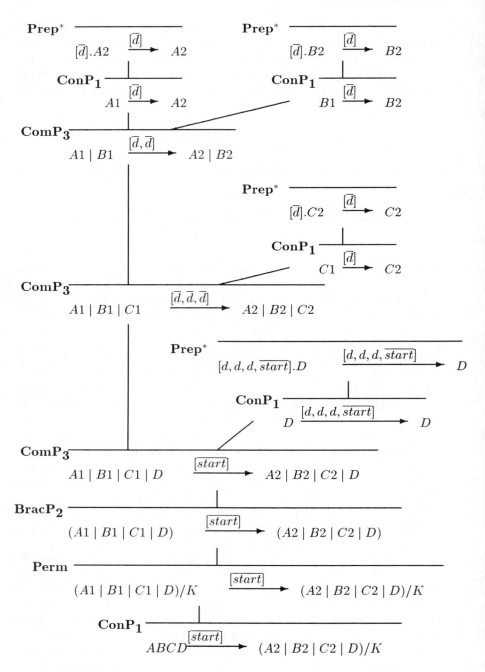

Figure 3.8. *Proof of the $\overline{[start]}$ transition for $ABCD$*

is very different if we make a slight modification to the prefix rule:

$$\textbf{PreP}^* \ \frac{}{\sigma.E \xrightarrow{\sigma} E}$$

We have simply said that prefixes must now be bags of atomic actions. Of course we can have a singleton bag, the bag that contains a single action, so we can still model all the existing systems but can now achieve the three-way synchronisation we were after:

$$
\begin{aligned}
A1 &\stackrel{\text{def}}{=} [\bar{d}].A2 \\
A2 &\stackrel{\text{def}}{=} [a].[a].[a].A1 \\
B1 &\stackrel{\text{def}}{=} [\bar{d}].B2 \\
B2 &\stackrel{\text{def}}{=} [b].[b].B1 \\
C1 &\stackrel{\text{def}}{=} [\bar{d}].C2 \\
C2 &\stackrel{\text{def}}{=} [c].C1 \\
D &\stackrel{\text{def}}{=} [d, d, d, \overline{start}].D \\
ABCD &\stackrel{\text{def}}{=} (A1 \mid B1 \mid C1 \mid D)/\{\overline{start}, a, b, c\}
\end{aligned}
$$

In its initial state $ABCD$ will have the following transition:

$$ABCD \xrightarrow{\overline{start}} (A2 \mid B2 \mid C2 \mid D)/\{\overline{start}, a, b, c\}$$

Under CCS*, as we shall call the new language, this will be the only transition for the initial state. The system will repeatedly return to this state when each agent's allotted number of as, bs or cs has been exhausted. Figure 3.8 gives a proof to demonstrate that this is indeed a valid transition. Note now that constructing these proofs for CCS* has become rather more complicated because every additional agent in a multi-way synchronisation greater than 2 must be introduced one at a time by an instance of the **Comp$_3$** rule.

EXERCISE 3.7

Construct an inference tree to prove that $\xrightarrow{[d]}$ is not a valid transition for the above agent.

EXERCISE 3.8

Given the CCS* definitions

$$
\begin{aligned}
P &\stackrel{\text{def}}{=} [a].P + [p].P \\
Q &\stackrel{\text{def}}{=} [b].Q + [q].Q \\
R &\stackrel{\text{def}}{=} [\bar{a}, \bar{b}].R + [\bar{a}].R + [\bar{b}].R \\
PQR &\stackrel{\text{def}}{=} (P \mid Q \mid R)/\{p, q\}
\end{aligned}
$$

prove the following transitions:

$$PQR \xrightarrow{[p]} PQR$$
$$PQR \xrightarrow{[q]} PQR$$
$$PQR \xrightarrow{[p,q]} PQR$$
$$PQR \xrightarrow{[]} PQR$$

Note that there are several ways of proving the last transition.

3.5 A synchronous calculus

We have now excluded the unwanted arcs from the graph in cases where we wished to force a particular concurrent transition. In doing this we have effectively removed the connection between concurrency and interleaving but we have had to do quite a lot of work to do so. A very interesting thing occurs if we now remove the two rules $\mathbf{ComP_1}$ and $\mathbf{ComP_2}$ from the operational semantics for CCS*. The result is a fully synchronous version of CCS*; we will call it SCCS*. With only $\mathbf{ComP_3}$, SCCS* does not allow sub-agents to idle unless they are specifically allowed to do so by being prefixed by the empty bag which we will now represent by '1'. The following is a definition for the idle version of an agent P which can delay as long as it wishes before performing the first action. We will use ':' for the prefix operator in SCCS* because of its synchronous nature.

$$P^I \stackrel{\text{def}}{=} 1 : P^I + P$$

This all has several effects on the behaviour associated with expressions and which can be illustrated by considering $ABCD$ under SCCS*. First of all, after the initial four-way synchronisation the whole system will deadlock because D wishes to perform three ds which are not in the permission set. We can overcome this by allowing idle states in appropriate places, thus giving rise to a new set of definitions:

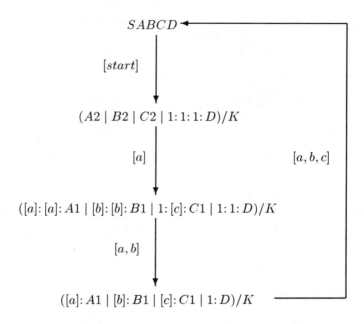

Figure 3.9. *SCCS* transition graph for SABCD*

$$A1 \stackrel{\text{def}}{=} [\overline{d}]\!: A2$$
$$A2 \stackrel{\text{def}}{=} [a]\!: [a]\!: [a].A1$$
$$B1 \stackrel{\text{def}}{=} [\overline{d}]\!: B2$$
$$B2 \stackrel{\text{def}}{=} 1\!: [b]\!: [b]\!: B1$$
$$C1 \stackrel{\text{def}}{=} [\overline{d}]\!: C2$$
$$C2 \stackrel{\text{def}}{=} 1\!: 1\!: [c]\!: C$$
$$D \stackrel{\text{def}}{=} [d, d, d, \overline{start}]\!: 1\!: 1\!: 1\!: D$$
$$SABCD \stackrel{\text{def}}{=} (A1 \mid B1 \mid C1 \mid D)/\{\overline{start}, a, b, c\}$$

This gets rid of the deadlock but gives rise to a system with a very simple cyclic behaviour as demonstrated in figure 3.9.

There is now a single ordering on the pattern of as, bs and cs and, furthermore, the initial four-way synchronisation on d and $\overline{d}$ becomes irrelevant as everything now synchronises anyway. We would have to considerably rethink $SABCD$ to allow it to match the behaviour of its CCS* predecessor because we will now have to build in the possible interleavings explicitly. The reason for this is that SCCS* effectively models an implicit global clock which causes each subprocess to perform some transition at every tick. We

CCS	Simple interleaving semantics Atomic transitions Two-way synchronisation
CCS$^+$	Straightforward semantics Concurrent transitions which can all be interleaved Cannot guarantee multi-way synchronisations
CCS*	A less intuitive semantics Concurrency not defined in terms of interleaving Can force multi-way synchronisation
SCCS*	As for CCS* but fully synchronous Agents can only idle when explicitly specified A superset of all the other languages

Figure 3.10. *Comparison of the CCS family of languages*

will not pursue this notion here but will return to it in chapter 7 which is devoted to the topic of time. It is worth observing the fact that CCS, CCS$^+$, CCS* and SCCS* are distinguished principally by their semantics and not by their syntax. It is also interesting that the first three are all subsets of SCCS*. Figure 3.10 gives a table which lists the languages we have developed and some of their distinguishing properties.

EXERCISE 3.9

If we were to interpret the agent PQR from exercise 3.8. as an SCCS* agent, changing '.'s for ':'s, which of the four transitions possible under CCS* would still be possible. Identify them and explain why?

EXERCISE 3.10

Respecify the agent $SABCD$ so that the actions a, b, and c are allowed to occur in the same patterns as $ABCD$. Hint: it is probably easier to see how to do this by allowing D to count occurrences of these actions as they are performed.

3.6 Summary and further reading

In this chapter we have studied the formal semantics of CCS and some closely related languages. Essentially, the formal semantics turns the concrete syntax of CCS, which we studied in the previous chapter, into a formal language by making precise the exact meaning of expressions. We did this by ascribing to each CCS agent a transition graph which captured the idea of the states of that agent and the particular actions which label allowable state changes or transitions. We then went on to show that operational semantics could be used both to formally define the operators in the language and to formalise the relationship between CCS expressions and their transition graphs. The latter was accomplished by using the operational semantics as a proof system to formally verify the transitions in a given transition graph. In the final two sections of the chapter we looked at some alternative but related characterisations of concurrency so as to illustrate more clearly what was meant by the term *interleaving semantics* and how this was related to, what we chose to call, true concurrency.

All the basic definitions formalising CCS are taken from Milner's book [Mil89]. Strictly speaking, we should have gone on to complete the formal definition of CCS by formally defining transition graphs in terms of a labelled transition system. This has been omitted because while transition graphs are intuitively quite straightforward a practical book, such as this, can do without them. Labelled transition systems and their connection with CCS are dealt with in [Mil89] as is also an alternative treatment of recursion in agent definitions. Milner's book is the best reference for SCCS, for which Milner is also responsible. SCCS uses an algebraic formulation of the notion of a concurrent transition and is defined by a far more elegant transitional semantics than that of SCCS*. The material on CCS$^+$, CCS*, and SCCS* was developed for teaching purposes and has not been published to date. The formulations for CCS$^+$, CCS*, etc. used in this chapter were adopted because they are defined in terms of concepts familiar to those who have followed an introductory course in Z or VDM. Anyone wishing to follow through these ideas in more detail would be advised to use SCCS as its theory is far better understood. Practical applications of SCCS have been found in the integration of structured and formal methods for concurrency [PCFP94].

Operational semantics for programming languages etc. were developed by Plotkin and the standard reference is [Plo81]. For a truly detailed analysis of the semantics of a language very similar to CCS the reader should consult [Hen88] which develops operational, denotational, and axiomatic semantics and the theory which links them. However, an understanding of universal algebra is really needed to gain full benefit from the latter work.

4

A first case study

In the previous chapter we studied the formal definition or semantics of CCS and saw how it could help us to understand not only the language itself but also the meaning of the systems we are specifying in the language. This chapter consists of a case study which is principally concerned with the practical problems of developing a specification of a rather more complex system than those already studied. Much of the discussion in this chapter will be of a *how to do it* variety with the technical content kept as familiar as possible to assist in this. Now that we have formally defined CCS we should have a far stronger sense of the meaning and applicability of expressions in the language. We will also emphasise the vital role of systems analysis in the development of specification despite the fact that we are using a formal specification method. A pragmatic approach to constructing formal specifications will be advocated which does not dogmatically require a single top-down approach nor does it assume the reader an absolute beginner nor a professor with years of experience in industry. We will also lay out some suggested guidelines for documenting formal specifications given in CCS.

4.1 Problem statement and analysis

```
------------
REQUIREMENTS
------------
```

```
A process stores three bits of data at a time. It assumes
that data is always transmitted and received least
significant bit first.

The process not only stores the current three bits but
```

also must maintain the integrity of the data held by
keeping bit patterns separate.

The process will transmit all or part of the current
three-bit pattern on request.

When requested to do so another process will analyse the
current three bits stored and output the messages odd,
even or zero as appropriate.

The conversion must be performed as many times as requested
on the current bit pattern.

In addition the system should be able to accommodate
other processes which might require access to the
three-bit store.

The system is not a large one but requires some careful thought. The most natural first step in building CCS specifications is to consider the system as the parallel composition of a number of simpler components with some appropriate restriction set. Looking at the requirements with little analysis leads us to decide that two processes could be used, a data-manager and an analyser or *converter*, as we shall refer to it. The former takes care of the correct storage and update of bit patterns and the latter is simply concerned with the conversion of the currently stored pattern. The data-manager would seem to be the more complicated.

Information is always considered in terms of patterns of three bits but no mention is made of packages. Assume that if we ask the question 'Do bits arrive singly or in packages of three?' that we are given the answer 'Always singly'. This means that the data-manager must be careful to count bits when it is inputting a new pattern and should never both input and output at the same time.

As for the converter, the requirement is actually to output $\overline{odd}$, $\overline{even}$ or $\overline{zero}$ as appropriate when requested to do so. The algorithm to determine the appropriate output on a given bit pattern is straightforward but needs to be expressed in CCS.

It would seem that we can already suggest a top-level CCS expression to define the required system:

$$DMConv \overset{\text{def}}{=} (DataMan \mid Conv)\backslash R$$

At this stage we obviously have no definitions for the agents *DataMan* and *Conv*, nor do we know what the restriction set R is going to be, but we

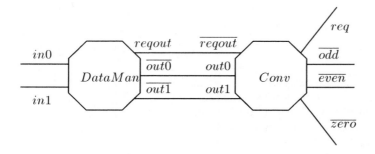

Figure 4.1. *First attempt at a flow graph and CCS definition*

have broken the problem down into smaller subproblems which we hope
will be easier to formally specify.

From this first attempt at a top-level system definition we can start to
build a flow graph which will capture the static configuration of the system.
In other words, what are the possible communications or actions in which
the system may engage during its operation? We are not concerned at
this stage with the ordering of these events and thus the agent definitions.
Working informally through the behaviour of the system we get a simple
set of actions. Zeros and ones are read into *DataMan* which outputs them
to *Conv* on request and when this *Conv* itself has received a conversion
request from the environment. The only other actions are the output of
the result of the conversion. Using our suggested CCS definition we can
draw a first attempt at what we think will be the top-level flow graph for
DMConv (fig. 4.1).

These first attempts are only guesses at this stage and we should be
ready to change them in the light of further development of the system.
The next step is to attempt to specify the two sub-agents identified in the
flow graph.

4.2 Defining the converter

If it were not for the requirement to treat the bit pattern 000 specially the
converter might be defined in the following manner:

$$Conv \stackrel{\text{def}}{=} out0.\overline{even}.Conv + out1.\overline{odd}.Conv$$

Unfortunately our task is a little more complex than this. An informal
description of the converter will be helpful at this stage and can be added
to the overall documentation of the completed specification. Essentially,
the converter must read 0s and 1s, least significant bit first, from the data–
manager until it can decide what output is necessary. We can begin by

using Method 2 from chapter 2 to determine the possible states which the converter may be in at any one time:

Converter

$Conv$	waiting for a request
$Conv1$	waiting for the first bit
$Conv2$	waiting for the second bit
$Conv3$	waiting for the third bit

Next we need to define patterns of behaviour which will connect the various states to give the desired behaviour. All we have to do is ask ourselves what choice of actions the agent has in any particular state.

$$Conv \stackrel{\text{def}}{=} req.\overline{reqout}.Conv1$$
$$Conv1 \stackrel{\text{def}}{=} out0.Conv2 + out1.\overline{odd}.Conv$$
$$Conv2 \stackrel{\text{def}}{=} out0.Conv3 + out1.\overline{even}.Conv$$
$$Conv3 \stackrel{\text{def}}{=} out0.\overline{zero}.Conv + out1.\overline{even}.Conv$$

Notice that the converter stops reading bits from the data-manager as soon as it is able to perform the required output. We should be aware of this when specifying the data-manager in the next section.

4.3 The data-manager

$DataMan$ is more complex and not only requires more thought but is not likely to be able to be specified using the same method we used for $Conv$. Instead we should look carefully at our analysis to date and break the subsystem down into yet smaller systems. In other words, we are going to give a flow graph for $DataMan$ and then attempt to define the sub-agents it introduces.

We have already established that we cannot allow the input of a new bit pattern in the middle of outputting an existing one or vice versa. These two activities seem to be mutually exclusive and so we could define them as separate subprocesses and use a semaphore to ensure the mutual exclusion. Of course, we also require an agent to actually store the current three-bit pattern. This agent will be accessible only by the input and output processes which in turn will only be able to access it if they have control of the semaphore. Figure 4.2 is a first attempt at a flow graph for $DataMan$ which could have the following definition:

$$DataMan \stackrel{\text{def}}{=} (Input \mid Output \mid Sem \mid Store) \backslash \{get, put, s0, s1, w0, w1\}$$

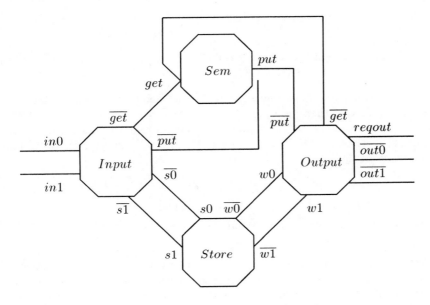

Figure 4.2. *First flow graph for DataMan*

One advantage of a language like CCS is that we can easily make use of agent definitions we already have, where appropriate. We will use the semaphore definition from chapter 2:

$$Sem \stackrel{\text{def}}{=} get.put.Sem$$

We might also at this stage decide to use a three-place buffer to store the current bit pattern. There are good reasons not to do so but we will ignore them for the moment. It is left as an exercise for the reader to specify the required buffer by modifying one of those already given in chapter 2.

We can now proceed to consider the two more complex systems, which are the inputting of new bit patterns and the outputting of the current bit pattern. If we first consider the input activity on its own the problem is really not that complex. Upon being asked to accept a new bit pattern the agent waits until it can gain control of the semaphore and then feeds three bits, one at a time into the buffer. Unlike the case of the converter, however, we don't seem to know when to start this activity for each new bit pattern. Assume that further questioning of the client makes it clear that the arrival of a new bit should trigger the input process. There is no request signal. We will need the following three states:

$Input$	the initial waiting state
$Read1$	waiting for the second bit
$Read2$	waiting for the third bit

The initial state $Input$ must wait for the arrival of the first bit in a new pattern and then gain control of the semaphore. Having done this it can send the new bit to the buffer and wait for the arrival of two further bits. The other states, $Read1$ and $Read2$, are quite straightforward. The definition of the agent will therefore be:

$$Input \stackrel{\text{def}}{=} in0.\overline{get}.\overline{s0}.Read1 + in1.\overline{get}.\overline{s1}.Read1$$
$$Read1 \stackrel{\text{def}}{=} in0.\overline{s0}.Read2 + in1.\overline{s1}.Read2$$
$$Read2 \stackrel{\text{def}}{=} in0.\overline{s0}.\overline{put}.Input + in1.\overline{s1}.\overline{put}.Input$$

This seems to be satisfactory, so we can proceed to the remaining sub-agent of the data-manager which deals with the output of the existing bit pattern. This process has much in common with the input process. The activity can only take place if control of the semaphore has been gained. Also, we have not said when the activity commences. In this case the decision is ours as this is an action which is internal to our specification and not affected by the requirements. We could try and use the converter's request for the output of the first bit to trigger the activity but that would mean sending the first bit before control of the semaphore has been gained. This could lead to problems if the input agent was active. We will have to add an extra synchronisation, $reqout$, to the top-level flow graph (fig. 4.3 below) to tell $Output$ that it needs to gain control of the semaphore. This must be reflected in the definition for $Output$ and will also require a slight change to the definition for $Conv$. The agent $Output$ can now be specified using the following states:

$Output$	initial waiting state
$Outready$	semaphore gained, ready to output first bit
$Out1$	ready to output second bit
$Out2$	ready to output third bit

The definitions should not surprise the reader:

$$Output \stackrel{\text{def}}{=} reqout.\overline{get}.Outready$$
$$Outready \stackrel{\text{def}}{=} w0.\overline{out0}.Out1 + w1.\overline{out1}.Out1$$
$$Out1 \stackrel{\text{def}}{=} w0.\overline{out0}.Out2 + w1.\overline{out1}.Out2$$
$$Out2 \stackrel{\text{def}}{=} w0.\overline{out0}.\overline{put}.Output + w1.\overline{out1}.\overline{put}.Output$$

We have now specified all the agents of the *DataMan* sub-agent of our specification and the top-level definition, repeated here, has remained unchanged:

$$DataMan \stackrel{\text{def}}{=} (Input \mid Output \mid Sem \mid Store) \backslash \{get, put, s0, s1, w0, w1\}$$

Our next task is the verification and validation of the specification. Do we have any technical problems with the system, deadlocks, unwanted behaviours, etc.? Have we specified a system that meets requirements? Before proceeding with this discussion you should attempt the exercise below which is concerned with just this problem. In the next section we will find out what problems there are with the specification to date.

EXERCISE 4.1

Build up a checklist of potential problems to do with flow of control, deadlocks, data and data structures, etc. Decide on some behaviour traces that will identify your problems and use the Verification Game or the Concurrency Workbench to check it all out. Hint: there are a number of severe problems with the specification as it stands.

4.4 Checking the system

Analysis of the specification shows, as the hint suggested, that we have a variety of problems which we can categorise in the following way:

1. Initialisation of *DataMan*

2. Definition of *Store*

3. *DataMan–Conv* communications

The first of these is a common one with building CCS specifications in that we did not consider how we were to initialise or startup *DMConv*. What we have actually specified is the normal *up and running* mode of operation. This could cause problems if *Conv* successfully requests a three-bit pattern before one has been entered into *Store*. In this case we would have the whole system deadlocked. Try animating the specification with the trace $req.\tau.\tau$ to see what actually happens. We have to make sure that *Store* receives its first three values before *Output* is activated. The changes are fairly straightforward but involve both *Input* and *Sem*. We will give the input process control of the semaphore from startup and simply get it

to read three bits and load them into *Store* before anything else is allowed
to happen. This requires a new definition for *Start* which is used once only:

$$Start \stackrel{\text{def}}{=} in0.\overline{s0}.Read1 + in1.\overline{s1}.Read1$$
$$Input \stackrel{\text{def}}{=} in0.\overline{get}.\overline{s0}.Read1 + in1.\overline{get}.\overline{s1}.Read1$$
$$Read1 \stackrel{\text{def}}{=} in0.\overline{s0}.Read2 + in1.\overline{s1}.Read2$$
$$Read2 \stackrel{\text{def}}{=} in0.\overline{s0}.\overline{put}.Input + in1.\overline{s1}.\overline{put}.Input$$

We need to make a slight change to the initial state of the semaphore so
that instead of waiting for *get* it starts waiting for *put*. Probably the easiest
way to do this is to leave the definition for *Sem* alone but to replace *Sem*
by *put.Sem* in the top-level definition for *DataMan* which now becomes

$$DataMan \stackrel{\text{def}}{=} (Start \mid Output \mid put.Sem \mid Store) \backslash \{get, put, s0, s1, w0, w1\}$$

Let us move on to the second problem on our list. You should have noticed
something wrong with the behaviour of the agent *Store*. The problem is
that when bits are output to the converter we are emptying the buffer and
so cannot perform another conversion on the same three bits if requested
to do so. This does not comply with requirements; having output a three-
bit pattern the data-manager should be able do so again as many times
as requested to do so. Our choice of a buffer to hold the bit patterns was
not correct and the problem is not difficult to identify in this context. A
buffer is a temporary store which holds data until some other agent requires
it. This is not to say we should not adopt the technique of agent re-use
nor evolutionary development, for they are natural and efficient ways of
building specifications. Quite the opposite, we are now going to introduce
a further operator into our language which will help us to do just this.

What we really need is something more like an array which holds data on
a more permanent basis. In this case all we really need are three variables to
store the separate bits. What we will do is define a generic variable of this
type and then build up the three instances of it we need. Our bit variable
has three possible states:

Var	uninitialised state
Var_0	holding a zero
Var_1	holding a one

The definition of the generic variable is now straightforward, but do
notice that we have decided to ignore attempts to access its uninitialised
state. This does not model *real life* where such programs invariably cause
a runtime error directly or pass junk data which then invariably leads to
error. Notice that this does not get us out of the initialisation problem for

the deadlock is already inevitable if *Output* has started to access *Store* variables.

$$Var \quad \stackrel{\text{def}}{=} \quad rd0.Var_0 + rd1.Var_1$$
$$Var_0 \quad \stackrel{\text{def}}{=} \quad \overline{wrt0}.Var_0 + rd0.Var_0 + rd1.Var_1$$
$$Var_1 \quad \stackrel{\text{def}}{=} \quad \overline{wrt1}.Var_1 + rd0.Var_0 + rd1.Var_1$$

We now need to build three specific instances of the array to hold the patterns of bits we are dealing with. We could do this by specifying three agents, $A1$, $A2$ and $A3$, just using the ideas from Var, but this is going to be time-consuming. Instead, we introduce a new operator which will allow us to define the three agents we require by relabelling actions of Var as appropriate. Let us look at a simple example first. You will recall the little two-place buffer we introduced in chapter 2:

$$Buff_2 \quad \stackrel{\text{def}}{=} \quad (C_1 \mid C_2)\backslash\{m\}$$
$$C_1 \quad \stackrel{\text{def}}{=} \quad in.\overline{m}.C_1$$
$$C_2 \quad \stackrel{\text{def}}{=} \quad m.\overline{out}.C_2$$

Remembering that we derived C_1 and C_2 from the agent C, defined as

$$C \stackrel{\text{def}}{=} in.\overline{out}.C$$

we could have defined C_1 and C_2 in the following manner:

$$C_1 \quad \stackrel{\text{def}}{=} \quad C[\overline{m}/\overline{out}]$$
$$C_2 \quad \stackrel{\text{def}}{=} \quad C[m/in]$$

where the intended meaning of the new notation,

$$C_1 \stackrel{\text{def}}{=} C[\overline{m}/\overline{out}]$$

is that C_1 behaves exactly like C except that the action $\overline{out}$ is always replaced by $\overline{m}$. We add the new operator to CCS by extending the operational semantics with the following rule:

$$\textbf{Rel}\frac{E \stackrel{l}{\rightarrow} E'}{E[f] \stackrel{f(l)}{\rightarrow} E'[f]}$$

where f is a function from $\mathcal{L}$ to $\mathcal{L}$ with the following additional properties. If f relabels l to l' then it also relabels $\bar{l}$ to $\overline{l'}$. In addition, f acts as the identity function on actions which do not occur complemented or uncomplemented in its domain. Notice that this new operator is static in the sense that it is not lost by the transition, much in the same way that parallel composition and restriction persist.

In the literature relabelling is always defined as above but it might be better to remember that we really mean the following rule:

$$\mathbf{RealRel}\frac{E \xrightarrow{l} E'}{E[f] \xrightarrow{[f](l)} E'[f]} \quad [f] = Id_{Act} \oplus f \oplus \overline{f}$$

This definition takes the partial function $f: \mathcal{L} \to \mathcal{L}$ and creates a total function $[f]: \mathcal{L} \to \mathcal{L}$ where Id_{Act} is the identity on actions, $\oplus$ is function override, and $\overline{f}$ is the function f with its domain and range complemented. We will use **Rel** as the rule for relabelling but you should always remember its full definition.

Using this new operator and our definition for Var we can redefine the $Store$ in the following manner:

$$
\begin{aligned}
Store &\stackrel{\text{def}}{=} (A1 \mid A2 \mid A3) \\
A1 &\stackrel{\text{def}}{=} Var[rd0A1/rd0, rd1A1/rd1, wrt0A1/wrt0, wrt1A1/wrt1] \\
A2 &\stackrel{\text{def}}{=} Var[rd0A2/rd0, rd1A2/rd1, wrt0A2/wrt0, wrt1A2/wrt1] \\
A3 &\stackrel{\text{def}}{=} Var[rd0A3/rd0, rd1A3/rd1, wrt0A3/wrt0, wrt1A3/wrt1]
\end{aligned}
$$

Remember that relabelling respects complements. Notice that we could have made our definition even more concise by indexing a single instance of the actual variable we require,

$$A_i \stackrel{\text{def}}{=} Var[rd0A_i/rd0, rd1A_i/rd1, wrt0A_i/wrt0, wrt1A_i/wrt1]$$

where $i \in \{1, 2, 3\}$.

Either way, the store now behaves in the manner we require but the flow graph for $DataMan$ and therefore the definitions for $Input$ and $Output$ must now be amended. The flow graph for $DataMan$ is given in the documentation of the completed specification towards the end of this chapter. The new definition for $Input$ is as follows:

$$
\begin{aligned}
Start &\stackrel{\text{def}}{=} in0.\overline{rd0A1}.Read1 + in1.\overline{rd1A1}.Read1 \\
Input &\stackrel{\text{def}}{=} in0.\overline{get}.\overline{rd0A1}.Read1 + in1.\overline{get}.\overline{rd1A1}.Read1 \\
Read1 &\stackrel{\text{def}}{=} in0.\overline{rd0A2}.Read2 + in1.\overline{rd1A2}.Read2 \\
Read2 &\stackrel{\text{def}}{=} in0.\overline{rd0A3}.\overline{put}.Input + in1.\overline{rd1A3}.\overline{put}.Input
\end{aligned}
$$

The definition for $Output$ will have to be similarly redefined but we will put this off for a moment and look at the behaviour of the overall system $DMConv$. There is our third major problem and it arises because of inconsistencies between the behaviours of $Conv$ and $Output$. The conversion process does not always require all three bits in order to be able to output the result $\overline{odd}$, $\overline{even}$ or $\overline{zero}$. However, the current specification of $Output$ always expects all three bits to be sent. There thus exists the possibility of deadlocks occurring where $Output$ is still waiting to send one or more bits

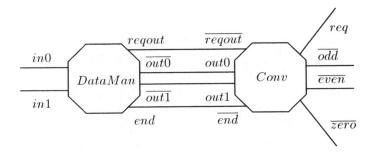

Figure 4.3. *Final flow graph for DMConv*

to *Conv* which has already made a conversion and is now attempting to respond to the next conversion request from the environment.

There are two ways round the problem. First of all, we could compel *Conv* to collect all three bits whether it needs them or not. Secondly, we could require *Conv* to inform *Output* when it has finished reading data. The second possibility seems the more reasonable, so we will adopt that and require *Conv* to send an $\overline{end}$ signal to *Output* to allow the latter to switch back to its initial state. Figure 4.3 gives the new flow graph for *DMConv* which will also mean a simple change to the flow graph for *DataMan*, figure 4.4.

It is best to amend the definition for *Conv* first and this simply amounts to performing the action $\overline{end}$ immediately before returning to its initial state if it has only read one or two bits:

$$
\begin{aligned}
Conv &\overset{\text{def}}{=} req.\overline{reqout}.Conv1 \\
Conv1 &\overset{\text{def}}{=} out0.Conv2 + out1.\overline{odd}.\overline{end}.Conv \\
Conv2 &\overset{\text{def}}{=} out0.Conv3 + out1.\overline{even}.\overline{end}.Conv \\
Conv3 &\overset{\text{def}}{=} out0.\overline{zero}.Conv + out1.\overline{even}.Conv
\end{aligned}
$$

There are various ways in which we could amend *Output* depending on how much we allow it to understand of the conversion algorithm. We could assume that the observation has been made that sometimes the second and/or third bits are not required and modify the agent accordingly. We could make the agent more robust and assume that it always requires an end-of-output signal until it has transmitted three bits. The latter case will make it easier to interface other agents which need access to the same data but for different reasons. We will specify this solution:

$$
\begin{aligned}
Output &\overset{\text{def}}{=} reqout.\overline{get}.Outready \\
Outready &\overset{\text{def}}{=} wrt0A1.(end.\overline{put}.Output + \overline{out0}.Out1)+ \\
&\qquad wrt1A1.(end.\overline{put}.Output + \overline{out1}.Out1) \\
Out1 &\overset{\text{def}}{=} wrt0A2.(end.\overline{put}.Output + \overline{out0}.Out2)+ \\
&\qquad wrt1A2.(end.\overline{put}.Output + \overline{out1}.Out2) \\
Out2 &\overset{\text{def}}{=} wrt0A3.(end.\overline{put}.Output + \overline{out0}.\overline{put}.Output)+ \\
&\qquad wrt1A3.(end.\overline{put}.Output + \overline{out1}.\overline{put}.Output)
\end{aligned}
$$

EXERCISE 4.2

Given the definition

$$ B \overset{\text{def}}{=} a.b.c.B $$

construct a specification, using B and the relabelling operator, that consists of four agents B_i, $i \in \{1,\dots,4\}$, composed in parallel, each of which fires its only observable action b_i cyclically. In other words, the only action sequence would be of the form $\overline{b_1}.\tau.\overline{b_2}.\tau.\overline{b_3}.\tau.\overline{b_4}.\tau.\overline{b_1}\dots$.

EXERCISE 4.3

In chapter 1 we discussed a mass transit system as an example of the type of system this book is concerned with. One feature of the system was the ability to run trains off into a siding when demand was low. Build a model of the siding based on the following diagram:

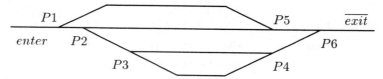

where $P1, P2, \dots$ are the names of the points and $enter$ and $\overline{exit}$ the actions refer to trains entering and leaving the siding.

Hint: approach the problem by defining a generic set of points which can be used in conjunction with relabelling to produce the switching possibilities.

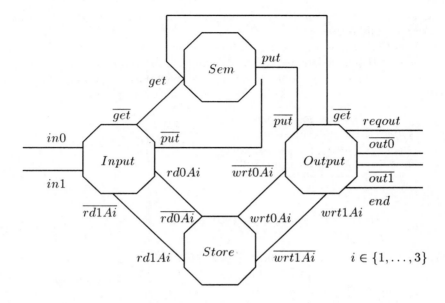

Figure 4.4. *Final flow graph for DataMan*

4.5 The completed specification

We can now collect together all the definitions and document them appropriately.

Specification of the data-manager–converter

The system is specified in terms of two sub-agents, *DataMan* and *Conv*, which model the storing of data and the conversion process respectively. Figure 4.3 gives the final flow graph for the top-level specification.

$$DMConv \stackrel{\text{def}}{=} (DataMan \mid Conv) \backslash R$$

$$R = \{reqout, out0, out1, end\}$$

The data-manager

The data-manager itself is specified in terms of the following sub-agents:

$$DataMan \stackrel{\text{def}}{=} (Start \mid Output \mid put.Sem \mid Store) \backslash D$$

$$D = \{get, put, rd0A1, rd1A1, \ldots, wrt0A1, wrt1A1, \ldots\}$$

Figure 4.4 gives the final flow graph for *DataMan*.

Start is used to ensure that the *Store* receives the first three-bit pattern before allowing *Conv* to attempt to access it. *Start* is called only once and is replaced by *Input* on all subsequent cycles.

The semaphore *Sem* is used to ensure the sub-agents *Input* and *Output* are mutually exclusive.

Input handles the updating of the store by accepting sequences of three bits from the environment. Upon receiving the first bit in a new pattern it attempts to gain control of the semaphore to enable it to update *Store*.

Start	waiting for the first three bits
Input	the initial waiting state
Read1	waiting for the second bit
Read2	waiting for the third bit

$$Start \stackrel{\text{def}}{=} in0.\overline{rd0A1}.Read1 + in1.\overline{rd1A1}.Read1$$

$$Input \stackrel{\text{def}}{=} in0.\overline{get}.\overline{rd0A1}.Read1 + in1.\overline{get}.\overline{rd1A1}.Read1$$

$$Read1 \stackrel{\text{def}}{=} in0.\overline{rd0A2}.Read2 + in1.\overline{rd1A2}.Read2$$

$$Read2 \stackrel{\text{def}}{=} in0.\overline{rd0A3}.\overline{put}.Input + in1.\overline{rd1A3}.\overline{put}.Input$$

The agent *Output* communicates bits to the agent *Conv* after synchronising on the action *reqout* and gaining control of the semaphore. The synchronisation on the action *end* terminates an output session if less than three bits have been sent.

Output	initial waiting state
Outready	semaphore gained, ready to output first bit
Out1	ready to output second bit
Out2	ready to output third bit

$$Output \stackrel{\text{def}}{=} reqout.\overline{get}.Outready$$

$$Outready \stackrel{\text{def}}{=} wrt0A1.(end.\overline{put}.Output + \overline{out0}.Out1) +$$
$$wrt1A1.(end.\overline{put}.Output + \overline{out1}.Out1)$$

$$Out1 \stackrel{\text{def}}{=} wrt0A2.(end.\overline{put}.Output + \overline{out0}.Out2) +$$
$$wrt1A2.(end.\overline{put}.Output + \overline{out1}.Out2)$$

$$Out2 \stackrel{\text{def}}{=} wrt0A3.(end.\overline{put}.Output + \overline{out0}.\overline{put}.Output) +$$
$$wrt1A3.(end.\overline{put}.Output + \overline{out1}.\overline{put}.Output)$$

The semaphore *Sem* is defined in the standard way:

$$Sem \stackrel{\text{def}}{=} get.put.Sem$$

The agent *Store* holds the current three-bit pattern in three sub-agent variables, *A1*, *A2* and *A3*, which are themselves defined by relabelling the generic variable *Var*. Figure 4.5 gives a generic flow graph for the three

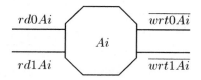

$$i \in \{1, \ldots, 3\}$$

Figure 4.5. *A generic flow graph for A1, A2, and A3*

sub-agents which communicate with *Input* and *Output* but not with each other.

$$Store \overset{\text{def}}{=} (A1 \mid A2 \mid A3)$$
$$A1 \overset{\text{def}}{=} Var[rd0A1/rd0, rd1A1/rd1, wrt0A1/wrt0, wrt1A1/wrt1]$$
$$A2 \overset{\text{def}}{=} Var[rd0A2/rd0, rd1A2/rd1, wrt0A2/wrt0, wrt1A2/wrt1]$$
$$A3 \overset{\text{def}}{=} Var[rd0A3/rd0, rd1A3/rd1, wrt0A3/wrt0, wrt1A3/wrt1]$$

Var	uninitialised state
Var_0	holding a zero
Var_1	holding a one

$$Var \overset{\text{def}}{=} rd0.Var_0 + rd1.Var_1$$
$$Var_0 \overset{\text{def}}{=} \overline{wrt0}.Var_0 + rd0.Var_0 + rd1.Var_1$$
$$Var_1 \overset{\text{def}}{=} \overline{wrt1}.Var_1 + rd0.Var_0 + rd1.Var_1$$

The converter

Upon receiving the signal *req* the agent *Conv* reads up to three bits from *DataMan* and outputs the message *odd*, *even* or *zero* as appropriate. If it is able to make the calculation on less than three bits it synchronises with *DataMan* on the action $\overline{end}$ to signal the termination of that particular session.

$Conv$	waiting for a request
$Conv1$	waiting for the first bit
$Conv2$	waiting for the second bit
$Conv3$	waiting for the third bit

$$Conv \quad \stackrel{\text{def}}{=} \quad req.\overline{reqout}.Conv1$$

$$Conv1 \quad \stackrel{\text{def}}{=} \quad out0.Conv2 + out1.\overline{odd}.\overline{end}.Conv$$

$$Conv2 \quad \stackrel{\text{def}}{=} \quad out0.Conv3 + out1.\overline{even}.\overline{end}.Conv$$

$$Conv3 \quad \stackrel{\text{def}}{=} \quad out0.\overline{zero}.Conv + out1.\overline{even}.Conv$$

End of specification

EXERCISE 4.4

Three extra conversion processes are required to be run in parallel with *DataMan* and *Conv*:

1. *Rev* outputs the reverse of the current three-bit pattern on request.

2. *LogicOr* outputs the logical *or* of the current three-bit pattern on request.

3. *LogicAnd* outputs the logical *and* of the current three-bit pattern on request.

Conv and the three new processes must be mutually exclusive in their interactions with the system as already defined. In other words, only one of the four may interact with *DataMan* at any one time.

EXERCISE 4.5

You may have noticed a certain similarity between *Conv* and *LogicOr*. Define *LogicOr* by relabelling *Conv* and then define *LogicAnd* by relabelling *LogicOr*.

4.6 Summary and further reading

The case study in this chapter was designed to make the reader think about the practicalities of using CCS to specify a system from requirements. A major point to arise is that using a formal method does not mean that all the usual tasks of systems analysis are to be forgotten. Indeed, we will see as the book progresses that we have to consider the integration of formal methods into the software lifecycle quite carefully. We also emphasised the fact that a simple top-down approach to specification construction was not necessarily appropriate and that iteration through the development process was inevitable for all but the simplest of systems. To this end we also advocated the use of bottom-up techniques for specification re-use and added a relabelling operator to the language to facilitate this. Later in the book we will pursue ideas concerning methods and the practical application of CCS further. It should also have become apparent just how important the verification and validation of CCS specifications is. Despite the simplicity of the language it allows us to specify very complex patterns of behaviour and we need to take great care they are the ones we want. In Part II of this book we will consider formal means of verification to enhance the testing techniques we have been using to date.

Now some specific points about the specification itself. Notice that for *Output* we have had to write out all the possible cases where an *end* signal might be received. This could get very cumbersome for a more complex agent and we would really like some kind of interrupt which forces *Output* to revert to its initial state without having to specify all the possible cases. In chapter 8 we will look at such extensions to the language. We should also observe at this stage that it is just as well our data is in bits and not natural numbers because we would not then be able to write out a state-based specification of the problem solution. More than this, we could quite reasonably observe that the *Store* itself looks far more like an implementation than a specification and has made us think too much about the *how* as opposed to the *what*. We will reconsider the topic of data and its transmission in the next chapter and see how it can benefit the readability and elegance of specifications.

As with the rest of the semantics for basic CCS the definition of the relabelling operator given in this chapter is taken from [Mil89] and is an essential part of the basic calculus. Its introduction was delayed in order to keep the earlier chapters as simple as possible. In fact there is one more aspect of the calculus to be covered before we have fully defined CCS as given in Milner's book, but we will deal with this in the next chapter.

5

Value passing

We saw in chapter 4 that basic CCS will have only limited use in specifying concurrent systems in which data and its communication play a significant part. Certainly, even the limited use of data made by the $DMConv$ in that chapter made a basically straightforward specification look somewhat cumbersome. In this chapter we will look at extensions to basic CCS which allow us to separate out behaviour from data. One of the intended benefits will be to simplify CCS specifications in that agents will now be used to specify processes in the more usual sense of the word and not data structures as they were forced to do in the last chapter. The new language will also allow us to specify systems more concisely in other ways.

We will demonstrate the notational additions to basic CCS first and then specify the semantics formally later on. It will turn out that the semantics of this new language can actually be given in terms of a translation into basic CCS. To illustrate the benefits of this apparently extended CCS we will rework some familiar examples from earlier chapters and compare them with their basic CCS counterparts.

5.1 Making values explicit

We saw in chapters 2 and 4 that we could give the effect of values in our specifications by the use of appropriate action names. A two place buffer that stores bits could be defined as

$$
\begin{aligned}
Cell_1 &\stackrel{\text{def}}{=} in0.\bar{z}.Cell_1 + in1.\bar{o}.Cell_1 \\
Cell_2 &\stackrel{\text{def}}{=} z.\overline{out0}.Cell_2 + o.\overline{out1}.Cell_2 \\
Buff_2^2 &\stackrel{\text{def}}{=} (Cell_1 \mid Cell_2)\backslash\{z,o\}
\end{aligned}
$$

where the actions $in0$ and $in1$ are intended to represent the inputting of a zero and a one respectively. If we were to try to use this technique to explicitly specify a two-place buffer that stored natural numbers, for example, then we should obviously not be able to write out all the cases. We can, however, use it as the basis of a translation between a value-passing calculus based on CCS and basic CCS itself.

The first step is to allow actions to have parameters which will consist of typed variables. The two-place buffer redefined for natural numbers would then be specified in the following manner:

$$Cell_1 \stackrel{\text{def}}{=} in(x).\overline{m}(x).Cell_1$$
$$Cell_2 \stackrel{\text{def}}{=} m(x).\overline{out}(x).Cell_2$$
$$Buff_2^N \stackrel{\text{def}}{=} (Cell_1 \mid Cell_2)\backslash\{m\}$$

We assume that all variables are of type natural number in this instance. This specification is obviously much simpler than the previous version and easier to understand by someone used to a programming language. There is now an important difference between $\alpha(x)$ and $\overline{\alpha}(x)$. The former binds all free occurrences of the variable x in the subexpression which $\alpha(x)$ prefixes and thus acts as a parameter-passing mechanism. In contrast, the action $\overline{\alpha}(x)$ is simply an output of a value for x and has no binding power. We will only consider cases where x becomes bound to some value expression e before the action $\overline{\alpha}(x)$ is possible.

Not only actions but agent constants may have parameters. We can define another version of the buffer in the following manner:

$$Buff_N^2(<>) \stackrel{\text{def}}{=} in(x).Buff_N^2(<x>)$$
$$Buff_N^2(<x>) \stackrel{\text{def}}{=} in(y).Buff_N^2(<y,x>) + \overline{out}(x).Buff_N^2(<>)$$
$$Buff_N^2(<x,y>) \stackrel{\text{def}}{=} \overline{out}(y).Buff_N^2(<x>)$$

Again, all variables are of type natural number and we are using the notation $< 5 >$ to represent the sequence which contains the single value 5. Notice that the actual variable names used within the parameters are less important than the order they are given in. In the second definition the agent $Buff^2(< x,y >)$ is called but the definition for this case has the variable names reversed, though if you check the right hand side of the definition you can assure yourself that the first value input is indeed the first value output. In a full formal specification of the buffer we should declare types for all variables used and specify abstract datatypes for any data structures, such as the sequences used above. At present we are concerned with the way values are communicated rather than their definition or calculation. We will return to consider these issues later in the chapter.

Notice that the scope of variables occurring in the left hand side of a constant definition extends to all free occurrences of that variable on the right-hand side. When the constant is *called*, its parameters should all be appropriately instantiated. The following are important points to note respecting the scoping of variables in the new calculus:

1. If a variable occurs as a parameter to an agent constant then its scope is the whole expression which defines that constant.

2. Variables occurring in input actions of the form $in(x)$ have as their scope the whole subexpression which that action prefixes.

3. Variables occurring as parameters to output actions of the form $\overline{out}(x)$ must always be in the scope of some input action or constant definition. In other words, output action parameters must always be given a value before their action is performed.

4. The scope of a variable never extends beyond the equation in which it occurs. In the definitions $C \stackrel{\text{def}}{=} in(x).C'$ and $C' \stackrel{\text{def}}{=} \overline{out}(x).C$ the scope of x ends with the call to C' and the x occurring in the definition for C' is a free variable which remains unbound despite any call to C'. Of course, this x could become bound if these definitions became part of a larger specification and in the scope of an input action with a variable parameter of that name.

We are also going to introduce a conditional statement to enable us to perform checks on values input. By way of an example, the following agent inputs two natural numbers and outputs the first divided by the second providing the latter is not zero in which case an error is reported:

$$Div \stackrel{\text{def}}{=} in(x).in(y).(if \ y = 0 \ then \ \overline{error}.Div$$
$$else \ \overline{output}(x \ div \ y).Div)$$

Notice that along with an appropriate definition of the natural numbers we are assuming definitions for operators defined over them as well. Again, what we should do is to add datatype definitions to our value-passing CCS specifications as well as some formal mechanism for typing variables.

The extensions to basic CCS provide a very natural means of specifying concurrent systems that handle data and data structures. Later in this chapter we will take a fresh look at the case study from chapter 4 and see how much more elegantly it can be modelled in value-passing CCS. Before that, we will see in the next section that we can translate the whole of this apparently extended calculus into basic CCS with the obvious benefit that all the semantic definitions we have studied will still hold when we consider value passing.

EXERCISE 5.1

1. Why do we need to introduce a conditional statement in the value-passing calculus but not for the basic calculus?

2. In the agent Div we used the two-armed conditional $if \ b \ then \ E \ else \ E'$ and yet it is only necessary to define a one-armed conditional $if \ b \ then \ E$. Why?

EXERCISE 5.2

1. Respecify the agents $Buff_4^2$, C and D from the producer–consumer problem from chapter 2 so that the buffer holds natural numbers instead of bits and interfaces correctly with the new versions of C and D which should output the mean and minimum of their inputs respectively. C accepts only odd values and D accepts only even values. You may assume definitions for operators, such as *mean*, *min*, *odd*, and *even*, that you may require.

2. Defining an agent to generate natural numbers instead of bits to input to the buffer, in the manner of A and B from the original, is problematic; can you see why?

EXERCISE 5.3

Respecify the filter so that $CVal$ and $DVal$ can take all output from the buffer until they can perform $\overline{mod3}$ or $\overline{mod4}$ respectively. Take a look at the solution to exercise 2.10 to see what is required.

EXERCISE 5.4

Specify a bounded buffer of size n along the lines of $Buff(<>)_2^N$ given above. You may assume sequence operators *head* and *tail*, with the expected meanings, as well as $x::s$ which adds a new element, x, to the front of the sequence, s.

5.2 The value-passing calculus

We will now state the syntax of the value-passing calculus in the context of a language which has a single type V. This can easily be extended to a language of multiple types by taking V to be the union of all the actual types required. Here, e is any value expression of type V, x is a variable of the same type, and b is any Boolean expression on V. The operators are given in descending order of precedence:

$$\mathcal{E}^+ \quad ::= \quad \mathbf{0}$$
$$| \quad \mathcal{E} \backslash R$$
$$| \quad \mathcal{E}^+[f]$$
$$| \quad l(x).\mathcal{E}^+$$
$$| \quad \bar{l}(x).\mathcal{E}^+$$
$$| \quad \alpha.\mathcal{E}^+$$
$$| \quad \mathcal{E}^+ \mid \mathcal{E}^+$$
$$| \quad \mathcal{E}^+ + \mathcal{E}^+$$
$$| \quad if \ b \ then \ \mathcal{E}^+$$

The three possible types of prefix expressions have several important implications for our new language. First of all, observable actions are not forced to take parameters but may be atomic as in basic CCS. We stipulate that no action may be both parameterised and unparameterised in the same specification. A further implication is that τ actions may not be seen to pass values. In addition, each agent constant A with arity n has a defining equation of the form $A(a_1, \ldots, a_n) \overset{\text{def}}{=} E$ where the only free variables in E are $x_1, \ldots, x_n$.

The translation relies on the idea that each action in the value-passing calculus has an associated set of actions in the basic calculus. For example, action $in(x)$ from our buffer example where x is of type natural number has the corresponding set $\{in_x \mid x \in \mathbf{N}\}$ of actions in the basic calculus. Actions with no variable need no translation. The translation is given in terms of a function

$$\|\text{-}\| \ \mathcal{E}^+ \to \mathcal{E}$$

such that for each expression $E \in \mathcal{E}^+$ without free variables we derive its translated form $\|E\| \in \mathcal{E}$. The function is defined by cases on the structure of value-passing expressions. We will make use of the notion of an indexed sum or choice operator

$$\sum_{i \in I} E_i$$

where I is an indexing set and the whole expression is syntactically equivalent to the agent

$$E_1 + \ldots + E_n \quad (\{1, \ldots, n\} = I)$$

Indexed sums are a generalisation of the binary sums we have been using to date and are defined by the following rule:

$$\mathbf{Sum_j} \ \frac{E_j \overset{\alpha}{\to} E_j'}{\sum_{i \in I} E_i \overset{\alpha}{\to} E_j'} \quad (j \in I)$$

Using indexed sums we can now define the semantic function $\|\text{-}\| \ \mathcal{E}^+ \to \mathcal{E}$ which translates expressions in the value-passing syntax into equivalent expressions in the syntax of basic CCS, for which of course we have an operational sematics.

$$\begin{array}{rcl}
\|l(x).E\| & = & \sum_{v \in V} l_v.\|E\{v/x\}\| \\
\|\bar{l}(e).E\| & = & \bar{l}_e.\|E\| \\
\|\alpha.E\| & = & \alpha.\|E\| \\
\|E + F\| & = & \|E\| + \|F\| \\
\|E \mid F\| & = & \|E\| \mid \|F\| \\
\|E\backslash R\| & = & \|E\|\backslash\{l_v \mid l \in R \wedge v \in V\} \\
\|E[f]\| & = & \|E\|[\widehat{f}] \ (\widehat{f}(l_v) = f(l)_v) \\
\|if\ b\ then\ E\| & = & \left\{ \begin{array}{ll} \|E\| & \text{if } b = true \\ \mathbf{0} & \text{otherwise} \end{array} \right. \\
\|P(e_1, \ldots, e_n)\| & = & P_{e_1, \ldots, e_n}
\end{array}$$

Essentially, we have given a denotational semantics for CCS in the sense that we are mapping syntactic expressions onto a mathematical object which constitutes the expression's meaning. Notice that we only consider output actions which are bound to some suitable value expression $\bar{l}(e).E$ and thus ensure that we do not attempt to translate free variables into basic CCS. The equation for restriction should include the case where an action in the restriction set is parameterised, in which case it remains unaffected. Notice also that there are several possible terminating cases for this function. If the indexing set on the generalised choice is the empty set then there are no E_i and 0 is simply returned. Another terminating case is when an agent constant, with or without parameters, is encountered. A further terminating case is when a boolean expression in a conditional expression evaluates to false. Equations for defining constants will be translated in the following manner:

$$\|P(x_1, \ldots, x_n) \stackrel{\text{def}}{=} E\| = P_{e_1, \ldots, e_n} \stackrel{\text{def}}{=} \|E\{e_1/x_1, \ldots, e_n/x_n\}\|$$

for all possible instantiations $e_1, \ldots, e_n$ of $x_1, \ldots, x_n$. In other words, there will be a separate definition for P for each possible instantiation of its parameter variable(s).

By way of an example we will redefine the generic agent Var from the case study in the last chapter and apply the translation function to it. The agent had the following definition:

$$\begin{array}{rcl}
Var & \stackrel{\text{def}}{=} & rd0.Var_0 + rd1.Var_1 \\
Var_0 & \stackrel{\text{def}}{=} & \overline{wrt0}.Var_0 + rd0.Var_0 + rd1.Var_1 \\
Var_1 & \stackrel{\text{def}}{=} & \overline{wrt1}.Var_1 + rd0.Var_0 + rd1.Var_1
\end{array}$$

We can produce a substantially simpler value-passing version even for this already simple specification:

$$VarVal \overset{\text{def}}{=} rd(x).VarVal(x)$$
$$VarVal(x) \overset{\text{def}}{=} \overline{wrt}(x).VarVal(x) + rd(y).VarVal(y)$$

We will apply the translation function to the defining expreression for $VarVal$ to see how the function actually achieves its task:

$$\|VarVal \overset{\text{def}}{=} rd(x).VarVal(x)\|$$
$$= VarVal \overset{\text{def}}{=} \|rd(x).VarVal(x)\|$$

This leaves us to translate the right hand side of the definition, which can be performed separately once we know what values have been substituted for any formal parameters; in this case there are none:

$$\|rd(x).VarVal(x)\|$$
$$= rd_0.\|VarVal(x)\{0/x\}\|$$
$$+$$
$$rd_1.\|VarVal(x)\{1/x\}\|$$
$$= rd_0.VarVal_0$$
$$+$$
$$rd_1.VarVal_1$$

Comparing the definitions for Var and $\|VarVal\|$ should convince you that they are virtually identical in this case, particularly if we had adopted the convention that $in0$ should always be represented as in_0 and so on. In practice, the translation should proceed by applying the function to the top-level definition first and then working down through the sub-agents and so on. This has the effect of identifying which particular instantiations for agents' parameter variables have to be evaluated. In the next section we shall put the value-passing calculus to work on the whole case study from the previous chapter to demonstrate the benefits to be gained from the new calculus.

EXERCISE 5.5

1. Use an indexed sum to give a derived definition for the null agent **0**.

2. Use an indexed sum to give a derived definition for the binary choice operator $E + F$.

EXERCISE 5.6

Use an indexed sum to solve the problem of generating natural numbers in exercise 2.2.

EXERCISE 5.7

Apply the translation function to the definition for $VarVal(x)$. This should generate two definitions, one for each value for x. Check this against the translation of $VarVal$ above.

EXERCISE 5.8

$Comms$ is a very simple model of a communications system with a transmitter (T), a receiver (R), and an unreliable medium (M). Messages are in ASCII and therefore all parameters are of the same type. Translate the $Comms$ system into basic CCS.

$$
\begin{aligned}
Comms &\stackrel{\text{def}}{=} (T \mid M \mid R)\backslash\{ok, s, r\} \\
T &\stackrel{\text{def}}{=} ok.send(x).\overline{s}(x).T \\
M &\stackrel{\text{def}}{=} \overline{ok}.s(x).(\overline{r}(x).M + \tau.M) \\
R &\stackrel{\text{def}}{=} r(x).receive(x).R
\end{aligned}
$$

5.3 An elegant data-manager

At the end of chapter 4 we made some comments to the effect that our specification of $DataMan$ had become unduly cumbersome because we were having to model data and behaviour in an essentially behaviourally oriented language. Let us now return to that specification and see how we can simplify it using the value-passing calculus. Remember that at the top level the system had the following definition:

$$DMConv \stackrel{\text{def}}{=} (DataMan \mid Conv)\backslash R$$

$$R = \{reqout, out0, out1, end\}$$

We can now take a look at the converter, for example, and see if we can improve it in any way by using the value-passing calculus. We still wish the converter to output *odd*, *even* or *zero* as appropriate for up to three bits received from $DataMan$ but we would like to simplify its definition. Here is the existing definition:

$$Conv \stackrel{\text{def}}{=} req.\overline{reqout}.Conv1$$
$$Conv1 \stackrel{\text{def}}{=} out0.Conv2 + out1.\overline{odd}.\overline{end}.Conv$$
$$Conv2 \stackrel{\text{def}}{=} out0.Conv3 + out1.\overline{even}.\overline{end}.Conv$$
$$Conv3 \stackrel{\text{def}}{=} out0.\overline{zero}.Conv + out1.\overline{even}.Conv$$

Looking at this original specification suggests that we should replace all occurrences of subexpressions of the form $in0. \ldots + in1. \ldots$ by $in(x). \ldots$, where $x \in \{0, 1\}$, and make use of the conditional expression. This would give us the following new specification:

$$ConVal \stackrel{\text{def}}{=} req.\overline{reqout}.ConVal1$$
$$ConVal1 \stackrel{\text{def}}{=} out(x).if \ x \neq 0 \ then \ \overline{odd}.\overline{end}.ConVal \ else \ ConVal2$$
$$ConVal2 \stackrel{\text{def}}{=} out(x).if \ x \neq 0 \ then \ \overline{even}.\overline{end}.ConVal \ else \ ConVal3$$
$$ConVal3 \stackrel{\text{def}}{=} out(x).if \ x \neq 0 \ then \ \overline{even}.ConVal \ else \ \overline{zero}.ConVal$$

Remembering that $DataMan$ was defined in the manner

$$DataMan \stackrel{\text{def}}{=} (Start \mid Output \mid put.Sem \mid Store) \backslash D$$

where

$$D = \{get, put, rd0A1, rd1A1, \ldots, wrt0A1, wrt1A1, \ldots\}$$

we could now go on to translate the sub-agents of this agent into the value-passing calculus. However, we can use the value-passing calculus to produce a far simpler and more abstract specification for $DataMan$ than this approach would give us. Instead of representing the store explicitly as an agent we can simply hold bit values as parameters to agent constants in the way we did for $Buff_N^2(\langle\rangle)$. For instance we can define the input process as

$$InVal \stackrel{\text{def}}{=} in(x).in(y).in(z).DMVal(x, y, z)$$

and the output process by

$$OutVal(x, y, z) \stackrel{\text{def}}{=} reqout.\overline{out}(x).OutVal1(x, y, z)$$
$$OutVal1(x, y, z) \stackrel{\text{def}}{=} end.DMVal(x, y, z) + \overline{out}(y).OutVal2(x, y, z)$$
$$OutVal2(x, y, z) \stackrel{\text{def}}{=} end.DMVal(x, y, z) + \overline{out}(z).DMVal(x, y, z)$$

and we simply define the data-manager as

$$DMVal(x, y, z) \stackrel{\text{def}}{=} InVal + OutVal(x, y, z)$$

The initial state of the system is now simply $InVal$. To complete the respecification it only remains to gather together all the definitions and document them appropriately.

The scope rules for variables are clearly illustrated if we replace $InVal$ with its defining expression in the definition for $DMVal$ itself, i.e.

$$DMVal(x, y, z) \stackrel{\text{def}}{=} in(x).in(y).in(z).DMVal(x, y, z) + OutVal(x, y, z)$$

The variables x, y and z have as their scope the whole expression on the left-hand side of the definition and do indeed bind all variables in the subexpression $OutVal(x, y, z)$. However, the occurrence of the three instances of the action in with parameters x, y and z means that while the parameters of the right-most call on $DMVal$ are again x, y and z and are in the scope of the left-most $DMVal(x, y, z)$ they are not bound by it. The reason is, of course, that they are all additionally within the scope of the three occurrences of the action in which actually bind them.

Specification of the data-manager–converter in the value-passing calculus

In the following definitions we assume all variables are of type bit. The system is specified in terms of two sub-agents, $DMVal$ and $ConVal$, which model the storing of data and the conversion process respectively:

$$DMConv \stackrel{\text{def}}{=} (InVal \mid ConVal)\backslash R$$

$$R = \{reqout, out, end\}$$

The data-manager

In the following definitions we assume that all variables are of type bit.

The data-manager itself is specified in terms of a choice between the input and output processes:

$$DMVal(x, y, z) \stackrel{\text{def}}{=} InVal + OutVal(x, y, z)$$

where $InVal$ handles the updating of the store by accepting sequences of three bits upon receiving the first from the environment:

$$InVal \stackrel{\text{def}}{=} in(x).in(y).in(z).DMVal(x, y, z)$$

$OutVal$ communicates bits to the agent $ConVal$ after synchronising on the action $reqout$. The synchronisation on the action end terminates an output session if less than three bits have been sent.

$OutVal$	initial waiting state
$OutVal1$	first bit output
$OutVal2$	second bit output

$$OutVal(x, y, z) \stackrel{\text{def}}{=} reqout.\overline{out}(x).OutVal1(x, y, z)$$

$$OutVal1(x, y, z) \stackrel{\text{def}}{=} end.DMVal(x, y, z) + \overline{out}(y).OutVal2(x, y, z)$$

$$OutVal2(x, y, z) \stackrel{\text{def}}{=} end.DMVal(x, y, z) + \overline{out}(z).DMVal(x, y, z)$$

The converter

Upon receiving the signal *req* the agent *ConVal* reads up to three bits from *DMVal* and outputs the messages *odd*, *even* or *zero* as appropriate. If it is able to make the calculation on less than three bits it synchronises with *DMVal* on the action $\overline{end}$ to signal the termination of that particular session.

Conv	waiting for a request
Conv1	waiting for the first bit
Conv2	waiting for the second bit
Conv3	waiting for the third bit

$$ConVal \stackrel{\text{def}}{=} req.\overline{reqout}.ConVal1$$

$$ConVal1 \stackrel{\text{def}}{=} out(x).if\ x \neq 0\ then\ \overline{odd}.\overline{end}.ConVal\ else\ ConVal2$$

$$ConVal2 \stackrel{\text{def}}{=} out(x).if\ x \neq 0\ then\ \overline{even}.\overline{end}.ConVal\ else\ ConVal3$$

$$ConVal3 \stackrel{\text{def}}{=} out(x).if\ x \neq 0\ then\ \overline{even}.ConVal\ else\ \overline{zero}.ConVal$$

End of specification

5.4 Values and indices

We have demonstrated the expediency of the value-passing calculus in the specification of concurrent systems where data is a significant consideration. However, we have skimmed over the actual definition of abstract datatypes and their role in the typing of parameters to actions and agent constants. In addition the semantic function assumes a single type for all variables but most practical specifications will require multiple datatypes and thus distinguished sets of variables to range over them. We should formalise our typing mechanisms and the declaration of type constructors and new operators for these types. In addition, we noted, in the previous chapter, the power of indices to simplify the definition of multiple agents in terms of a generic definition and appropriate relabelling functions. It would be useful if the use of indices could also be formalised. The outcome of all this should be a complete definition of value-passing CCS which made the use of user-defined datatypes and indexing schemes quite unambiguous. We will present the *completed* value-passing CCS here by way of example and briefly discuss its semantics.

We need to extend the syntax of value-passing CCS to allow us to define types for indices and parameters for both actions and agents. We will therefore need various new forms of definition in addition to that for agents. We will introduce these by example by *completing* the definition of *DMConv* from earlier in this chapter. First of all we will declare a set and an associated constant name for the type bit:

$$const \ bit \stackrel{\text{def}}{=} \{0,1\}$$

Having declared the type bit we can associate typed parameters and indices with action names. We will call these complex structures as *labels*. For $DMConv4$ we will need to declare the following labels:

$$label \ in(bit), out(bit), \overline{out}(bit)$$

Notice that we declare types for action parameters and not for particular variables. In general the context in which these are used will determine their type. We can now demonstrate the definition of the agent $OutVal$ in its completed form:

$$agentOutVal(x\!:\!bit, y\!:\!bit, z\!:\!bit) \stackrel{\text{def}}{=} reqout.\overline{out}(x).OutVal1(x,y,z)$$

The definitions for $OutVal1$ and $OutVal2$ will follow a similar pattern. We leave it as an exercise for the reader to complete the conversions of the remaining definitions into value-passing form as they should now contain no surprises.

In this specification we have no indices but we can illustrate their use by defining the generic variable from which we built the array in the previous chapter, pages 61–62:

$$
\begin{aligned}
const \quad & index \stackrel{\text{def}}{=} \{0,1,2\} \\
label \quad & rd_{index}(bit), wrt_{index}(bit) \\
agent \quad & Var \stackrel{\text{def}}{=} rd(x).Var(x) \\
& Var(x\!:\!bit) \stackrel{\text{def}}{=} \overline{wrt}(x).Var(x) + rd(y).Var(y)
\end{aligned}
$$

We can now specify the three agents formally in the following manner:

$$agent \ A_i\!:\!bit \stackrel{\text{def}}{=} Var[rd_i/rd, \overline{wrt_i}/\overline{wrt}]$$

The combination of relabelling and values, particularly indices, allows us to specify systems using appropriate levels of abstraction whilst at the same time preserving much of the simplicity of basic CCS.

This, *completed*, version of the value-passing calculus also allows parameters to be sets or lists. The natural numbers and the usual operators over them are also included in the language definition. For instance, we have already used the operator *div* and boolean operators such as '=' and '≠'. In the rest of the book we will use this version of the value-passing calculus where appropriate and introduce additional operators as they are required.

EXERCISE 5.9

Complete the definition of the elegant data-manager given in section 5.3.

EXERCISE 5.10

$$Const\ B\ =\ \{t, f\}$$
$$Label\ in(B), out(B), m(B), novalue$$

$$Queue \stackrel{\text{def}}{=} (Q1 \mid Q2)\backslash\{m\}$$
$$Q1 \stackrel{\text{def}}{=} in(x).Q1'(x)$$
$$Q1'(x : B) \stackrel{\text{def}}{=} \overline{m}(x).Q1$$
$$Q2 \stackrel{\text{def}}{=} m(x).Q2'(x) + \overline{novalue}.Q2$$
$$Q2'(x : B) \stackrel{\text{def}}{=} \overline{out}(x).Q2$$

Translate $Queue$ and all its associated definitions into basic CCS. Notice that the constant and label definitions make the translation of the restriction set far clearer.

EXERCISE 5.11

Define an agent $Logic$ which attempts to read two Boolean values from $Queue$ and outputs the *and* or *or* of them as requested. $Logic$ cannot wait and so if *novalue* is returned then the additional truth value u (undefined) is recorded. Truth tables for three-value *and* and *or* will be needed.

EXERCISE 5.12

Compose $Logic$ with $Queue$ to build a single specification $LogSys$ and translate the whole into basic CCS.

5.5 Summary and further reading

In chapter 4 we identified the need for a new version of CCS which would allow us to model systems with a significant data component. We have shown that we did not have to extend basic CCS in order to produce a value-passing calculus but that it was possible to define a semantic function which translated value-passing expressions into basic CCS. In addition we found that the new value-passing calculus made it possible to produce specifications which were simpler and more abstract than was possible with basic CCS. The basic reference for this extension to basic CCS is [Mil89]. We looked briefly at one way of *completing* the value-passing calculus, by which we mean the extension of the language definition to formally model abstract datatypes. This version is due to Bruns [Bru91] and has the additional advantage that if the types used are finite then there is software support to automatically translate value-passing expressions into their basic CCS form. In the next chapter we will study another solution to the problem of extending a basic process algebra to allow explicit value passing.

6

Traffic lights

In this chapter we will return to CCS but once again concentrate on its practical application. Therefore, much of the discussion will again focus on *how* to build specifications As the title suggests we are going to consider the specification of a traffic lights system for the reason that these are well known and we can concentrate on their specification in CCS without expending too much effort on the systems analysis side of the problems. This system will not only require consideration of concurrency and communication but also safety-critical aspects of systems. After some thought we will adopt a pragmatic, bottom-up approach to constructing the system and first of all consider simplifications of it in order to fix our ideas on the problem at hand. We will use these simplified specifications to help us build the complete system as the chapter progresses. The examples in this chapter are control problems and are intended to switch the reader's attention away from value passing and onto other more specifically real-time issues. This will lead us into considering a real-time version of CCS in the next chapter. As with chapter 4, we will continue the process of critically evaluating CCS and pointing out small but practical extensions we might wish to make to the language to help the building of specifications.

6.1 Getting started

```
    ------------
    REQUIREMENTS
    ------------
A control system must ensure the safe and correct
functioning of a set of traffic lights at a T-junction
between a major and a minor road. The lights will be
set to green on the major road and red on the minor
road unless a vehicle is detected by a sensor in the
road just before the lights on the minor road.
```

In this case the lights will be switchable in the
standard manner and allow traffic to leave the minor
road. After a suitable interval the lights will revert
to their default position to allow traffic to flow on
the major road again. Once a vehicle is detected the
sensor will be disabled until the minor-road lights
are set to red again.

There is also to be a pedestrian crossing a short
distance down the minor road but beyond the sensor.
There is a button on each side of the road for
pedestrians to indicate they wish to cross. The
crossing should only allow people to cross when the
'minor lights' are set to red in order to minimise
waiting times for traffic on the minor road. All
requests for service from either the sensor or the
button must eventually be complied with.

A first reading of the requirement establishes that there are actually two
sets of lights which must cooperate in certain circumstances: there are the
traffic lights actually on the junction and there are the pedestrian lights
some way down the minor road. We could therefore attempt a top-down
decompostion of the system into these two subsystems and proceed much
in the way we did with the data-manager–converter in chapter 4. There are
other ways of tackling problems, however. A common and useful technique
in formal methods is to specify a simplified version of the required system
in order to focus ideas and assess potential problems and complexities. I
therefore suggest we adopt a highly pragmatic approach and build half
of the system first and then see how to extend it. Specifically, I suggest
we literally cut the requirements document in half and work on the top
paragraph first. Doing this generates the following interim requirement:

THE TOP HALF

A control system must ensure the safe and correct
functioning of a set of traffic lights at a T-junction
between a major and a minor road. The lights will be
set to green on the major road and red on the minor
road unless a vehicle is detected by a sensor in the
road just before the lights on the minor road.
In this case the lights will be switchable in the
standard manner and allow traffic to leave the minor

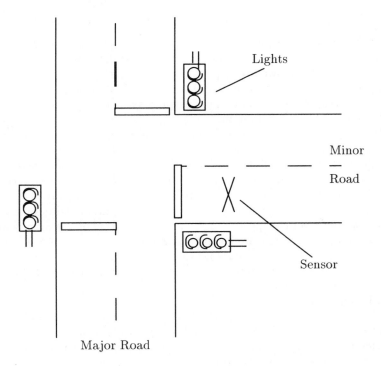

Figure 6.1. *The simple road junction*

road. After a suitable interval the lights will revert
to their default position to allow traffic to flow on
the major road again. Once a vehicle is detected the
sensor will be disabled until the minor-road lights
are set to red again.

There are a number of good reasons for adopting this approach. First of
all we obviously have a simpler system to consider. Secondly, the top half
of the problem shares some basic problems with the complete requirements
document in the sense that both require lights to be modelled and switched
on and off. We will only have to solve these problems once. Having made
life easier for ourselves, at least for the time being, we can proceed to model
the top half. Figure 6.1 gives a pictorial view of the simplified system.

6.2 The simple road junction

First of all some initial observations on the requirements. It is obvious
that certain combinations of light settings would be dangerous and must
therefore not be allowed to happen. Basically, the system invariant should
state that at any one time either the major lights or the minor lights must
be set to red. Whatever else happens we must get this right to ensure the
safe functioning of the system.

There are also several points to note concerning the correct functioning
of the system. If a vehicle does trigger the sensor then it should eventually
be permitted by the lights to leave the minor road. If the sensor never
communicates the arrival of a vehicle then the system could be considered
safe but would certainly not be correct because it would stay in its default
setting with the major lights on green and the minor lights on red. The
lights would never change although the frame of mind of any drivers waiting
on the minor road might well change – for the worst we assume. The correct
functioning of the sensor and its communication with other components in
the system will be an important consideration in the correct behaviour of
the system as a whole.

Thinking back to the way we broke down the system in chapter 4 the
obvious way to specify this particular system might be to build a central
controller working all the lights and a separate sensor to which the controller must respond safely and correctly. A top-level CCS expression to
represent the system specified in this way would be

$$J1 \stackrel{\text{def}}{=} (Controller \mid Sensor)\backslash L$$

where L would be the restriction set that determined the observable behaviour of *Lights*.

However, there are a variety of other ways in which we could make the
initial decomposition of the system. Remember that we are building a specification of a system and not implementing it, and so the degree of concurrency present at this stage does not necessarily reflect the degree of
concurrency which will be present in the implementaton. We can specify
more agents at this level than we would actually expect to find in the even-
tual implementation. Very often it is easier to adopt this approach to start
with because it allows us to distribute the complexity of a system over a
number of simpler concurrent processes. In the case of the traffic lights we
could specify each individual colour of light on both the major and minor
roads as a concurrent agent, in which case our initial CCS expression might
take the following form:

$$J2 \stackrel{\text{def}}{=} \begin{aligned}(MaRed \mid MaAmber \mid MaGreen \mid MiRed \mid MiAmber \\ \mid MiGreen \mid Sensor)\backslash Q\end{aligned}$$

We might wish to ask if $J1$ is an implemenation of $J2$, in other words that they are equivalent in some sense. In chapter 10 we will show that we can calculate the less distributed system by reducing the degree of concurrency within the other specification. We will consider both $J1$ and $J2$ in this chapter but start with an intermediate solution. Taking a further look at the requirements we can derive a list of sub-agents that we think we will need both by analysis of that document and by considering the number of sub-agents that we believe will make our task more manageable. Further to our point about the degree of concurrency in a specification, we do not have to make our concurrent decomposition of the system match the expected implementational decomposition. It will turn out that this too we can manipulate. What it does mean is that we can, for instance, consider the major and minor lights as separate processes along with the sensor which certainly should be autonomous. From this decision we can state a top-level specification for the whole system in the following manner:

$$Lights1 \stackrel{\text{def}}{=} (Major \mid Minor \mid Sensor) \backslash L$$

We now have three possible decompositions of the system but we will pursue $Lights1$ for the time being. At this stage we should ask ourselves how we are actually going to represent the state of the lights and the sensor which constitute the system state. Remember, we have no notion of data in basic CCS. States of the system record only possible next actions which in this case will be concerned with switching lights on or off. Furthermore, the agent $Major$ may be in a state which records the fact that the only possible next action is to switch the red light off but does not record the fact that the red light is currently switched on. We could assume that to get to this state the red light had to be switched on and is still on. A more complex model might allow us to check whether or not particular lights are on or off but it is easier to avoid this additional complexity at this stage. We will need a set of actions which will allow us to switch any of the lights on and off. For the sensor we will need an observable action that records the arrival of a vehicle.

Let us first consider the sensor, as this is potentially, at least, fairly straightforward. The sensor tells the system that a vehicle has been detected and it is this information alone which can trigger a change from the system's default state. We can give a very simple definition for the sensor in the following way:

$$Sensor \stackrel{\text{def}}{=} press.\overline{s}.Sensor$$

where the action $press$ records the detection of a vehicle and the action $\overline{s}$ communicates this fact to the rest of the system.

If we accept this first attempt at a definition for the sensor we can proceed to do the same for the lights themselves. The requirement stipulates that no changes can occur at the minor road until the lights on the major road have been set to red and it is therefore the major lights which require the information communicated by the *Sensor*. On receiving this information the major lights should be set to red in the appropriate manner and inform the minor lights of this fact. If we adopt the convention that G, A, R will stand for the colour of lights and that, for instance, maG_{on} and miG_{on} identify the actions for switching the major green light and the minor green lights on respectively, then the definition for this part of the system becomes quite straightforward. In chapter 2 we noted two outline approaches to this problem. We can continue to decompose the agents we have identified or we can use the state-based approach to specify each of our sub-agents as a sequential system. The present system is simple enough to allow us to do the latter:

$$Major \quad \overset{\text{def}}{=} \quad s.maG_{off}.maA_{on}.maA_{off}.Ma1$$
$$Ma1 \quad \overset{\text{def}}{=} \quad maR_{on}.\overline{ma}.Majorwait$$

The agent *Majorwait*, as its name suggests, is the state in which the major lights are set to red and must wait until it is safe to return to green again. We could now consider the behaviour of the major lights commencing from the state *Majorwait* but we can also defer this until we have considered the behaviour of the minor lights. In the case of this system the latter is probably slightly easier.

The communication *ma* tells the minor lights that it is now safe to allow traffic to leave the minor road and sets off a sequence of light changes which we can define by the following set of definitions:

$$Minor \quad \overset{\text{def}}{=} \quad ma.miA_{on}.miR_{off}.miA_{off}.Mi1$$
$$Mi1 \quad \overset{\text{def}}{=} \quad miG_{on}.miG_{off}.miA_{on}.miA_{off}.Mi2$$
$$Mi2 \quad \overset{\text{def}}{=} \quad miR_{on}.\overline{mi}.Minor$$

Normally, of course, the red and amber lights will be switched off at the same time, but for the moment we have switched red off and then amber off. Later on in this chapter we will return to think again about this problem. The final thing to do is to switch the major lights back to green and wait for another vehicle:

$$Majorwait \overset{\text{def}}{=} mi.maA_{on}.maR_{off}.maA_{off}.maG_{on}.Major$$

We have now specified all of the agents given in the top-level DFD and arrived at a flow graph for the whole system given by figure 6.2. In the next section we will try to find out whether or not *Lights*1 behaves as required, but before reading on undertake the next exercise and find out for yourself.

EXERCISE 6.1

Amend the definitions for *Minor* and *Majorwait* so that the red and

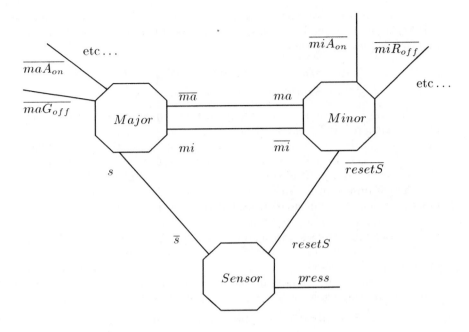

Figure 6.2. *The flow graph for Lights*1

amber lights are switched off at the same time.
Hint: In CCS your answer will be something of a compromise.

EXERCISE 6.2
   Construct a test plan and use the CWB or the Verification Game to see whether or not *Lights*1 behaves as expected and required.

6.3 Validating *Lights*1

Your answer to exercise 6.2 should have convinced you that all is not well. Once again, we have forgotten to specify how we are to start the lights up. Notice that if we do not do this then there will be no lights on at all until the first vehicle is responded to and then only major lights will be on but not minor lights until after the signal *mi* has been received. This is a fairly simple matter to solve with the following two definitions which should be self-explanatory, though you should ask yourself why we have required the synchronisations on m and w:

$$StartMajor \overset{\text{def}}{=} start.\overline{m}.maG_{on}.w.Major$$
$$StartMinor \overset{\text{def}}{=} m.miR_{on}.\overline{w}.Major$$

If the system is correctly started up then it appears safe. There is always at least one red light on. It is not correct, however, because there is a problem with the way *Sensor* interacts with the rest of the system. Once a vehicle has been detected and the information sent to the agent *Major* the *Sensor* reverts to its initial state ready for the next vehicle, but that vehicle may arrive immediately after the one just detected, in which case it will move off when the lights go to green but the sensor will still record its arrival and use this information to trigger another change of lights even though there may be no vehicles waiting on the minor road at all by then. We must make sure that no more vehicles are responded to until the *Minor* lights are switched back to red. We can achieve this by adding a synchronisation between *Minor* and *Sensor* in the appropriate state. With these slight amendments the whole system can be specified in the following manner.

Specification of the simple road junction

The system is defined in terms of three subprocesses which correspond to the major lights, minor lights and sensor. The processes *StartMajor* and *StartMinor* represent the startup states for the major and minor lights which are then specified in terms of cyclical behaviours which commence with *Major* and *Minor* respectively.

$$Lights1 \overset{\text{def}}{=} (StartMajor \mid StartMinor \mid Sensor)\backslash L$$
$$L = \{ma, mi, resetS, s, m, w\}$$

The major lights

After being initialised by *StartMajor*, which has to synchronise with *StartMinor* to make sure it has started up correctly, before commencing normal running the major lights enter a cyclical behaviour which revolves around the three definitions for *Major*, *Ma*1 and *Majorwait*. Of these, *Major* represents the state where the major road has priority, with *Ma*1 being simply a convenient place to break up the definition. *Majorwait* represents the state where the minor road is active and the major road is set on red.

$$StartMajor \overset{\text{def}}{=} start.\overline{m}.maG_{on}.w.Major$$
$$Major \overset{\text{def}}{=} s.maG_{off}.maA_{on}.maA_{off}.Ma1$$
$$Ma1 \overset{\text{def}}{=} maR_{on}.\overline{ma}.Majorwait$$
$$Majorwait \overset{\text{def}}{=} mi.maA_{on}.maR_{off}.maA_{off}.maG_{on}.Major$$

The minor lights

The minor lights have a slightly simpler definition than the major in that after startup they are either dormant, $Minor$, or active, $Mi1$ and $Mi2$:

$$StartMinor \stackrel{\text{def}}{=} m.miR_{on}.\overline{w}.Minor$$

$$Minor \stackrel{\text{def}}{=} ma.miA_{on}.miR_{off}.miA_{off}.Mi1$$

$$Mi1 \stackrel{\text{def}}{=} miG_{on}.miG_{off}.miA_{on}.miA_{off}.\overline{resetS}.Mi2$$

$$Mi2 \stackrel{\text{def}}{=} miR_{on}.\overline{mi}.Minor$$

The sensor

The sensor is very simple in that it records the arrival of a vehicle and then attempts to transmit this information to $Major$ via the action s. It then has to wait to be reset, $resetS$, before being able to detect a further vehicle:

$$Sensor \stackrel{\text{def}}{=} press.s.resetS.Sensor$$

End of specification

6.4 The red–amber problem

In practice we would expect the red and amber lights to be switched off at the same time and it would be far nicer if our specification could reflect this. Of course if we were using CCS* we would be able to do this quite easily, but in this chapter we are working in basic CCS. For a moment let us consider possible solutions to exercise 6.1 which we might wish to incorporate into the final definition for the $Lights1$ system. Referring to the interleaving semantics given for CCS, the only way to say that two observable actions can occur concurrently is to say they can happen in any order and always reach the same state. We have inadvertently suggested the solution to this problem when we added the startup procedure to $Lights1$. After the action $start$ we used two synchronisations to guarantee that both maG_{on} and miR_{on} occurred before any further observable actions were allowed. In effect we have said these two actions took place in parallel because they could be interleaved. Draw the transition graph for the first few steps of $Lights1$ to see what is meant here if you are in doubt. In the case of the red and amber lights the necessary behaviour can be captured by the expression

$$maR_{off}.maA_{off}.Major' + maA_{off}.maR_{off}.Major'$$

This solution has to rely on the fact that concurrency can be defined in terms of choice because we only have sequential systems available here. This produces as close a specification of the behaviour as is possible in basic CCS, although it is rather cumbersome. Notice that we cannot use the following expressions:

$$maR_{off}.Major' \mid maA_{off}.Major'$$

or

$$(maR_{off} \mid maA_{off}).Major'$$

Both are incorrect, the first because it generates multiple copies of the agent $Major'$ and thus an incorrect and unsafe behaviour for the system and the second because it is syntactically incorrect and thus produces a meaningless specification. There is something appealing about the second, however, because it does seem to capture the desired intentions behind the system and does so in a neat and compact way. People learning CCS are often tempted to write expressions of this form. The intended meaning of the expression

$$(maR_{off} \mid maA_{off}).Major'$$

is exactly the same as

$$maR_{off}.maA_{off}.Major' + maA_{off}.maR_{off}.Major'$$

It is relatively easy to introduce the new form of expression by means of a syntactic abbreviation. We will use the operator '$\ddagger$' to stand for the parallel composition of actions so as not to confuse it with the parallel composition of agents. The particular expression we are looking for will therefore be

$$(maR_{off} \ddagger maA_{off}).Major'$$

and its meaning is captured by the following syntactic equivalence:

$$(\alpha \ddagger \beta).E \equiv \alpha.\beta.E + \beta.\alpha.E$$

We can define a more general form of the expression in the following manner:

$$
\begin{aligned}
& (\alpha_1 \ddagger \ldots \ddagger \alpha_n).E \\
\equiv\ & \prod_{i \in I}^{\ddagger} \alpha_i.E && (I = \{1, \ldots, n\}) \\
\equiv\ & \sum_{i \in I} \alpha_i.(\prod_{j \in J}^{\ddagger} \alpha_j).E && (J \neq \{\} \wedge i \notin J) \\
& \text{or} \\
& \alpha_i.E && J = \{\}
\end{aligned}
$$

A point to note is that

$$(\alpha_1 \ddagger \alpha_2).(\beta_1 \ddagger \beta_2).E$$

is a well-formed expression but should not be considered as equivalent in any sense to the well-formed expression

$$(\alpha_1 \ddagger \alpha_2 \ddagger \beta_1 \ddagger \beta_2).E$$

Drawing the transition graphs for the two expressions should convince you of their differing behaviours.

Using our new notation we can amend the definitions for *Lights*1 to include these, more realistic, behaviours for red and amber lights. We will call this version of the system *Junction*1 to distinguish it from *Lights*1:

$$
\begin{aligned}
Junction1 &\overset{\text{def}}{=} (StartMajor \mid StartMinor \mid Sensor)\backslash L \\
L &= \{ma, mi, resetS, s, m, w\} \\
StartMajor &\overset{\text{def}}{=} start.\overline{m}.maG_{on}.w.Major \\
Major &\overset{\text{def}}{=} s.maG_{off}.maA_{on}.maA_{off}.Ma1 \\
Ma1 &\overset{\text{def}}{=} maR_{on}.\overline{ma}.Majorwait \\
Majorwait &\overset{\text{def}}{=} mi.maA_{on}.(maR_{off} \ddagger maA_{off}).maG_{on}.Major \\
StartMinor &\overset{\text{def}}{=} m.miR_{on}.\overline{w}.Minor1 \\
Minor1 &\overset{\text{def}}{=} ma.miA_{on}.(miR_{off} \ddagger miA_{off}).Minor2 \\
Minor2 &\overset{\text{def}}{=} miG_{on}.miG_{off}.miA_{on}.(miA_{off} \ddagger \overline{resetS}).Mi2 \\
Minor3 &\overset{\text{def}}{=} miR_{on}.\overline{mi}.Minor \\
Sensor &\overset{\text{def}}{=} press.\overline{s}.resetS.Sensor
\end{aligned}
$$

Notice that using this new notation we could have specified the startup in the manner

$$Start \overset{\text{def}}{=} (maG_{on} \ddagger miR_{on}).Junction1$$

where *Junction*1 is simply

$$
\begin{aligned}
Junction1 &\overset{\text{def}}{=} (Major \mid Minor \mid Sensor)\backslash L \\
L &= \{ma, mi, resetS, s\}
\end{aligned}
$$

An important point to note is that we have specified the system in its startup and operating mode but we have not said how we are to stop it safely.

Before building the specification *Junction*1 we considered various other decompositions of the simplified system, and it will be worthwhile giving these some thought. We will then go on to extend *Junction*1 so that it models the whole system including the pedestrian lights.

EXERCISE 6.3

Extend the definition of *Lights*1 to model the means of switching it off. At what point in the system's operating mode would you consider it safe to turn the system off? Furthermore, can you guarantee that it will switch off when told to?

6.5 Other approaches

Let us think for a moment about the development process we have just been through. We adopted a top-down approach very much as advocated in chapter 2. We identified sub-agents of the system and developed them separately in order to build up the whole system. We could have decomposed the sub-agents further but we chose to adopt the other method from chapter 2 which uses a state-based approach to build a sequential specification of a system. Finally we investigated the system's behaviour both by way of animation and by building its transition graph, where appropriate, and thus checking behaviour against requirements. There are other ways we could have gone about the process. We could have explored the necessary communications between the three agents identified and gradually built up a flow graph before formally specifying the agents. This can often work quite well for systems with relatively simple communications patterns.

We did suggest other approaches. One was to specify each light individually before using composition and relabelling to build them up into the larger system required. The other was to think directly in terms of a central control system very much in the way the system would be implemented. It is worth exploring this technique further, as, contrary to much traditional computer science wisdom, the bottom-up approach can be very useful. Furthermore, it is very often unavoidable in the specification and design of control and safety-critical systems because the physical system on which the software is to operate is very often either already built or its design is at an advanced stage before the software has even been thought of. We will also consider the latter situation as it leads to an interesting specification which gives a different view of the problem to hand.

First of all the lights. The basic principle behind these is that they receive signals which tell them to change state. They will be either on or off and will receive a signal to change to the other state. Due to the fact that CCS does not represent data but only atomic actions we can only refer to the state of a light in terms of the next observable action of which it is capable. A very basic light would have the following definition:

$$Light \stackrel{\text{def}}{=} ok.on.off.\overline{std}.Light$$

The intended meaning of this is that the light is off until it receives the ok-to-proceed signal, at which point the light is switched on for an unspecified period before switching off and reporting that it has returned to its unlit state. We are actually recording events as well as actions here because *on* and *off* refer as much to the fact that an observer might see the light go on or off as to the action of achieving the changes. This is irrelevant to the formal definition of CCS but is worth noting with respect to the intuitions which support our modelling of systems in the language. In some ways an event is more abstract than an action which denotes more of the *how* rather than just the *what*.

It would be nice if we could take our basic light and use relabelling to build all the various lights we need and compose them in parallel to produce the system we require:

$$
\begin{aligned}
MaGreen &\stackrel{\text{def}}{=} Light[miG_{on}/on, miG_{off}/off, \overline{m1}/\overline{std}] \\
MaAmber &\stackrel{\text{def}}{=} Light[m1/ok, miA_{on}/on, miA_{off}/off, \overline{m2}/\overline{std}] \\
MaRed &\stackrel{\text{def}}{=} Light[m2/ok, miR_{on}/on, miR_{off}/off] \\
Sequence &\stackrel{\text{def}}{=} (MaGreen \mid MaAmber \mid MaRed)\backslash\{m1, m2\}
\end{aligned}
$$

The agent *Sequence* uses the action *ok* to commence a sequence of light switches from green to amber to red and then reports successful completion. Problems arise, however, with the traffic lights because some lights have to wait while they are on red while others wait while they are on green and others may require concurrent state changes. It is best to consider each light individually and then build them up into sequences. First of all let us look at the lights on the major road. We assume the initial state where the green light is on and the red and amber are off. Nothing happens until a signal is received from the sensor. The green light is switched off and a signal sent to the amber light. The green light stays off until a return signal allows it to turn on again. The amber light simply turns on, then off, and sends a signal to the red light to go on. After turning on, the red light sends a signal to the minor lights and then waits for permission to proceed. The agents are straightforward to define up to this point:

$$
\begin{aligned}
MajG &\stackrel{\text{def}}{=} s.maG_{off}.\overline{c1}.c6.maG_{on}.MajG \\
MajA &\stackrel{\text{def}}{=} c1.msA_{on}.maA_{off}.\overline{c2}.MajA \\
MajR &\stackrel{\text{def}}{=} c2.maR_{on}.\overline{ok1}.MajRon
\end{aligned}
$$

At this stage we have left the major lights on red awaiting permission from the minor lights to return to green again. Let us suppose that this permission arrives in the form of a synchronisation on the action $ok2$. The first action should be to switch on the amber light and then to switch both the red and amber lights off concurrently. The $ok2$ synchronisation could be received by either $MajA$ or $MajRon$ – it makes no real difference. The problem occurs after the amber light is switched on because we now need somehow to achieve this concurrent switching off of the two lights. However, it is difficult to use our new parallel operator in this situation because it is defined for parallel actions performed by a single agent and we not only require two agents to perform their actions in parallel but also require that both actions be accomplished before control passes to the green light. This makes the pattern of communications a little more difficult and means that we will require a second definition for the amber light. The full definition for the three lights is now

$$MajG \stackrel{\text{def}}{=} s.maG_{off}.\overline{c1}.c6.maG_{on}.MajG$$

$$MajA1 \stackrel{\text{def}}{=} c1.msA_{on}.maA_{off}.\overline{c2}.MajA2$$

$$MajA2 \stackrel{\text{def}}{=} c3.maA_{on}.\overline{c4}.maA_{off}.c5.\overline{c6}.MajA1$$

$$MajRoff \stackrel{\text{def}}{=} c2.maR_{on}.\overline{ok1}.MajRon$$

$$MajRon \stackrel{\text{def}}{=} ok2.\overline{c3}.c4.maR_{off}.\overline{c5}.MajRoff$$

$$MajorPL \stackrel{\text{def}}{=} (MajG \mid MajA1 \mid MajRoff)\backslash\{c1,\ldots,c6\}$$

Notice that the only way we could achieve the desired concurrent switching off of the red and amber lights was to enable both, $c3$, but to make sure by means of an additional synchronisation, $c5$, that both have taken place before the green lights are enabled again. This is, in fact, another solution to the problem from section 1 of this chapter. The alternative definition would have been

$$Majorwait \stackrel{\text{def}}{=} mi1.maA_{on}.(maR_{off}.done.maG_{on}.Major$$
$$\mid maA_{off}.\overline{done}.0)$$

$$Minor1 \stackrel{\text{def}}{=} ma.miA_{on}.(mir_{off}.done.Minor2 \mid miA_{off}.0)$$

which achieves the desired effect but without the benefit of the clarity of our abbreviated syntax. In this solution we would also have an ever-growing number of null agents composed in parallel with our active agents and the question arises as to whether the various systems are the same because of this. We will leave the specification of $MinorPL$ as an exercise (6.5) and complete the specification of this view of the simple junction by

$$JunctionPL \stackrel{\text{def}}{=} (MajorPL \mid MinorPL \mid Sensor)\backslash\{s, ok1, ok2, resetS\}$$

In this particular case we could have arrived at the same solution by continuing with the top-down approach adopted in chapter 1. Another possibility was to simply give a state-based description of the whole system in the first place, although complications would arise because of the independent behaviour of the sensor at various stages in the operation of the system as a whole. The important thing to learn from this chapter so far is to reflect upon the ways we have gone about our modelling problems and to try and add to your repertory of problem-solving intuitions.

EXERCISE 6.4

Specify $MinorPL$ in the same style as $MajorPL$. What comparisons can you make between the two agents?

EXERCISE 6.5

Attempt to draw the first part of the transition graph for $Junction1$ with the new $Majorwait$ and $Minor1$ agents.

1. What do you observe about the graph?

2. How does the behaviour recorded by this graph compare with the behaviour of the graph for the previous version of $Junction1$?

EXERCISE 6.6

Yet another way to specify the system is to adopt a central controller which takes charge of switching on or off all lights. Specify the junction in this manner but make sure that the lights do exactly what they are told and do not anticipate instructions.

6.6 The complete system

We can now return to the original requirements document and consider how to add in the bottom half that we have been ignoring so successfully to date. For your convenience the bottom half of the requirements is given below and figure 6.3 gives the pictorial representation of the complete problem.

```
    ---------------
    THE BOTTOM HALF
    ---------------


    There is also to be a pedestrian crossing a short
    distance down the minor road but beyond the sensor.
    There is a button on each side of the road for
    pedestrians to indicate they wish to cross. The
    crossing should only allow people to cross when the
    'minor lights' are set to red in order to minimise
    waiting times for traffic on the minor road. All
    requests for service from either the sensor or the
    button must eventually be complied with.


    ---------------
```

In the full system we must make sure not only that the original invariant that at least one red light must be on all the time holds but also that either

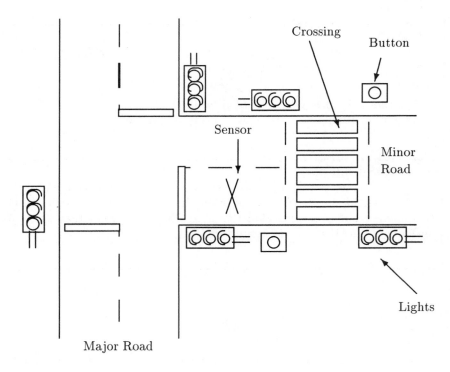

Figure 6.3. *A more complex junction*

the minor lights or the crossing lights must be red also. When we say the
crossing lights are *on red* we shall mean for the pedestrians. In essence
we have a mutual exclusion problem here with the *greenness* of the minor
and pedestrian lights being exclusive properties. Like the minor lights the
crossing lights will be a simple sequence of switches. The only complication
in the new system is ensuring the mutual exclusion property. We could
introduce a semaphore to do this as with the system Mx in chapter 2 or we
could extend an existing agent to give us the desired additional behaviour.
In this case we can use the agent $Major$ because all the while it is in its
initial state the minor lights must be on red and therefore the crossing can
allow people to cross should they have requested to do so.

We define the button in a similar manner to the *Sensor*:

$$Button \stackrel{\text{def}}{=} press.\bar{b}.resetB.Button$$

The button can be pressed, after which a message is sent to the crossing, $\bar{b}$,
and the button then waits for a reset command, $resetB$, which will come
from the crossing. The crossing has itself to gain permission from the agent
$Major$ before it can go any further. We can define the agent *Crossing* in

the following manner:

$$Crossing1 \stackrel{\text{def}}{=} b.\overline{cr1}.crA_{on}.crA_{off}.crR - on.Crossing2$$
$$Crossing2 \stackrel{\text{def}}{=} redman_{off}.greenman_{on}.greenman_{off}.$$
$$redman_{on}.resetB.Crossing3$$
$$Crossing3 \stackrel{\text{def}}{=} crA_{on}.(crR_{off} \ddagger crA_{off}).crG_{on}.\overline{cr2}Crossing1$$

We do not have to alter the behaviour of $Minor$ because it will not interact with $Crossing$. We will have to extend the definitions for the major lights to include the interactions with the crossing. In fact the changes are not complex. We introduce a new agent, $Newmajor$, to operate the mutual exclusion property:

$$Newmajor \stackrel{\text{def}}{=} cr1.cr2.Newmajor + s.Major'$$

The definition of $Major'$ is exactly that of $Major$ except that it eventually returns control to $Newmajor$ instead of itself. The full definition of the new system can be given as

$$Junction2 \stackrel{\text{def}}{=} (Newmajor \mid Minor \mid Sensor)\backslash L$$
$$Newmajor \stackrel{\text{def}}{=} cr1.cr2.Newmajor + Major'$$
$$Major' \stackrel{\text{def}}{=} s.maG_{off}.(maA_{on} \ddagger maA_{off}).Ma1$$
$$Ma1 \stackrel{\text{def}}{=} maR_{on}.\overline{ma}.Majorwait$$
$$Majorwait \stackrel{\text{def}}{=} mi.maA_{on}.(maR_{off} \ddagger maA_{off}).maG_{on}.Newmajor$$
$$Minor \stackrel{\text{def}}{=} ma.miA_{on}.miR_{off}.miA_{off}.Mi1$$
$$Mi1 \stackrel{\text{def}}{=} miG_{on}.miG_{off}.miA_{on}.(miA_{off} \ddagger \overline{resetS}).Mi2$$
$$Mi2 \stackrel{\text{def}}{=} miR_{on}.\overline{mi}.Minor$$
$$Crossing1 \stackrel{\text{def}}{=} b.\overline{cr1}.crA_{on}.(crR_{off} \ddagger crA_{off}).Crossing2$$
$$Crossing2 \stackrel{\text{def}}{=} redman_{off}.greenman_{on}.greenman_{off}.$$
$$redman_{on}.Crossing3$$
$$Crossing3 \stackrel{\text{def}}{=} (crR_{off} \ddagger crA_{off}).crG_{on}.\overline{cr2}Crossing1$$
$$Sensor \stackrel{\text{def}}{=} press.s.resetS.Sensor$$
$$Button \stackrel{\text{def}}{=} push.b.resetB.Button$$
$$L = \{ma, mi, resetS, s\}$$

The flow graph for the extended system, figure 6.4, gives some idea as to the patterns of communication.

Further reflection on the behaviour of the system $Lights2$ should have pointed out a serious flaw with respect to the requirements document. In particular we should study the effects of non-determinism on the behaviour of the system as a whole. Suppose the whole system is in its default state and both the button and sensor are triggered. The question is, can we guarantee that the minor lights will definitely go to green or that the pedestrians

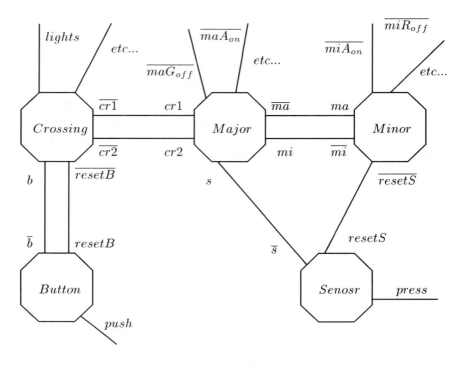

Figure 6.4. *A flow graph for the complex junction*

will definitely be allowed to cross at some time in the future? The answer is *no* for the current specification. The problem is that there is nothing to stop the system continually favouring the sensor rather than the button or vice versa. Animating the system shows just this state of affairs. In fact we shall see that removing unwanted non-determinism from CCS specifications can be extremely difficult and in some cases modelling desirable behaviour such as the interruption of processes is not possible at all without adding to the language.

In this case, however, we can prevent the possibility of the perpetual exclusion of either the crossing or the pedestrian lights by checking to see that if the minor lights have gone to green and back then we can force a check to see if the crossing is waiting and so on. If we can specify such a mechanism then equal access to green lights should be guaranteed.

We need to look at the definition of the major lights to see at what point we should add our checks. There are two points where these should be. The first is after the major lights have received the communication $cr2$ from the crossing. At this point a check should be made to see if the sensor has been pressed or not. If it has then the minor lights should be enabled whereas otherwise no action should be taken and the major lights may go back to their initial state. The other important state is when the major lights receive the signal $mi1$ from the minor lights because this means that they are now back on red and the crossing may be enabled if necessary. Of course, no action should be taken if the button has not been pressed. Notice that we do not wait for the major lights to get back to red as the requirements document makes no mention of the state of these lights with respect to enabling the crossing.

These checks have several effects on the existing specification. First of all there are the obvious extensions to the definitions for the major lights, but there is also the question of what happens to the *Sensor* and the *Button*, for these must always be able to say which state they are in, i.e. active or inactive. Here are the necessary changes to *Junction2* to make the system fair with respect to the minor lights and the pedestrian crossing:

$$
\begin{aligned}
Button & \stackrel{\text{def}}{=} bno.Button + press.\overline{b}.resetB.Button \\
Sensor & \stackrel{\text{def}}{=} sno.Sensor + press.\overline{s}.mi1.Sensor \\
Newmajor & \stackrel{\text{def}}{=} cr1.cr2.(\overline{sno}.Newmajor + Major) + Major \\
Majorwait & \stackrel{\text{def}}{=} mi1.Majorcheck \\
Majorcheck & \stackrel{\text{def}}{=} \overline{bno}.maA_{on}.(maR_{off} \ddagger maA_{off}).maG_{on}.Newmajor \\
& \quad + \\
& \quad cr1.maA_{on}.(maR_{off} \ddagger maA_{off}). \\
& \qquad maG_{on}.cr2.Newmajor
\end{aligned}
$$

EXERCISE 6.7

We have used CCS to model the traffic lights as a purely event-driven system.

1. Consider how you could use SCCS to extend *Junction1* so that it models the following timing requirements:

   (a) Minor green lights stay on for 30 seconds.

   (b) All other light settings stay on for 5 seconds.

2. What is the relationship between actions and time in SCCS?

6.7 Summary and further reading

In this chapter we have returned to the practical problems of using CCS to specify concurrent systems. This system was designed to avoid problems involving data and value passing so that we could concentrate on behavioural control. Despite the fact that it was apparently simpler than *DMConv* from the previous case study, we nevertheless encountered problems of control, particularly with respect to actions which we wished to be genuinely concurrent. We found that we could approximate truly concurrent actions by their fair interleaving and introduced a derived operator '$\ddagger$' to make such statements more succinct. In fact, '$\ddagger$' is a derived operator of the author's and is not to be found in Milner's presentation of CCS. Milner [Mil89] does, however, define a *sequential composition* operator ';' which can be used to similar effect. The expression $E; F$ is defined in such a way that on successful completing of its allotted task(s) the agent E passes control to F.

We encountered the problem of *fairness* when considering whether or not the minor lights and the pedestrian crossing would be allowed to become active if they were requested to do so. This type of problem will be further investigated in a later case study when its correct handling will be required to ensure the safe operation of a system. In addition, we very quickly observed that this was a somewhat odd requirement, and therefore specification, in that real traffic lights take time to turn lights on and off whereas ours did not. If we are to build a believable model of a traffic light system we will need to model time as well. In the next chapter we will build on the reader's experiences in trying to answer exercise 6.6 and develop a timed version of CCS.

7

Time

So far, in this book, we have only concerned ourselves with the ordering of events within concurrent systems. This is an important part of any real-time system but very often the timing of events can be critical as well. In this chapter, as its title suggests, we will be considering the importance of making time explicit in specifications. Indeed, you might be surprised that it has taken us so long to get to this stage, given the importance of timing in safety-critical and real-time systems. You might on the other hand be surprised at just how far we managed to get with our very simple first language. However, whichever view you take, we have to consider this issue to allow our specifications to cope with the types of problems that engineers are typically faced with.

7.1 Concepts of time

There are various ways of adding time to specifications. Doing the exercise at the end of the last chapter should have given you some ideas. An obvious way in which time can be modelled is by making all agents synchronise on some global clock. In fact, Milner's Synchronous Calculus of Communicating Systems (SCCS), mentioned in chapter 3, uses the idea that every process in a system must perform some action at every tick of the clock unless it is specifically allowed to delay until the next tick. In this manner neither the global clock, nor indeed time itself, is actually modelled specifically, but the effect is exactly a global clock which ticks incessantly and which cannot be ignored.

There are other possibilities; we could, for instance, attach to each action the length of time it takes to complete from start to finish. This would have the effect of recording the passage of time in terms of the combined behaviours of the system's subprocesses. Presumably the complements of actions would have to require the same amount of time to complete. We would then have to add in some invisible actions which did nothing except cause specified periods of time to pass. This is a similar approach to the one forced by many real-time programming languages which require the programmer to program in time-consuming loops which delay the performance of a command.

Another way of introducing time is to take a language such as CCS and add to it a further type of action which models the performance of specified time delays. In other words we make agents wait before they are able to perform some next action. If we think back to the traffic lights in chapter 6 it is easy to see how we would like to expand those specifications to include the length of time particular lights should remain switched on. For instance, the definition of $Mi1$ on page 92 of the same chapter might be amended to be

$$Mi1 \stackrel{\text{def}}{=} miG_{on}.5.miG_{off}.1.miA_{on}.5.miA_{off}.Mi2$$

which simply specifies the delays we require between the actions of switching on or off various lights. We have thus modelled the intervals during which the major green and amber lights are on. We have also modelled the delays we require when the agent is inactive, e.g. the one second delay between turning the green light off and the amber light on. This notion of time relies on the slightly strange idea that atomic actions take no time at all. Even then there are several ways of interpreting a delay, depending on whether a process simply becomes available on the expiry of some delay or is forced to perform some action at that point in time. Delays can therefore be strong or weak and this will also affect the semantic definitions of such languages.

There are, thus, a number of possibilities for adding time to formal specifications of real-time systems. We are going to study a language which adds time to specifications in terms of delays. Despite the questions posed in the previous paragraph there are a number of advantages to be gained from adopting this approach. First of all we will not have to change existing definitions of the operators already introduced and which are well understood. Our notion of time will, more or less, fit in around what we already have. Secondly, many of the important uses of time in real-time systems are of the waiting type. A choice of what to do next depends to some extent on how long a process has to wait before being able to perform its next action. The length of time a particular action takes may be modelled by defining two actions, e.g. $aStart$ and $\overline{aEnd}$, which specify the period over which a is active and then placing a delay between them. So the modelling of time in terms of explicit delays seems to present the possibility for quite an expressive language.

7.2 Timed CCS (TCCS)

We are going to study one particular style of timed CCS which uses strong delays, in other words delays which force some action the moment they expire. We will, briefly, return to the other possibilities later in the chapter. As with value passing we will take a fresh look at some of the simpler examples from chapter 2 and see how they behave in the presence of delays.

First of all we will consider how delays interact with parallel composition by studying what happens when we add delays to the mutual exclusion example, Mx, which you should recognise from chapter 2. Instead of atomic actions $c1$ and $c2$ to mark the critical sections we will now specify the start and finish points for both actions in the following way:

$$
\begin{aligned}
Mx &\stackrel{\text{def}}{=} (P1 \mid P2 \mid Sem)\backslash\{get, put\} \\
NewP1 &\stackrel{\text{def}}{=} \overline{get}.startc1.endc1.\overline{put}.NewP1 \\
NewP2 &\stackrel{\text{def}}{=} \overline{get}.startc2.endc2.\overline{put}.NewP2 \\
Sem &\stackrel{\text{def}}{=} get.put.Sem
\end{aligned}
$$

The obvious use of time would be to state how long each of the critical sections actually takes by adding delays to the processes $NewP1$ and $NewP2$ to make clear the length of time between the start and end points of the two critical sections. This will now give us the following system:

$$
\begin{aligned}
NewMx &\stackrel{\text{def}}{=} (TP1 \mid TP2 \mid Sem)\backslash\{get, put\} \\
TP1 &\stackrel{\text{def}}{=} \overline{get}.startc1.(5).endc1.\overline{put}.TP1 \\
TP2 &\stackrel{\text{def}}{=} \overline{get}.startc2.(4).endc2.\overline{put}.TP2 \\
Sem &\stackrel{\text{def}}{=} get.put.Sem
\end{aligned}
$$

This now says that the critical sections $c1$ and $c2$ take 5 seconds and 4 seconds to complete respectively. But this introduces a problem in that we have not said what agents are allowed to do when they are inactive but time can pass for other agents. In the $NewMx$ example with the new definitions $TP1$ and $TP2$ the system may evolve to the following state by performing a τ-action followed by $startc1$:

$$((5).endc1.\overline{put}.TP1 \mid TP2 \mid put.Sem)\backslash\{get, put\}$$

In this state $TP1$ has a 5 second delay but the other two agents have no delays at all and indeed are also temporarily deadlocked as their next actions are also restricted. This will lead us to a rule which states that agents composed in parallel can only delay if they can all delay for the same period of time. There are two possible ways of satisfying this requirement: we allow any agent without a specific delay to idle for as long as it wants or, alternatively, we do not allow agents to delay unless they have an explicit delay specified. If we adopt the former then it might be difficult in some circumstances to force an action to be performed in preference to some further unspecified delay. If we adopt the latter approach then this system is deadlocked in terms of both time and action which does not seem a desirable state of affairs. Despite this our first version of timed CCS adopts the second approach.

We can try to eliminate the temporal deadlock by giving the semaphore a 5 second delay, which is fine if it is being controlled by $TP1$ but no good if it is being controlled by $TP2$ which only has a 4 second delay. Another deadlock will occur and perhaps we should have a choice of delays for the semaphore. The problem for the other two processes is far worse than this because the non-determinism in the system means that $TP2$, for instance, might have a long delay before it becomes active or indeed it might never become active. We will have to introduce the notion of an arbitrary delay which specifies that an agent is in an idle state. Syntactically, we will identify such an agent by underlining it and we will mean by this the agent that can delay indefinitely. The only way an agent can get out of an idle state is to perform some action. Using this new idea we can complete the timed version of Mx:

$$TMx \stackrel{\text{def}}{=} (TP1 \mid TP2 \mid TSem)\backslash\{get, put\}$$
$$TP1 \stackrel{\text{def}}{=} \overline{get}.startc1.(5).\overline{endc1}.\overline{put}.TP1$$
$$TP2 \stackrel{\text{def}}{=} \overline{get}.startc2.(4).\overline{endc2}.\overline{put}.TP2$$
$$TSem \stackrel{\text{def}}{=} get.\underline{put}.TSem$$

Notice that $TSem$ can only delay when it is busy and not when it is free. The result of this is that no delay between active critical sections is allowed: either the action $c1$ or $c2$ must be in progress. Adding an extra idle state to the semaphore by

$$IdleSem \stackrel{\text{def}}{=} \underline{get}.\underline{put}.IdleSem$$

would allow a possibly infinite delay between active critical sections.

Just as with basic CCS, we can draw transition graphs to capture the possible behaviour of a specification. Figure 7.1 gives the transition graph for TMx and you should note that in the diagram $\rightarrow$ can represent both an action and a delay transition. We will make a distinction between these in the formal semantics.

It is relatively clear what we mean by the interactions of delays and parallel composition but less so with the choice operator. For instance, what does the following specification mean?

$$ArbD \stackrel{\text{def}}{=} (5).a.ArbD + (7).b.ArbD$$

Can we wait 5 time units and guarantee that an a happens and can we only get a b after 5 or more time units? What happens after 7 time units have elapsed? Do we lose both possibilities or is the action b forced to be performed? Are we even allowed to wait more than 5 time units in this case?

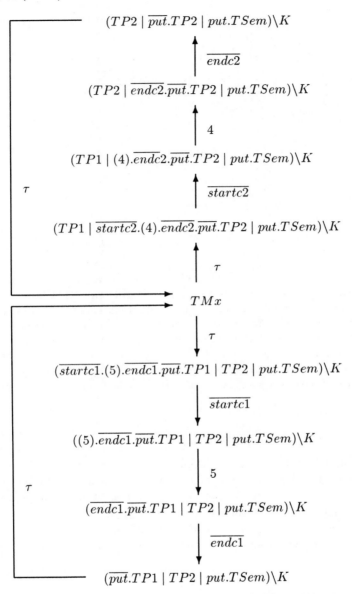

Figure 7.1. *Transition graph for* TMx

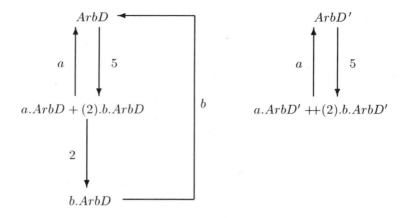

Figure 7.2. *Transition graph for ArbD and ArbD'*

It is convenient to specify two choice operators which differ in the manner they handle delays. Strong choice $E +\!\!+ F$ will only allow a delay if both E and F are capable of that delay, while weak choice $+$ will also allow a choice to be made in favour of the agent which can delay the longest. Figure 7.2 gives the transition graph for $ArbD$. In this case the action a becomes available after exactly 5 units of time but is lost if it is not performed immediately. A further delay of 2 will force the action b to take place. In the case of weak choice delays can actually affect the observable behaviour of agents.

Notice that if we replace $+$ by $+\!\!+$:

$$ArbD' \stackrel{\mathrm{def}}{=} (5).a.ArbD' +\!\!+ (7).b.ArbD'$$

then the resulting transition graph (see fig. 7.2) is quite different. In this example, the right hand side of the choice is never possible because after a delay of 5 the action a is forced and the transition graph demonstrates that it behaves just as the agent $D5 \stackrel{\mathrm{def}}{=} (5).a.D5$.

We have demonstrated informally how adding delays affects the apparent behaviour of agents and in the next section we will formalise these ideas for all the operators of basic CCS.

EXERCISE 7.1

Some useful derived operators can be defined which model common patterns of behaviour involving the interaction of time and actions:

1. $[t].E \stackrel{\mathrm{def}}{=} \ldots$ is intended to define the agent E prefixed by a *soft* delay. In other words, E becomes *available* after t units of time.

2. $E_t \overset{\text{def}}{=} \dots$ is the agent E which is only available for t units of time after which it will not allow time to progress. Hint: use the composition operator here.

EXERCISE 7.2

Being able to specify agents which are *timed out* after a specified delay has occurred is very important and different types of delay can be specified:

1. $TimeOut1_t(\alpha.P, Q) \overset{\text{def}}{=} \dots$ defines the agent which allows P up to t units of time to perform its first action otherwise either P or Q must perform an action after the passing of exactly t units of time.

2. $TimeOut2_t(\alpha.P, Q) = \overset{\text{def}}{=} \dots$ defines the agent which allows P up to t units of time to perform its first action otherwise some action from Q only is forced after exactly $t + 1$ units of time.

3. What does the agent $TimeOut1_t(P, \mathbf{0})$ define?

EXERCISE 7.3

$$A1 \overset{\text{def}}{=} (1).a.A1$$
$$A2 \overset{\text{def}}{=} (2).a.A2$$
$$B2 \overset{\text{def}}{=} (2).b.B2$$
$$B3 \overset{\text{def}}{=} (3).b.B3$$

Draw transitions graphs for the following agents:

1. $A1 \mid B2$
2. $A2 \mid B3$
3. $A1 + B2$
4. $A1 +\!\!+ B2$
5. $TimeOut1_3(a.A1, b.B2)$

7.3 The formal semantics for TCCS

Timed versions of CCS, unlike value-passing CCS, are extensions to the basic language and will require additions to the operational semantics. However, because time and actions do not interact the semantics for timed

TCCS makes use of the operational semantics already given for basic CCS with the addition of rules for time delays. We will see that most of the operators interact very naturally with delays although we shall have to be careful how we define the two timed versions of choice, $+\!\!\!\!+$ and $+$.

The syntax for the language is as follows with the operators presented in descending order of precedence as for CCS etc:

$$
\begin{aligned}
\mathcal{E}^T \quad ::= \quad & \mathbf{0} \\
| \quad & \underline{\mathbf{0}} \\
| \quad & A \\
| \quad & \mathcal{E}^T[f] \\
| \quad & \mathcal{E}^T \backslash R \\
| \quad & \alpha.\mathcal{E}^T \\
| \quad & (t).\mathcal{E}^T \\
| \quad & \underline{\alpha}.\mathcal{E}^T \\
| \quad & \mathcal{E}^T \mid \mathcal{E}^T \\
| \quad & \mathcal{E}^T + \mathcal{E}^T \\
| \quad & \mathcal{E}^T +\!\!\!\!+ \mathcal{E}^T
\end{aligned}
$$

In addition we assume a set of agent definitions $P \overset{\text{def}}{=} E$, one for each constant P. The transitional semantics for TCCS formalises, in a similar manner as for CCS, the transitions in the extended form of transition graphs presented in section 7.2. Of course, we now have time transitions in addition to action transitions. We will take $\mathcal{T}$ to be the set of allowable delays which gives rise to the relation $\{\overset{t}{\leadsto} \mid t \in \mathcal{T}\}$ which characterises transitions via delays. For most of this chapter, we will take $\mathcal{T}$ to be the set $\{1, 2, 3, \ldots, \omega\}$ which will mean that all delays must be discrete and that delays of 0 are not allowed. The two types of transitions must satisfy the operational rules for TCCS which will consist of the rules for basic CCS given in chapter 2 with some additions. The first additions are a few extra rules to make precise the action transitions for agents constructed using the new operators. To begin with, we will simply state that both strong and weak choice behave as expected with respect to actions:

$$
\textbf{Sum}_1\textbf{op} \quad \frac{E \overset{\alpha}{\to} E'}{E\,\text{op}\,F \overset{\alpha}{\to} E'} \qquad \textbf{Sum}_2\textbf{op} \quad \frac{F \overset{\alpha}{\to}'}{E\,\text{op}\,F \overset{\alpha}{\to} F'} \qquad \text{op} \in \{+, +\!\!\!\!+\}
$$

We also need to define the action transitions allowed for agents which are in their idle state:

$$
\textbf{Idle}_1 \quad \frac{}{\underline{\alpha}.E \overset{\alpha}{\to} E}
$$

The second and major set of additions defines the rules for delayed transitions, but let us just recap briefly the additions to the syntax of basic CCS. The agent $\underline{\mathbf{0}}$ is the agent which is deadlocked in terms of actions but which may allow time to pass indefinitely. The agent $(t).E$ is the agent that has to wait exactly t units of time before becoming the agent E, at which time some action from E must be performed unless E itself allows a further delay. This is the strong notion of delay referred to in the previous section. We use $\underline{\alpha}.E$ to refer to an unspecified delay on the action α. This agent can delay its next action for as long as it likes and represents the agent $\alpha.E$ in its idle state. In other words, $\underline{\alpha}.E$ will be allowed to delay indefinitely until it performs the action α, at which point it will no longer be idle unless, of course, E itself is allowed to idle. The following rules formalise the notions of timed and idle prefixes:

$$\textbf{Idle}_2 \quad \frac{}{\mathbf{0} \overset{t}{\leadsto} \mathbf{0}} \qquad \textbf{Idle}_3 \quad \frac{}{\underline{\alpha}.E \overset{t}{\leadsto} \underline{\alpha}.E}$$

$$\textbf{Time}_1 \quad \frac{}{(t).E \overset{t}{\leadsto} E} \qquad \textbf{Time}_2 \frac{}{(s+t).E \overset{s}{\leadsto} (t).E}$$

$$\textbf{Time}_3 \quad \frac{E \overset{s}{\leadsto} E'}{(t).E \overset{s+t}{\leadsto} E'}$$

Idle$_2$ says that the agent $\mathbf{0}$ can always allow time to pass. **Idle$_3$** says that an agent that can idle can delay for some specific t and remain idle. **Time$_1$** is straightforward, while **Time$_2$** says that if we know an agent can wait for a specified period of time then we know that it can also wait for any period of time s less than that, $0 < s \le t$. **Time$_3$** says that if we know E can wait s units of time then prefixing E by (t) simply increases the possible delay by t to $s + t$ units of time.

It is relatively clear what we mean by the interactions of delays and action prefixes but less so with the choice operators. In the previous section we found it convenient to adopt two choice operators which differ in the manner they handle delays. Strong choice $+\!\!\!+$ will commit an agent to the lesser of two possible delays and weak choice $+$ will also allow the environment to choose the longer of two possible delays. Before we proceed any further with the delay rules we need to specify some rules which will allow us to prove whether or not a given TCCS agent is capable of a particular delay:

$$\frac{}{\mathbf{0} \uparrow t} \qquad \frac{}{\underline{\alpha}.E \uparrow t}$$

$$\frac{}{(t).E \uparrow s} \ (s \le t) \qquad \frac{E \uparrow t_0}{(t).E \uparrow s} \ (s \le t_0 + t)$$

$$\frac{E \uparrow t}{E + F \uparrow t} \qquad \frac{F \uparrow t}{E + F \uparrow t}$$

$$\frac{E \uparrow t, \ F \uparrow t}{E +\!\!\!+ F \uparrow t} \qquad \frac{E \uparrow t, \ F \uparrow t}{E \mid F \uparrow t}$$

$$\frac{E \uparrow t}{E \backslash R \uparrow t} \qquad \frac{E \uparrow t}{E[f] \uparrow t}$$

$$\frac{E \uparrow t}{P \uparrow t} \quad (P \stackrel{\text{def}}{=} E)$$

Using these additional proof rules we can now specify the possible behaviours for the two choice operators of which strong choice is the more restrictive:

$$\textbf{TWSum}_1 \quad \frac{E \stackrel{t}{\rightsquigarrow} E', \; F \uparrow t}{E + F \stackrel{t}{\rightsquigarrow} E'}$$

$$\textbf{TWSum}_2 \quad \frac{F \stackrel{t}{\rightsquigarrow} F', \; E \uparrow t}{E + F \stackrel{t}{\rightsquigarrow} F'}$$

$$\textbf{TWSum}_3 \quad \frac{E \stackrel{t}{\rightsquigarrow} E' \quad F \stackrel{t}{\rightsquigarrow} F'}{E + F \stackrel{t}{\rightsquigarrow} E' + F'}$$

$$\textbf{TSSum} \quad \frac{E \stackrel{t}{\rightsquigarrow} E' \quad F \stackrel{t}{\rightsquigarrow} F'}{E +\!\!+ F \stackrel{t}{\rightsquigarrow} E' + F'}$$

In practical terms these two choice operators only make sense when either one of the delays is δ or there is a choice between a delay and an action.

The timed rule for composition says simply that two agents in parallel may only delay t units of time if they can both do so separately. Thus $(t).E \mid 0$ will deadlock for any t:

$$\textbf{TCom} \quad \frac{E \stackrel{t}{\rightsquigarrow} E' \quad F \stackrel{t}{\rightsquigarrow} F'}{E \mid F \stackrel{t}{\rightsquigarrow} E' \mid F'}$$

The remaining operators are unaffected by the passing of time:

$$\textbf{TRes} \quad \frac{E \stackrel{t}{\rightsquigarrow} E'}{E\backslash L \stackrel{t}{\rightsquigarrow} E'\backslash L}$$

$$\textbf{TRel} \quad \frac{E \stackrel{t}{\rightsquigarrow} E'}{E[S] \stackrel{t}{\rightsquigarrow} E'[S]}$$

$$\textbf{TCon}_1 \quad \frac{E \stackrel{t}{\rightsquigarrow} E'}{P \stackrel{t}{\rightsquigarrow} E'}(P \stackrel{\text{def}}{=} E) \qquad \textbf{TCon}_2 \quad \frac{E \stackrel{t}{\rightsquigarrow} E'}{E \stackrel{t}{\rightsquigarrow} P}(P \stackrel{\text{def}}{=} E')$$

Figure 7.3 gives a proof of the timed transition of 7 for the agent $ArbD$ discussed in section 7.2. The proof is much the same as the proofs in chapter 3 except for the additional hypothesis for weak choice which uses the delay rules to demonstrate that the maximum delay for $(5).a.ArbD$ is, of course, 5 and thus the delay of 7 is not possible. Proofs for action transitions are the same as for basic CCS except for the additional rules for weak choice and agents which are idle.

$$\text{Time}_1 \dfrac{\rule{7cm}{0.4pt}}{(7),b.ArbD \overset{7}{\leadsto} b.ArbD}$$

$$\dfrac{(5).a.ArbD \uparrow 5}{(5).a.ArbD\neg \uparrow 7}$$

$$\text{TWSum}_2 \dfrac{(5).a.ArbD + (7).b.ArbD \overset{7}{\leadsto} b.ArbD}{}$$

$$\text{Con}_1 \dfrac{}{ArbD \overset{7}{\leadsto} b.ArbD}$$

Figure 7.3. *Proof of the transition $ArbD \overset{7}{\leadsto} b.ArbD$*

EXERCISE 7.4

Prove correct the following transitions from exercise 7.3:

$$A1 \mid B2 \overset{1}{\leadsto} a.A1 \mid (1).b.B2$$
$$A1 +\!\!+ B2 \overset{2}{\leadsto} b.B2$$

EXERCISE 7.5

Draw the transition graph for TMx and prove the timed transitions for one of the branches of the graph.

7.4 Still at the traffic lights

As a first example of the use of time we will complete the process, started at the beginning of this chapter, of adding time in the form of appropriate delays to the traffic lights problem from chapter 6. In this particular case we are using a soft notion of time in the sense that the ordering on events is more important than the actual times involved which can in fact be varied at will to suit particular traffic junctions. We will take time units to be seconds in this section. However, introducing time will cause us some new problems. To jog your memory, here is the definition of the simple road junction before we concerned ourselves with the red–amber problem:

$$
\begin{aligned}
Lights1 &\stackrel{\text{def}}{=} (StartMajor \mid StartMinor \mid Sensor)\backslash L \\
StartMajor &\stackrel{\text{def}}{=} start.\overline{m}.maG_{on}.w.Major \\
Major &\stackrel{\text{def}}{=} s.maG_{off}.maA_{on}.maA_{off}.Ma1 \\
Ma1 &\stackrel{\text{def}}{=} maR_{on}.\overline{ma}.Majorwait \\
Majorwait &\stackrel{\text{def}}{=} mi.maA_{on}.maR_{off}.maA_{off}.maG_{on}.Major \\
StartMinor &\stackrel{\text{def}}{=} m.miR_{on}.\overline{w}.Minor \\
Minor &\stackrel{\text{def}}{=} ma.miA_{on}.miR_{off}.miA_{off}.Mi1 \\
Mi1 &\stackrel{\text{def}}{=} miG_{on}.miG_{off}.miA_{on}.miA_{off}.\overline{resetS}.Mi2 \\
Mi2 &\stackrel{\text{def}}{=} miR_{on}.\overline{mi}.Minor \\
Sensor &\stackrel{\text{def}}{=} press.s.resetS.Sensor \\
L &= \{ma, mi, resetS, s, m, w\}
\end{aligned}
$$

We established in the previous chapter that the specification models the correct order in which lights should be switched on and off but not the durations for which lights are in their on or off states. Let us impose some timing constraints and add them to $Lights1$:

- Minor lights stay on green for 30 seconds.
- The major lights must be on green for at least 30 seconds in every cycle but must respond to the sensor immediately after that.
- All interim lights stay on for 5 seconds.
- There is a one second delay between switching one light off and another on.

It seems straightforward to add appropriate delays at the appropriate points and arrive at the following specification:

$$
\begin{aligned}
TLights1 &\stackrel{\text{def}}{=} (StartMajor \mid StartMinor \mid Sensor)\backslash L \\
StartMajor &\stackrel{\text{def}}{=} start.\overline{m}.maG_{on}.w.Major \\
TMajor &\stackrel{\text{def}}{=} (30).s.maG_{off}.(1).maA_{on}.(5).maA_{off}.(1).TMa1 \\
TMa1 &\stackrel{\text{def}}{=} maR_{on}.\overline{ma}.TMajorwait \\
TMajorwait &\stackrel{\text{def}}{=} mi.maA_{on}.(5).maR_{off}.maA_{off}.(1).maG_{on}.TMajor \\
StartMinor &\stackrel{\text{def}}{=} m.miR_{on}.\overline{w}.Minor \\
TMinor &\stackrel{\text{def}}{=} ma.miA_{on}.(5).miR_{off}.miA_{off}.(1).TMi1 \\
TMi1 &\stackrel{\text{def}}{=} miG_{on}.(30).miG_{off}.(1).miA_{on}.(5).miA_{off}. \\
&\qquad (1).\overline{resetS}.TMi2 \\
TMi2 &\stackrel{\text{def}}{=} miR_{on}.\overline{mi}.TMinor \\
Sensor &\stackrel{\text{def}}{=} press.s.resetS.Sensor \\
L &= \{ma, mi, resetS, s, m, w\}
\end{aligned}
$$

Notice that we have said nothing about any timing constraints on the startup precedure or the *Sensor* because none were stated in the additional requirements. We have translated all the timing information in the additional requirements into delays in the specification. We now need to animate the model to see if it really behaves in the manner required. In fact, the specification as it now stands is seriously flawed and does not at all specify the system we require. To see what the problem is it is easier to consider a smaller example first.

Consider a very simple system that can at any time perform the action a but which will perform the action b every 5 seconds. A definition in the style of $TLights1$ above would look like the following:

$$A \stackrel{\text{def}}{=} a.A$$
$$B \stackrel{\text{def}}{=} (5).b.B$$
$$AB \stackrel{\text{def}}{=} A \mid B$$

Far from performing the action a at arbitrary intervals and b every 5 seconds AB performs an infinite sequence of as but allows no time to pass at all. The problem is that AB is in a state of temporal deadlock because B wishes to wait but A cannot wait at all. However, because in our timed semantics actions take no time the only behaviour possible is the infinite repetition of a. If you take a look at the definition for parallel composition in respect of time you will see that we need to make it possible for A to wait indefinitely between each action. To do this we make use of the arbitrary delay δ to give us the new specification:

$$A \stackrel{\text{def}}{=} \underline{a}.A$$
$$B \stackrel{\text{def}}{=} (5).b.B$$
$$AB \stackrel{\text{def}}{=} A \mid B$$

The point is that when a parallel agent has both an action and a delay only the action is possible as both agents have to agree the delay. In this case A can either delay up to 5 seconds with B or perform a. However, B can only delay until 5 seconds have passed, at which point it cannot delay and must do the action b thus causing a temporal deadlock until it has done so. The implication for the traffic lights and for all timed specifications is that idle agents must be thus enabled by a δ prefix. The traffic lights can now be correctly specified by identifying all points at which an agent becomes idle:

$$
\begin{aligned}
TLights1 &\stackrel{\mathrm{def}}{=} (StartMajor \mid StartMinor \mid Sensor) \backslash L \\
StartMajor &\stackrel{\mathrm{def}}{=} start.\overline{m}.maG_{on}.w.Major \\
TMajor &\stackrel{\mathrm{def}}{=} (30).\underline{s}.maG_{off}.(1).maA_{on}.(5).maA_{off}.(1).TMa1 \\
TMa1 &\stackrel{\mathrm{def}}{=} maR_{on}.\overline{ma}.TMajorwait \\
TMajorwait &\stackrel{\mathrm{def}}{=} \underline{mi}.maA_{on}.(5).maR_{off}.maA_{off}.(1).maG_{on}.TMajor \\
StartMinor &\stackrel{\mathrm{def}}{=} m.miR_{on}.\overline{w}.Minor \\
TMinor &\stackrel{\mathrm{def}}{=} \underline{ma}.miA_{on}.(5).miR_{off}.miA_{off}.(1).TMi1 \\
TMi1 &\stackrel{\mathrm{def}}{=} miG_{on}.(30).miG_{off}.(1).miA_{on}.(5).miA_{off}. \\
 &\qquad (1).\overline{resetS}.TMi2 \\
TMi2 &\stackrel{\mathrm{def}}{=} miR_{on}.\overline{mi}.TMinor \\
Sensor &\stackrel{\mathrm{def}}{=} press.\overline{s}.\underline{resetS}.Sensor \\
L &\equiv \{ma, mi, resetS, s, m, w\}
\end{aligned}
$$

This is not the end of the story, however, because we have only specified idle points for agents in their first cycle. If you analyse the system carefully you will find there is a potential problem with the *Sensor* and the *Major* if a vehicle is detected before the major lights have returned to green. The sensor wishes to synchronise with the major lights on $\overline{s}$ but the major lights are not yet willing to do so. Eventually a delay on the major lights will be encountered which will cause a temporal deadlock. A possible solution is to treat

$$\overline{s}.\underline{resetS}.Sensor$$

as an idle state and in the following manner:

$$\underline{\overline{s}}.\underline{resetS}.Sensor$$

This avoids the temporal deadlock but introduces the possibility of an infinite delay for the whole junction. A sort of temporal divergence.

A more sensible solution is to treat the sensor differently on its second and subsequent cycles. We would like to specify a maximum delay after the sensor has been activated. During this time the synchronisation on $\overline{s}$ should always be possible but at the end of this period this synchronisation must take place. We can use the derived timeout operator to specify this

$$Sensor2 \stackrel{\mathrm{def}}{=} \overline{s}.\underline{resetS}.Sensor \mathbin{+\!\!+} (36).\mathbf{0}$$

We have defined an agent which is timed out by $\mathbf{0}$. This may seem rather odd but the definition forces the restricted action $\overline{s}$ and thus guarantees that the *Sensor* will be responded to at most 36 seconds after a vehicle has been detected.

EXERCISE 7.6
Amend the version of the traffic lights which included a pedestrian crossing on the minor road so that it now models time appropriately.

EXERCISE 7.7
Rework the automated train examples from earlier chapters so that sections of track may remain idle unless a train arrives, in which case an appropriate amount of time should pass before the train clears each section.

7.5 Fault-tolerant reactor control system

```
-----------
REQUIREMENTS
-----------
```

```
A fault-tolerant reactor control system is required
which monitors the core temperature and drops rods into
the core if the temperature becomes too high. Six
temperature sensors provide readings simultaneously
to three periodic processes called assessors. Each
assessor evaluates the six sensor readings and sends
the result to a voter process which waits asynchronously
to receive the readings. The voter produces a vote on
the three values received and sends this to an actuator
process which drops rods or maintains the status quo
depending on the value of the vote. In addition the
actuator will automatically timeout and drop rods into
the core if no message is received from the voter in a
predetermined time. All computations take finite times
to complete.
```

```
-----------
```

We can identify four types of processes from the requirements. A sensor (six), an assessor (three), a voter (one), and an actuator (one). Of these, we need not model the six sensors but only the values received from them. Note that the time taken by the various computations must be made explicit, as must the values communicated by processes. This means we must use TCCS with value passing. We could probably manage without value passing if it were not for the temperature values provided by the sensors, whose range precludes writing out all possible cases. First we will assume the type *Boolean* and declare a type to represent the temperature range along with the variables and functions we will need. We assume the temperature range is bounded:

$$
\begin{aligned}
Temp &= -272 \dots Maxtemp \\
x_i &: \quad Temp \quad\quad (i \in \{1, \dots, 6\}) \\
y_j &: \quad Boolean \quad (j \in \{1, 2, 3\}) \\
f &: \quad Temp \times Temp \times Temp \times Temp \times Temp \times Temp \to Boolean \\
v &: \quad Boolean \times Boolean \times Boolean \to Boolean
\end{aligned}
$$

Let us begin modelling the system by considering the assessors, although as they have a common pattern of behaviour we need provide only one generic definition:

$$
Assessor_n \stackrel{\text{def}}{=} (s_1(x_1) \ddagger \dots \ddagger s_6(x_6)).(p).\bar{c}_n(f(x_1, \dots, x_6)).Assessor_n
$$

$$
n \in \{1, 2, 3\}
$$

In the assessor specification, (p) is the computation time for the function f which we have not defined at this stage. Note the use of the derived operator $\ddagger$ from the traffic lights chapter. The absence of delays means effectively that we require all the temperature values to arrive at the same moment in time in any order. Without this operator we would have had to have specified all possible patterns in which the six sensor readings could have arrived.

The voter is similar to the assessors except that it must wait on each individual assessor communication:

$$
Voter \stackrel{\text{def}}{=} (c_1(y_1) \ddagger \dots \ddagger c_3(y_3)).(q).\bar{a}(v(y_1 \dots y_3)).Voter
$$

Again, (q) is the length of time taken to complete the computation v, which we have also put off defining till later. The reader should note that the use of the $\ddagger$ notation here is inconsistent with the operator's definition in chapter 6. Undertaking the following exercise should help to remedy the situation.

The actuator has three possible courses of action in each cycle. If it receives a timely message from the voter it will respond accordingly. Otherwise it must initiate some emergency procedure which starts by dropping some rods into the core:

$$
\begin{aligned}
Actuator &\stackrel{\text{def}}{=} a(x).Actuator'(x) + (t).\overline{drop}.Alarm \\
Actuator' &\stackrel{\text{def}}{=} if\ x = tt\ then\ \overline{drop}.Actuator\ else\ Actuator
\end{aligned}
$$

We can complete the specification by composing the various agents in parallel and restricting accordingly:

$$System \stackrel{\text{def}}{=} (Assessor_1 \mid \ldots \mid Assessor_3 \mid Voter \mid Actuator) \backslash \{c_1, c_2, c_3, a\}$$

This specification illustrates the natural manner in which systems involving time and data may be specified in TCCS. Once again the abstraction powers of the value-passing calculus have been amply demonstrated. The following exercise requires the use of the full language of CCS with time, value passing, and indexing. It might appear at first to be virtually the same problem as the reactor control system but it is actually quite different.

EXERCISE 7.8

Specify in TCCS a system which consists of a monitor process and three bit registers. The monitor has a cycle which consists of checking the value held by as many registers as it needs to decide whether or not to switch to an alarm state. It will do this if only one register returns 1 whereas if two or more return 1 then the next cycle can begin. Each register is updated by a different device in the environment and all registers must be modelled. The following timing constraints apply:

- Each register may idle while it is waiting for the next value to arrive.

- On receiving a new value each register will wait a specific number of seconds for that value to be read, after which interval it will lose that value and switch back to its idle state to wait for a new value to arrive. The registers have the following delays:

  1. Register 1 will wait 4 seconds

  2. Register 2 will wait 5 seconds

  3. Register 3 will wait 3 seconds

- The monitor expects a reading from a register at least every 4 seconds. If no reading is available in that period a timeout occurs and the monitor switches to its alarm state.

- At the end of each successful cycle the monitor will wait 10 seconds before commencing the next.

Hint: there are various ways of doing this with or without value passing but the most elegant way uses value passing and indexed sums.

7.6 In other times ...

So far we have considered a single possible way of adding time to CCS in the form of specific, or strong, delays: in other words, delays which prescribe a specific amount of time after which some action must take place with the possibility of a further delay only if it is explicitly specified. To introduce arbitrary delays we introduced δ as an additional delay prefix. This view of time is not the only one available to us. In the introduction to this chapter we referred to SCCS which effectively synchronises processes on each tick of a global clock. We also mentioned the possibility of weak delays which only specify a minimum wait. We also considered the possibility of associating actions with a number which represents the time the action takes to complete. In this section we will briefly investigate the last two possibilities, still in the context of CCS.

We will refer to the language we have been studying as sTCCS, or strong timed CCS. Weak timed CCS (wTCCS) extends basic CCS with processes of the form $[t].P$, which is intended to mean the process P delayed by at least t units of time. The first rule for this states that $[t].P$ may delay as long as it likes – even for times greater than t:

$$\textbf{WTime} \quad \frac{\rule{3cm}{0.4pt}}{[t].P \overset{t'}{\leadsto} [t \dot{-} t'].P}$$

where

$$t \dot{-} t' = \begin{cases} t - t' & \text{if } t' \leq t \\ 0 & \text{otherwise} \end{cases}$$

This means that delays of greater than t will set the delay prefix to 0 which still allows arbitrary delays of the form

$$[0].P \overset{t}{\leadsto} [0].P$$

This in turn would seem to suggest that we should equate agents of the form $[0].P$ in wTCCS with idle agents in sTCCS. The next rule reinforces this observation

$$\textbf{ActTime} \frac{P \overset{\alpha}{\to} P'}{[0].P \overset{\alpha}{\to} P'}$$

This rule says that an agent that has waited for at least its minimum delay is always able to perform an action of which it is capable or it may continue to wait. This is useful as it models the type of delays which can be implemented in the real-time programming language Ada where the real-time kernel cannot be guaranteed to notice exactly when a specified delay has expired. The agent $[0].\mathbf{0}$ is equivalent to the agent $\underline{\mathbf{0}}$ in sTCCS; in other words they both represent the deadlocked agent that can only allow time to pass but will never perform any action. Despite the different approach to delays the strong version of TCCS is more fundamental in that there is a straightforward translation of wTCCS expressions into sTCCS expressions. We simply take expressions of the form $[t].P$ and translate them into expressions of the form $(t).\underline{P}$ where we take $\underline{P}$ to be the agent P with all its initial actions allowed to idle. We will not pursue wTCCS further here, but refer the reader to the literature.

In all the variants of timed CCS considered so far, other time domains are possible so long as they satisfy the constraint that they are totally ordered and have a unique least element. Thus the rational numbers and the positive reals are also possible time domains. In specifying systems where possible delays may be very small, fractions of a second, this is a far more practical technique than taking the time domain $\mathbf{N}^+$ to denote time units in milliseconds. In sTCCS with the positive reals as a time domain, transitions of the following form are allowed:

$$\underline{\alpha}.E + (5).F \overset{2.5}{\leadsto} \underline{\alpha}.E + (2.5).F$$

EXERCISE 7.9

Use the operational semantics for sTCCS with the positive reals as a time domain to prove the above transition to be true.

7.7 Summary and further reading

In this chapter we have investigated the addition of time to basic CCS. In the language of TCCS we accomplished this by adding the concept of delays to the syntax of basic CCS and then expanding the operational semantics to model transitions of time. We then went on to *complete* the specification of the traffic lights from the previous chapter by adding in appropriate delays to model the time lights were actually lit. We then went on to show that, because value-passing CCS can be embedded in basic CCS, we also had a timed version of value-passing CCS as well. We used this language to give a clear and *abstract* definition of the reactor control system. Finally we looked briefly at other characterisations of time for CCS.

The reference [FC92] covers TCCS, [MT89] covers sTCCS, and [Tof89] covers both sTCCS and wTCCS. The reactor control system in this chapter was adapted from the example they used to introduce sTCCS.

8

The home heating system

In this third case-study chapter we are going to consider the development of a system which, like the reactor control system in the previous chapter, will require the use of TCCS with value passing. The requirements document is more realistic both in terms of the size of the system and also in that it stipulates both high-level requirements and various low-level features to do with the system's implementation. As with previous case-study chapters we will attempt to evaluate the performance of CCS in this context and point out useful additions to the language and to the techniques which we bring to bear on specification construction. We will continue to adopt a pragmatic approach to the developement of the specifications and thus continue to reflect, in some manner, on the way such specifications are constructed in real life. In particular, we are going to specify the whole system and not just potential software components. In chapter 14 we will return to the whole problem of systems analysis and deciding which components should be specified and which should be part of the system's and therefore the specification's environment.

8.1 Requirements

```
------------
REQUIREMENTS
------------
```

A temperature sensing device compares the differences between
Ta, the temperature sensed in the house, and the reference
temperature Tr, which is the desired house temperature. The
difference between these two, the error in the temperature,
is measured and sent to the controller. Users may set the
reference temperature within the range 0...35 degrees Celsius.

The controller will attempt to keep the house temperature

within 2 degrees either way of the reference temperature by
turning a furnace on or off as the allowable limits of the
range are reached. To achieve this the controller sends
discrete signals to start an ignition system and then a motor
and to shut them down in the reverse order.

The furnace sends discrete signals to the controller to
indicate the current state of motor rpm and ignition. If
the motor does not reach its optimum speed
on startup the furnace will signal an error which should
abort the startup sequence. The controller will wait 5
seconds for a successful motor status signal from the
furnace. It will terminate the ignition sequence if the
unsuccessful signal is received or if no signal arrives
within 5 seconds.

On receiving an ignition error signal from the furnace, the
controller will shut the system down and set an appropriate
light on an abnormal status panel. If an error indicator is
set on, a manual reset is required before the system may
restart.

There is a master switch which may be set on or off by users
who may also set two pairs of start/stop times for any 24
hour period.

A minimum of 5 minutes must elapse between turning off the
furnace and restarting it. The furnace must be shut down
within 5 seconds if any furnace error is detected or the
master switch is set to off.

   The requirement given above is for a hot-air heating system rather then
the sort of hot-water system which is more conventionally found in Great
Britain. It works by heating air in a chamber and then blowing the hot air
through ducts set in the walls of the building. The hot air emerges through
grilles set near the floor in each room.
   We are presented with a problem which has a variety of competing requirements all of which have, obviously, to be satisfied. The system has
strong behavioural constraints with regard to the correct and safe functioning of the heating system. There are also specific timing constraints and
some particular constraints concerning data and how it should be handled.
One way of approaching such diverse requirements is to adopt Boehm's spi-

ral model of the lifecycle [Boe91]. This approach suggests we should tackle
that aspect of the system which is liable to cause us the greatest problems
in the case of error or failure.

We should ask ourselves: what would be the worst mistake we could make
in specifying this system?

The system we are asked to specify is essentially a control system with
timing constraints. The timing constraints are *hard* in the sense that they
are an integral part of the system's behaviour but they are essentially constraints on behaviour. The behavioural control aspects of the system are
quite complex and would have to be well understood before explicit references to time could be considered. When we review the requirements
document for its concern with data, we see that much space is given over
to temperature values which control the conditions under which the furnace
is switched on or off and the manner in which the particular calculation
is made. However, in many such cases we can abstract away from particular values and concentrate on threshold values which are going to directly
influence the behaviour of the system. In other cases this approach is im-
practical if various subsets of values trigger particular behaviours. In the
present case there are essentially only two threshold values in terms of temperature: the high value, 2 degrees above the reference temperature, and
the low value, 2 degrees below the reference temperature. The actual value
of the required temperature is unimportant and need not be considered in
our first, purely behavioural, specification. The same holds for the speed
of the motor, which we can model as acceptable or not without worrying
about particular values for its rpm. We can thus model data in terms of
atomic actions which represent threshold values. It has been shown in this
book and in other places that it is often possible to abstract away from
data and time and still construct valuable analyses of systems.

The answer to the question posed above should be, I suggest, that we
must first ensure that the basic behaviour of the system is as required. In
other words, ensuring the correct order of events should be our first priority.
We will then return to consider data and time and decide how to amend
the model to best accommodate them.

8.2 Valueless home heating in no time

Even without time and data the system is complex enough and as usual we
will start by considering how to decompose it into manageable subsystems.
Reading through the requirements we immediately come across the need
for a temperature sensor or thermostat. The thermostat interacts directly
with a controller which activates and deactivates the furnace. We seem to
need a controller and a furnace. The controller is also responsible for setting
error lights and responding to the master switch so we will add a status
indicator and a master switch to our list. Initially we will model all these

as separate sub-agents. The first guess for the top-level decomposition thus looks like this:

$$Hhs \stackrel{\text{def}}{=} (Master \mid Controller \mid Status \mid Furnace \mid Sensor)\backslash H$$

Having suggested a possible top-level decomposition of the home heating system, we now have to decide what to do next. In previous examples we have adopted various approaches. In the case of the data-manager we adopted a pragmatic approach and quickly put together prototype specifications, making use of known components, and then tested them to see if they interacted correctly. After a few iterations we arrived at an overall specification which, we were confident, satisfied requirements. For the traffic lights we first specified a simplified system, the major–minor lights, which had a simpler pattern of behaviour than the whole system. We completed the specification only when we were confident about the behaviour of its simpler counterpart. This time we will adopt yet another approach. The home heating system consists of a controller which sits in the middle of an environment which itself consists of a number of devices of varying degrees of complexity. Some of these devices, such as the temperature sensor and the master switch, influence the behaviour of the controller without being influenced by it. Other devices, such as the abnormal status indicator and the furnace, influence and are influenced by the controller. Given this situation it would seem a good idea to model the environment in which the controller has to exist and tackle the controller when we know what its interfaces to the other devices are. Let us also put off considering the furnace until the rest of the environment has been dealt with.

We begin, then, with the master switch. We can observe that it has always to be in one of two states, either on or off. A first guess might make use of the semaphore idea from earlier chapters:

$$Switch \stackrel{\text{def}}{=} on.off.Switch$$

but this approach is too simplistic because a switch always has two distinct roles in a system: some person or device sets the current state of the switch, while the switch itself influences other devices by signalling its current state. The master switch must satisfy these two roles if it is to function correctly. In our solution the actions on and off represent the user setting the switch and the actions $setOn$ and $setOff$ are the resulting signals to the controller. Obviously the former cause a change of state while the latter do not:

$$MasterOff \stackrel{\text{def}}{=} \overline{setOff}.MasterOff + on.MasterOn$$
$$MasterOn \stackrel{\text{def}}{=} \overline{setOn}.MasterOn + off.MasterOff$$

We now turn our attentions to the abnormal status indicator which is similar to the master switch in that it is set either on or off but it must also have indicator lights which can be set to register the presence or absence of various faults. Whenever the device changes state through a reset, any lights lit must also be turned off. We can use our experiences from the traffic lights to model lights in terms of the actions of switching them on or off. The two possible faults to register are in the motor speed and the combustion status. To make matters easier for ourselves we will model a generic fault action and its corresponding indicator light. This leaves open the possibility of using the value-passing calculus to extend the specification to indicate particular faults. The indicator is set on by the controller but can only be reset by the user, and we use the actions $absOn$ and $\overline{reset}$ to model these respectively. We will use the actions $\overline{flitOn}$ and $\overline{flitOff}$ to register this generic fault on the indicator panel. Finally, the actions $\overline{rdabsOff}$ and $\overline{rdabsOn}$ signal the state of the device. The specification may now be completed in the following manner:

$$StatOff \stackrel{\text{def}}{=} \overline{rdabsOff}.StatOff + absOn.\overline{flitOn}.StatOn$$
$$StatOn \stackrel{\text{def}}{=} \overline{rdabsOn}.StatOn + reset.\overline{flitOff}.StatOff$$
$$+ absOn.StatOn$$

We now have the temperature sensor or thermostat to consider before we think about the furnace. In the previous section it was pointed out that we need only model two threshold temperatures and these can be modelled by the atomic actions $\overline{highT}$ and $\overline{lowT}$. The thermostat can register one or the other but never both at the same time. A tempting specification is

$$Sensor \stackrel{\text{def}}{=} \overline{highT}.Sensor + \overline{lowT}.Sensor$$

but this is not correct. Consider the mutual exclusion example, Mx from chapter 2, in which we rejected the specification

$$Spec_1 \stackrel{\text{def}}{=} c1.Spec_1 + c2.Spec_2$$

on the grounds that it meant both $c1$ and $c2$ were possible next actions, which would violate the mutual exclusion property we were after. A similar criticism applies to $Sensor$ in that it asserts that both threshold temperatures could always happen as the next action. We can get round this by imposing τ-actions to register the temperature transitions which give rise to either extreme:

$$Sensor \stackrel{\text{def}}{=} \tau.\overline{highT}.Sensor + \tau.\overline{lowT}.Sensor$$

There are many other ways we could have specified $Sensor$. It is very often tempting to overspecify devices such as this by attributing to them too much knowledge of the physical system in which they exist. The following specification assumes that after a low there will always be a high and vice versa:

$$Sensor1 \stackrel{\text{def}}{=} \tau.\overline{highT}.Sensor2$$
$$Sensor2 \stackrel{\text{def}}{=} \tau.\overline{lowT}.Sensor1$$

The specification we have chosen assumes that once a threshold is reached it should be held until the controller responds to it which again is not necessarily what we want. We could have used a third τ-action to model the fact that neither of the two threshold values has been reached:

$$Sensor \stackrel{\text{def}}{=} \tau.\overline{highT}.Sensor + \tau.\overline{lowT}.Sensor + \tau.Sensor$$

The problem here is that we have introduced the possibility of an infinite sequence of τ-actions into the specification, which now potentially *diverges*. Even though we are going to stick with *Sensor* in its original form we will encounter the problem of feedback loops as we develop our model of the home heating system.

There are yet further possibilities. We could specify quite formally the relationship between the thermal capacity of the heating system and heat loss from the building and the way this affects the efficiency of the heating system and thus the relationship between successive temperature readings. This could become quite important when we consider adding time and data to the specification. It would be very interesting to use such information to derive a far more complete specification but we will not be able to pursue such ideas in this book.

We shall move on and consider the furnace which would appear to have a more complex behavioural pattern than the components we have already specified. Notice that in terms of functionality we can really only model the control aspects of the furnace, which consist of the way it responds to control signals and the occurrence of faults. We cannot model the production of heat. It is the occurrence of faults which will cause us the most problems. The two possible faults which can occur arise in the motor during startup and in a loss of ignition whilst heat is being generated. We have to make sure that such faults generate error messages which we can guarantee will be received by the controller. In fact, the generation of error messages as appropriate is the only autonomous action of the furnace and arises internally from the states of its subsystems. All other activity is directed by the controller and, as with the sensor, we should be careful not to attribute too much behavioural capability to the furnace itself.

The furnace has two subsystems of interest to us, the motor and the ignition system, neither of which interacts with the other. With these observations in mind we can define the initial state of the furnace in the following way, where M stands for motor and I for ignition, of course:

$$Furnace \stackrel{\text{def}}{=} MOff \mid IOff$$

The behaviours of the two devices are somewhat similar in that they both have states which correspond to the idle state when the subsystem is off, the normal running state when the component is active but no errors have been detected, and the error state when the component is active but a fault has been detected. We can suggest the need for the following definitions:

DeviceOff	the off state
DeviceOn	operating normally
DeviceOnError	operating but fault detected

We will also assume that actions such as *deviceOn* and *deviceOff* be used to control these subsystems. When heat is required the controller should first request that the furnace be ignited and follow that by requesting that the motor be started. We may as well deal with the subsystems in this order. In its off state the ignition system must obviously respond to an *iOn* signal but it must also accept but ignore an *iOff* signal. Although we are not able to model the actual output of heat from the furnace it is useful to identify the intervals in which the production of heat should be taking place. We can do this in the manner of the traffic lights by using the actions $\overline{heatOn}$ and $\overline{heatOff}$ to signal the start and finish of such intervals. In fact, if we did not do this an observer of our system would not know whether the heating system was operational or not.

$$IOff \stackrel{\text{def}}{=} iOn.\overline{heatOn}.IOn + iOff.IOff$$

This effect is actually better achieved in SCCS* by using the concurrent action

$$[iOn, \overline{heatOn}]$$

which has the advantage that it does not result in extra interleavings with a resulting increase in the size of the state space which will be generated in the CCS version we are actually using.

Once it is switched on and in normal operation the ignition system must respond to both the *iOff* and *iOn* signals but must also model the fact that a fault might be detected. We can use a τ-action to model the unobservable switch to a faulty state. Additionally, the action $\overline{iOk}$ will be used to tell the controller that the ignition system is in normal operation:

$$IOn \stackrel{\text{def}}{=} \begin{aligned} &iOn.IOn + iOff.IOff \\ &+ \overline{iOk}.IOn + \tau.IOnErr \end{aligned}$$

The requirements state that the controller be forced to respond to an error message and so the third definition is somewhat simpler than the others:

$$IOnErr \stackrel{\text{def}}{=} \overline{iErr}.iOff.IOff$$

The definitions for the motor subsystem are similar except that there is a startup phase in which a fault might be detected. Also, the end of a heat production interval occurs when the motor is turned off, and this has to be incorporated into the definitions:

$$MOff \overset{\text{def}}{=} mOn.(\tau.MOn + \tau.MOnErr) + mOff.MOff$$
$$MOn \overset{\text{def}}{=} mOn.MOn + mOff.\overline{heatOff}.MOff + \overline{mOk}.MOn$$
$$MOnErr \overset{\text{def}}{=} \overline{mErr}.mOff.\overline{heatOff}.MOff$$

We have now completed our first attempt at modelling the environment in which the controller has to exist. Our next task is obviously to model the controller and use the Verification Game to see if it works as we would hope. In the usual way we would begin by identifying some important states which the controller might be in and then building definitions for them. In this case the behaviour pattern is determined by the environment which we have already specified, so we can build the required definitions by following this pattern through. There has to be an off state which is dependent on the current setting of the master switch and the abnormal status indicator. If the former is on and the latter is off then heating can begin. The action *setOn* from the master switch is the signal which allows the heating system to begin operation and the action *rdabsOff* allows it to proceed:

$$COff \overset{\text{def}}{=} setOn.(rdabsOff.COn1 + rdabsOn.COff)$$

The startup phase will then only proceed if and when the sensor signals a low enough temperature. Should this occur then the controller has to begin synchronising with the furnace. This means requesting ignition followed by motor startup. For the latter this depends on receiving mOk to allow the sequence to continue, while receiving $mErr$ means the sequence is aborted. If the sequence continues then the startup phase is complete. If the motor fault is detected then the abnormal status indicator is set on and the controller reverts back to its off state. Notice that the requirement does not require us to check whether or not the ignition system is functioning correctly at this stage.

$$COn1 \overset{\text{def}}{=} lowT.\overline{iOn}.COn2$$
$$COn2 \overset{\text{def}}{=} \overline{mOn}.(mOk.COnRun + mErr.\overline{mOff}.\overline{absOn}.COff)$$

In its normal running state the controller must look at three different devices in order to determine what it should do next:

- An error in the furnace should cause shutdown and set an error light on the abnormal status indicator.

- A *highT* from the sensor should signal normal shutdown.

- A *setOff* from the master switch should also cause normal shutdown.

From this we determine two shutdown patterns depending on whether or not a fault light needs to be set:

$$COnRun \stackrel{\text{def}}{=} iErr.CStopErr + setOff.CStop + highT.CStop$$
$$CStop \stackrel{\text{def}}{=} \overline{iOff}.\overline{mOff}.COff$$
$$CStopErr \stackrel{\text{def}}{=} \overline{iOff}.\overline{mOff}.\overline{absOn}.COff$$

Now we can compose together the initial states of all the subsystems and impose a suitable restriction set:

$$Hhs1 \stackrel{\text{def}}{=} (MasterOff \mid COff \mid StatOff \mid Furnace \mid Sensor) \backslash H$$
$$H \stackrel{\text{def}}{=} \{setOn, setOff, absOn, absOff, rdabsOn, rdabsOff,$$
$$lowT, highT, mOn, mOff, mErr, mOk,$$
$$iOn, iOff, iErr, iOk\}$$

We have now completed our first attempt at the specification of the behavioural part of the home heating system. In the next section we will try to establish any behavioural problems we may inadvertently have introduced.

EXERCISE 8.1

Animate the specification as it stands and identify the problems, of which there are a number.

8.3 Verifying the home heating system

The obvious question follows: does our system specify the required behaviour? In animating the home heating system we should have certain specific questions in mind:

1. Does the system ever deadlock?

2. Does the controller always respond to devices?

3. Does the controller always respond correctly to devices?

The deadlock question turns out to be quite subtle because of the presence of loops such as the repeated turning on and off of the master switch. For this reason it is not possible for the whole system to deadlock, as far as CCS is concerned, in spite of the fact that major components are liable to local deadlock. In other words, it is possible to have a livelock situation where something is always happening but necessary behaviours are locked out. One solution is to set the switch on and leave it on while the system is being animated.

So, assuming that you have already turned the master switch on, allow the sensor to perform a τ so that it wishes to signal *lowT*. This will have the effect of starting up the system. Further, assume that the motor starts up correctly which will in turn result in both controller and furnace achieving their normal running states. Suppose now that a furnace error is detected but ignoring this for the moment the controller responds to a *highT* from the sensor. Which shutdown procedure will result? If you have animated the system correctly you should now see that the controller and furnace are deadlocked. The furnace wants to shut down with an error signalled but the controller is capable of only a normal shutdown. However, there is no general system deadlock because, as we have already pointed out, the master switch can always be reset.

We have to change the controller definition so that the local deadlock is removed and the furnace will always be shut down correctly. The controller must take account of a furnace error and then set the abnormal status indicator even if shutdown was activated normally via the sensor or the master switch. Of course, whatever originates a shutdown, the correct sequence should be followed once any error has been responded to.

$$
\begin{aligned}
COnRun &\overset{\text{def}}{=} iErr.CStopErr + setOff.CStop1 + highT.CStop1 \\
&\quad + lowT.COnRun \\
CStop1 &\overset{\text{def}}{=} CStop2 + iErr.CStopErr \\
CStop2 &\overset{\text{def}}{=} \overline{iOff}.\overline{mOff}.COff \\
CStopErr &\overset{\text{def}}{=} \overline{mOff}.\overline{iOff}.\overline{absOn}.CStop1
\end{aligned}
$$

There is another way of viewing the problem we have just solved. Instead of making provision for the controller to respond to all messages in various orders we could assert that some messages take priority over others. In other words, error messages should be responded to in preference to messages from the master switch or the sensor. As CCS is currently defined this is going to be a problem due to the inherent non-determinism of the choice operator. In fact, eliminating unwanted non-deterministic behaviour from CCS specifications can be a major problem in itself. However, we don't want to banish non-determinism from CCS altogether as it can be a useful specification technique when used carefully. Think back to the mutual exclusion example, Mx in section 2.2, for an illustration of the usefulness of non-determinism. What we are lacking is an interrupt operator of the sort defined in LOTOS and made available in many implementation environments. It is possible to define an interrupt operator for CCS, in the manner of its LOTOS counterpart, and respecify the controller appropriately. The definitions for the operator are, in some ways, a mixture of those for choice and composition. Notice that because we have no specific notion of successful termination in CCS, the definitions are a little simpler than those for LOTOS:

$$\textbf{Int}_1 \quad \frac{E \xrightarrow{\alpha} E'}{E \wedge F \xrightarrow{\alpha} E' \wedge F} \qquad \textbf{Int}_2 \quad \frac{F \xrightarrow{\alpha} F'}{E \wedge F \xrightarrow{\alpha} F'}$$

In other words, the definitions assert that any agent which consists of a sub-agent E with interrupt agent F will behave just as E until F performs its first action, at which point E (or the state it has evolved to) will be lost. Essentially the interrupt occurs when the environment chooses to select an action of F. The third rule says that an agent and another agent which might interrupt it can only delay if they can both delay for that amount of time. We will use interrupts in timed specifications later in this chapter. We can now return to the problem at hand and respecify $ConRun$:

$$ConRun_{int} \stackrel{\text{def}}{=} (\overline{setOff}.CStop1 + highT.CStop1) \wedge iErr.CStopErr$$

It is important to consider what we have done here in relation to the definitions for the new interrupt operator. If an error is detected then $CStopErr$ will take over. However, if no error is detected then eventually $CStop1$ will take effect but the effect of the latter is to leave the interrupt in place even though the furnace has been shut down. This might cause problems and could mean that the interrupt will have to be disabled sometimes in order to ensure correct behaviour.

We are not finished, however. If we rerun the startup sequence that caused the error but assume a $highT$ signal from the sensor is available, then you should see that another deadlock occurs. This time it is because the controller cannot respond to a $highT$ but the sensor demands to send its signal. There are various ways out of this; we can either remodel the controller so that it responds in addition to $highT$ or we can remodel the sensor so that it does not have to send all signals. We could also, of course, make both changes. Certainly it seems reasonable that the sensor should not have to send all signals but that the temperature read might change before it is transmitted. In addition we should be able to turn the system off in the period when the controller is waiting for the temperature to drop and heating is required. The following changes are made:

$$COn1 \stackrel{\text{def}}{=} lowT.\overline{iOn}.COn2 \\ + highT.COff$$

Further work with the Verification Game should assure you that there are no further major problems with the definitions in terms of deadlocks and so on. Whether or not we are happy with the definitions themselves and the way they model expected behaviour is another matter. As already pointed out in the development of the sensor, it is possible to make devices too *clever* and thus inadvertently avoid confronting problems which will be vital to the safe and/or correct functioning of the implementation. We might decide to take a further look at the furnace from this point of view. Essentially, the furnace currently forces the controller to act correctly or not at all but, in reality, the furnace should simply respond to whatever messages it gets from the controller. We might alternatively say that we have specified the correct behaviour and not concerned ourselves with this set of possible errors. We should probably continue to add erroneous behaviours so that we can model the system and its problems in a manner closer to the actual world it will operate in. Yet another criticism of the furnace might be that any subset of the three possible errors might be active at any one time. Perhaps we should model the furnace as four concurrent subsystems, of which three would be error sensors. We leave the reader to consider these matters further and adapt the specifications as an exercise should they think fit.

EXERCISE 8.2

There is, in fact, still a problem with the specification given. It is left as an exercise for the reader to find.

EXERCISE 8.3

Investigate the behaviour of the home heating system and determine whether or not the interrupt can cause problems. Respecify the system appropriately so that the interrupt remains and the expected behaviour is maintained.

EXERCISE 8.4

Remodel the furnace so that it includes the following behaviours:

1. It is always ready to respond to any message from the controller.
2. The three error messages can occur simultaneously and must all be communicated to the controller.

8.4 Definitions for Version 1

We can now collect together all the definitions and document them appropriately. Notice that although we did not draw up a state table for the controller as part of the development of its specification we have included one in the documentation to make it easier for others to read.

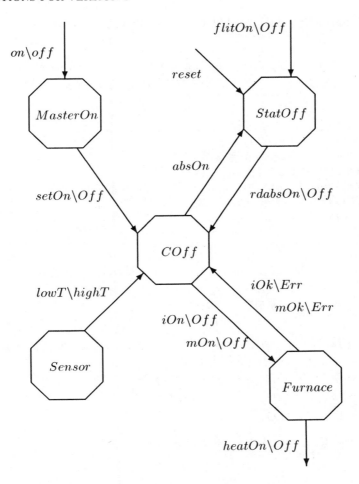

Figure 8.1. *Flow graph for the home heating system*

The home heating system - Version 1

$$Hhs3 \overset{\text{def}}{=} (MasterOff \mid COff \mid StatOff \mid Furnace \mid Sensor)\backslash H$$
$$H \overset{\text{def}}{=} \{setOn, setOff, absOn, absOff, rdabsOn, rdabsOff,$$
$$lowT, highT, mOn, mOff, mErr, mOk,$$
$$iOn, iOff, iErr, iOk\}$$

The master switch

The master switch can be in one of two states where it is either set off or
set on. The actions *on* and *off* represent the user setting the switch while

the actions *setOn* and *setOff* tell the controller the current state of the switch:

$$MasterOff \stackrel{\text{def}}{=} \overline{setOff}.MasterOff + on.MasterOn$$

$$MasterOn \stackrel{\text{def}}{=} \overline{setOn}.MasterOn + off.MasterOff$$

The controller

$COff$	the off state
$COn1$	begin startup
$COn2$	start furnace
$COnRun$	normal running, waiting for $highT$ or error
$CStop1$	normal closedown with error check
$CStop2$	normal closedown
$CStopErr$	error closedown, set error light

$$COff \stackrel{\text{def}}{=} setOn.(rdabsOff.COn1 + rdabsOn.COff)$$

$$COn1 \stackrel{\text{def}}{=} lowT.\overline{iOn}.COn2$$
$$+ highT.COff$$

$$COn2 \stackrel{\text{def}}{=} \overline{mOn}.(mOk.COnRun + mErr.\overline{mOff}.\overline{absOn}.COff)$$

$$COnRun \stackrel{\text{def}}{=} iErr.CStopErr + setOff.CStop1 + highT.CStop1$$
$$+ lowT.COnRun$$

$$CStop1 \stackrel{\text{def}}{=} CStop2 + iErr.CStopErr$$

$$CStop2 \stackrel{\text{def}}{=} \overline{iOff}.\overline{mOff}.COff$$

$$CStopErr \stackrel{\text{def}}{=} \overline{iOff}.\overline{mOff}.\overline{absOn}.CStop1$$

NB: the alternative definition of *ConRun* with an interrupt is given below:

$$ConRun_{int} \stackrel{\text{def}}{=} (\overline{setOff}.CStop1 + highT.CStop1) \; {}^{\wedge} error.CStopErr$$

Abnormal status indicator

This sets a light on $(\overline{flitOn})$ or off $(\overline{flitOff})$ in response to the signals $\overline{rdabsOn}$ and $\overline{rdabsOff}$ respectively.

$$StatOff \stackrel{\text{def}}{=} \overline{rdabsOff}.StatOff + absOn.\overline{flitOn}.StatOn$$

$$StatOn \stackrel{\text{def}}{=} \overline{rdabsOn}.StatOn + reset.\overline{flitOff}.StatOff$$
$$+absOn.StatOn$$

The furnace

$$Furnace \stackrel{\text{def}}{=} MOff \mid IOff$$

$DeviceOff$	the off state
$DeviceOn$	operating normally
$DeviceOnError$	operating but fault detected

$$MOff \quad \overset{\text{def}}{=} \quad mOn.(\tau.MOn + \tau.MOnErr)$$
$$+ mOff.MOff$$

$$MOn \quad \overset{\text{def}}{=} \quad mOn.MOn + mOff.\overline{heatOff}.MOff$$
$$+ \overline{mOk}.MOn$$

$$MOnErr \quad \overset{\text{def}}{=} \quad \overline{mErr}.mOff.\overline{heatOff}.MOff$$

$$IOff \quad \overset{\text{def}}{=} \quad iOn.\overline{heatOn}.IOn + iOff.IOff$$

$$IOn \quad \overset{\text{def}}{=} \quad iOn.IOn + iOff.IOff$$
$$+ \overline{iOk}.IOn + \tau.IOnErr$$

$$IOnErr \quad \overset{\text{def}}{=} \quad \overline{iErr}.iOff.IOff$$

The temperature sensor

This version of the temperature sensor models only the two extreme thresholds of $highT$ and $lowT$. The two τ-actions model the intervening temperature changes.

$$Sensor \quad \overset{\text{def}}{=} \quad \tau.\overline{highT}.Sensor + \tau.\overline{lowT}.Sensor$$

End of specification

While this is, in a strictly behavioural sense, a complete specification, we must remember that we have decided to deliberately ignore important aspects of the requirements document so as to make our first attempts at a specification easier. Reflecting on the problems we have already encountered, and solved, this would seem to have been a good idea. It is now time to return to that document and try to extend the specification to meet all requirements. This will be the task of the next two sections of the chapter.

8.5 Real temperatures

So far we have not modelled actual temperature values in our specification but have restricted ourselves to atomic actions with which to represent threshold values. Let us now consider where we could usefully make explicit reference to actual values in our specification so as to better satisfy requirements. We have already decided to model specific furnace errors using the value-passing calculus so as to simplify our definitions for the furnace, the controller, and the abnormal status indicator. This should not require any major modifications to the existing specification. The obvious area where value passing can help us is in the modelling of temperature and the calculations to be made using this data. Perhaps we should reconsider

Sensor first as we have, so far, managed to produce a home heating system in which temperature plays no part at all.

In the average house the temperature sensor consists of a dial which allows the desired temperature to be set and some internal mechanism which senses the air temperature and calculates the current difference between the two. The new device specification will thus have to model the repeated task of measuring the current air temperature and allowing the desired temperature to be reset by the user at will. The temperature difference will be passed to the controller on request. We will assume the range of the temperatures that may be set by the user is a subset of the possible house temperatures and that all are given in Celsius. Such sensors are commercially available devices which operate within a limited range.

$$
\begin{aligned}
DesTemp &= \{0, \ldots, 35\} \\
ActTemp &= \{-10, \ldots, 50\} \\
Tr &: DesTemp \\
Ta, Td &: ActTemp \\
SenInit &\stackrel{\text{def}}{=} desT(Tr).actT(Ta).SensorV(Tr, Ta) \\
SensorV(Tr, Ta) &\stackrel{\text{def}}{=} (actT(Ta').SensorV(Tr, Ta')) \\
&\quad {}^{\wedge}\ desT(Tr').SensorV(Tr', Ta)) \\
&\quad {}^{\wedge}\ \overline{diffT}(Ta - Tr).SensorV(Tr, Ta)
\end{aligned}
$$

Notice that we have had to initialise the sensor so that it has both a desired temperature and a current reading to allow it to begin operation. Notice also that we have used interrupts to make sure that communicating the current temperature difference takes precedence over setting a new desired temperature. In turn this takes precedence over reading a new value for Ta. In this situation the interrupt does not cause problems because it always returns the state $SensorV(Tr, Ta)$, for some values of Tr and Ta, and there is no need to disable it. We must now take a fresh look at the controller to see how it is affected by the more complicated behaviour we have given the sensor.

There are two definitions for the controller which refer to $lowT$ or $highT$ and these are $Con1$ and $ConRun$ which will both need to be amended. The controller receives the temperature difference Td from the sensor via the action $diffT$. If the furnace is off and $Td \geq 2$ then heating should commence, whereas if the furnace is on and $Td \leq -2$ then heating should stop. However, we have to be careful now that we are not dealing simply with threshold values. In the states $Con1$ and $ConRun$ we now have to continually check the current temperature difference to see if it has reached the appropriate threshold or not. This means that we have to set up two continuous checking loops which read the current value for Td and respond appropriately. Very importantly, we have to make sure that shutdown requests override the checking loop and are themselves overridden by error messages. Notice that it is easier to introduce new definitions to specify the actual checking of the current value for Td:

$$COn1V \quad \overset{\text{def}}{=} \quad setOn.diffT(Td).Check1(Td)$$

$$Check1(Td) \quad \overset{\text{def}}{=} \quad if\, Td \geq 2\, then\, \overline{iOn}.COn2$$
$$else\, COff$$

$$COnRunV \quad \overset{\text{def}}{=} \quad diffT(Td).if\, Td \leq -2\, then\, CStop1$$
$$else(setOff.CStop1$$
$$+iErr.CStopErr$$
$$+(setOn \ddagger iOk).ConRunV)$$

It is interesting to compare our new specification with the previous one given in basic CCS. Essentially the switch from threshold values to actual temperature differences has forced us to introduce a control loop to look for threshold values rather than simply waiting for them to appear. The value-passing specification is, effectively, a reification of its basic CCS predecessor, in the sense that we were forced to introduce implementation-oriented behaviour in order to fully meet requirements. We now have a specification that could be treated as a design from which to implement the system. You should not think, however, that the effect of introducing value-passing constructs into a specification always has this effect. Reflecting back on the value-passing version of the data-manager makes it clear that it is quite possible for the reverse to be true. It all depends on the nature of the system to be specified. In the case of the home heating system we could identify threshold values and ignore the rest, while in the case of the data-manager the patterns of behaviour were heavily dependent on the patterns of bits stored. It is still the case, though, that representing data structures as processes forces a lower-level view of the system.

EXERCISE 8.5

Use value passing to further modify the home heating system so that the abnormal status indicator has separate lights for the two types of errors. What complications does this introduce?

EXERCISE 8.6

Suppose that the home heating system were further modified so as to make motor speed explicit. What complications does this introduce and do the extra effort and detail justify themselves?

8.6 In the meantime

Our final task, in this chapter, is to extend the model so that it admits
all the timing constraints given in the requirements document. First let us
extract this information and consider how we are to respond to it.

```
        -------------------

        TIMING INFORMATION
        -------------------


The controller will wait 5 seconds for the motor status
signal from the furnace and will terminate the ignition
sequence if one does not arrive.

The user may set two pairs of start/stop times for any
24 hour period.

A minimum of 5 minutes must elapse between turning off the
furnace and restarting it. The furnace must be shut down
within 5 seconds if any furnace error is detected or the
master switch is set to off.


        -------------------
```

Notice that we cannot build a complete timed version of the home heating system because we do not know how long all the various actions and
physical processes such as turning on or off of values actually take. However, the timing requirements we have got present us with some interesting
problems, as we shall see. Before commencing to amend the specification
to include the timing information it is interesting to categorise it because
our responses to it are going to have to be quite different:

1. The length of time particular operations take

2. Limitations on how long complex activities are allowed to take

3. Allowing some timings to change dynamically

   Point 1 requires us to build in delays to obtain a real-time version of the
untimed home heating system we have already built. As with the traffic
lights we will have to check that we do not introduce temporal deadlocks
and eliminate them if we do. This means identifying the specific points
where agents are allowed to idle. Point 2 is really referring to temporal
properties of the whole system; these are not timing constraints to be added
as delays to the specification but constraints on general behaviour which
will have to be checked as part of the verification process. This has much
in common with the safety property of the traffic lights that either the
major or minor lights must always be set on red. Again this is a property

of the system and not a behavioural aspect of some specific subsystem. Point 3 is interesting because it represents a dynamic timing constraint in that specific timings or delays can change while the system is operational. Points 1 and 3 can be satisfied by amending the existing specification but 2 must wait until later in this book when we will investigate the verification of such temporal properties.

We will look, in particular, at the requirement to allow the user to set specific on/off times, as this requires some thought. All the timing constraints we have had to consider so far have been static in that they are set within the specification and thus are unaffected by the system's behaviour. In this case, however, the system's behaviour does indeed affect the timing constraints in that the user can set them while the heating system is operational. In turn the changing timings set by the user affect the operational behaviour of the heating system. So let us consider the case where the user may set a single pair of on/off times. Using the value-passing calculus it is not difficult to see how we could model the input of such a pair by the user,

$$SetTimer \stackrel{\text{def}}{=} input(on).input(off).Timer(on, off)$$

and it is tempting to then go on to model the timer in its operational mode:

$$Timer(on, off, r) \stackrel{\text{def}}{=} \overline{toff}.(on).\overline{ton}. \\ (off).\overline{toff}.(r).Timer(on, off, r) \,^\wedge SetTimer$$

Notice the use of the interrupt to incorporate the reset operation in a natural manner. The additional delay of r is necessary because the timings are set daily and after the heating has been turned off the whole system has to wait until the start of the next day. We would need to have three parameters to the operational timer definition $Timer(on, off, r)$, where $SetTimer$ would calculate r from on and off, which would not be difficult given that we would need a type for the number of time units per day ($tupd$). However, there is a far greater problem which has to do with when in the day the user decides to reset the timer. At present we seem to be assuming that the user resets the on/of setting at the start of a new day or rather that the effect of inputting a new setting is to start a new day as far as the timer is concerned. This obviously does not model a very useful, or indeed, typical system.

One of the problems you should have encountered, in the above exercise, is that you needed to know what time of day it was when the reset was to be made, but TCCS does not naturally give you access to this as it is concerned with the passage of time and not some observable clock. If we could model an observable clock in some way then we would need a rather clumsy agent which calculated the current on/off delays applicable. We can model a *readable* clock quite straightforwardly and then use it to model the timer in a fairly natural way also, but not in terms of the specific delays which are proving rather cumbersome:

$$
\begin{aligned}
midnight &= 60 \times 60 \times 24 \\
tupd &= \{0, \ldots, midnight\} \\
t &: \quad tupd \\
Clock(t) &\stackrel{\text{def}}{=} \overline{time}(t).Clock(t) \\
&\quad + (1).Clock(t + 1 \bmod midnight)
\end{aligned}
$$

What we have done is not to actually read the time as such but to hold a separate variable which records the passage of time. It is the current value of the variable which can be read. Notice that this solution only works if the time domain chosen is the natural numbers. If the positive reals had been chosen then fractions of time units would be allowed to pass which would then prevent the clock from being read until one complete time unit had elapsed. Notice also that, because of the way TCCS has been defined, reading the current time takes no time at all! This oddity aside, the clock suggests a way of specifying on/off settings in terms of value parameters instead of delays. Additionally, we should consider what happens if no on/off times have been set.

$$
\begin{aligned}
on, off, t &: \quad tupd \\
AlwaysOn &\stackrel{\text{def}}{=} \overline{timOn}.AlwaysOn \\
TimerSet &\stackrel{\text{def}}{=} input(on).input(off).time(t).if\ on \leq t \vee t \geq off \\
&\qquad then\ (TimerOff(on, off)\ ^\wedge TimerSet) \\
&\qquad else\ (TimerOn(on, off)\ ^\wedge TimerSet) \\
TimerOff &\stackrel{\text{def}}{=} time(t).if\ t = on\ then \\
&\qquad \overline{timOn}.(1).TimerOn(on, off) \\
&\qquad else\ \overline{timOff}.(1).TimerOff(on.off) \\
TimerOn &\stackrel{\text{def}}{=} time(t).if\ t = off\ then \overline{timOn}.(1).TimerOff(on, off) \\
&\qquad else\ \overline{timOff}.(1).(TimerOff(on, off) \\
Timer &\stackrel{\text{def}}{=} (Clock(0)\ |\ (AlwaysOn\ ^\wedge TimerSet))\backslash\{time\}
\end{aligned}
$$

In order to complete the timed specification we have to integrate $Timer$ with the existing specification which means modifying the specification for the controller and then modifying the other sub-agents as required to include their timing constraints. It will then be necessary to identify all states where a sub-agent may be allowed to idle so as to prevent any temporal deadlocks occurring.

EXERCISE 8.7

Attempt to extend the current definition of the timer so that it does allow a new on/off pair without *starting a new day.*

EXERCISE 8.8

Although we have used interrupts here we have not yet defined how they interact with time. Extend the definitions given for $^\wedge$ above so that it interacts with time in an appropriate manner.

8.7 Summary and further reading

The purpose of this chapter has been to bring together the application of basic CCS and its timed and value-passing variants to the specification of a larger system. We chose to adopt a pragmatic approach, based on Boehm's spiral model of the lifecycle [Boe91], and model the basic behaviour of the home heating system before going on to consider value passing and time. In the process of doing so we looked at an interrupt operator ' $^\wedge$ ' which had applications in the area of ensuring responses to error messages. The interrupt operator for CCS is introduced and discussed in [Mil89]. We also observed that the use of the value-passing calculus did not always lead to more abstract specifications. In chapter 14 we will return to the subject of formal specification building, for large systems, in the context of structured methods. However, until then we will leave the problem of building formal specifications for real-time systems and address the subject of their formal verification, for which CCS is well provided.

II

Reasoning about Specifications

9

Theories of equivalence

Rather than getting straight on with the main business of this chapter it is worthwhile to reflect on the stage we have reached and what else we can usefully consider. So far we have concentrated on building formal specifications of concurrent and real-time systems. In order to be able to do this we gradually built up a highly expressive language, really a set of related languages, with which we can model various types of concurrent and/or real-time systems. Because of the complexity of concurrent systems we had to find ways of establishing the *correctness* of specifications expressed in these languages. To help us in this task we have used animation techniques, the Concurrency Workbench or the Verification Game, to verify our models. While both techniques are based on the formal semantics of the various versions of CCS we were using they are essentially *testing* techniques which work in much the same way as if we were testing a program in C or Pascal. This remark is not meant to be at all disparaging for the author firmly believes such techniques have a valuable contribution to make in the verification of specifications whether they be formal or informal. Testing models prior to building the real thing is sound engineering practice and we should make use of it whenever we can.

The obvious advantage of animating a formal specification is that the semantics of the language in which it is expressed give us precise guidelines as to how the animation may be allowed to proceed and what the results mean. This is not to say, however, that we should be satisfied with our efforts at verification as they currently stand. Indeed, the very fact that CCS includes the word 'calculus' in its name suggests that we can not only build specifications but can perform calculations of some sort upon them. Given that the CCS family of languages are essentially algebras we should be able to define equivalence between expressions, agents that is, of these algebras. With a formal definition of equivalence we can then build up equational laws, of the sort taught in high school algebra, and use them to simplify and restructure specifications. In the next two chapters we investigate such equivalences and the equational laws they generate. We will also see that just as the definitions of the formal languages themselves required *design* decisions so will our definitions of equivalence.

In the final two chapters of this section of the book we will go on to look at the problem of verifying properties of a specification such as those discussed for the traffic lights and the home heating system. In the former case we needed to be sure that either the major or minor lights were always on red. Similar properties were considered for the heater. What we will wish to do is express such properties formally and then *prove* whether or not particular specifications satisfy such required properties. Formal reasoning and in particular *proof* are usually considered by non-formal-methods people to be *the* reason for bothering with formal methods at all. In fact such techniques are but part of the picture and supplement the basic process of expressing and clarifying one's ideas in a formal language. Many companies which use formal methods do so for this reason rather than the benefits formal proof can deliver. If formal methods are to be used successfully then they have to be both useful, cost-effective, and properly integrated within the organisation and its other demands. The latter is essentially the subject of the final part of the book and for now we return to the real business of this chapter.

As already stated, this chapter introduces the reader to some of the possible theories of equivalence usually associated with CCS. We will concentrate on the basic calculus and then show how value passing and time may also be accommodated. The notion of equivalence used is called *bisimulation* and is based on the idea of processes mimicking each other's behaviour. Several forms are developed to take into account all possible actions of a process or only observable actions when we try to ignore τ-actions whenever possible. The chapter uses case studies to demonstrate the value of equivalence in showing that different views or specifications of a system may be equivalent. In particular, we will demonstrate that a centrally controlled solution to a problem and a distributed solution to the same problem may be proved behaviourally the same. This in turn begins to show how reification of specifications towards implementations may be accomplished.

9.1 Characterising equivalence

A number of times in earlier chapters we have begun to consider, in an informal way, just when we might consider two agents equivalent. It was apparent from early on that it was possible to characterise equivalence in a number of different ways. In chapter 2 we compared the processes D_3 and D_4 by observing that they seemed capable of the same sequences of actions although their definitions seemed to give them different choices between actions in their various states. In chapter 3 we used transition graphs as a diagrammatic means of characterising the behaviour of agents. We also defined labelled transition systems as a means of formalising the diagrams. Several times in chapter 3 we compared various transition graphs with a view to informally establishing equivalence. In chapter 3 we again compared D_3 and D_4 but we noted that they possessed different transition graphs and thus appeared to be capable of different behaviours. Also in chapter 3 we compared transition graphs for $Buff_2$ and $B0$ and noted that they appeared to be the same except for the presence of a τ-action in the graph for $Buff_2$.

It seems important that we characterise equivalence in terms both of all possible sequences of actions and in terms of choices of actions for a given state. For this reason we would not want D_3 and D_4 to be identified as equivalent by our notion of equivalence. If we reconsider the two versions of the simple buffer from chapter 2:

$$
\begin{aligned}
Buff_2 &\overset{\text{def}}{=} (C_1 \mid C_2)\backslash\{m\} \\
C_1 &\overset{\text{def}}{=} in.\overline{m}.C_1 \\
C_2 &\overset{\text{def}}{=} m.\overline{out}.C_2
\end{aligned}
$$

$$
\begin{aligned}
B0 &\overset{\text{def}}{=} in.B1 \\
B1 &\overset{\text{def}}{=} in.B2 + \overline{out}.B0 \\
B2 &\overset{\text{def}}{=} \overline{out}.B1
\end{aligned}
$$

we might wish, perhaps, that $Buff_2$ and $B0$ should be identified as being equivalent. They are both capable of the same sequences of actions and always have the same choice of observable actions, that is, ignoring τ-actions. Notice that if we redefine $B0$ in the following manner then $Buff_2$ and $B0'$ are equivalent on all choices, including τ-actions:

$$
\begin{aligned}
B0' &\overset{\text{def}}{=} in.B1' \\
B1' &\overset{\text{def}}{=} \tau.(in.B2' + \overline{out}.B0') \\
B2' &\overset{\text{def}}{=} \overline{out}.B1'
\end{aligned}
$$

We seem to have two slightly different notions of equivalence developing: a stronger notion of equivalence which does not differentiate between internal and external actions and a weaker notion that attempts to consider only external actions. Both of these rely on the fact that two processes must first of all generate the same set of action sequences. We can give a general outline of these notions using the following ideas:

1. Two agents might be equivalent if they are both capable of the same sets of action sequences.

2. The choices of next action available to each agent after any sequence of actions must be the same.

3. The choices of next action available to each agent after any sequence of

actions must be the same except that allowances are made for τ-actions where possible.

We would wish to say that $B0'$ and $Buff_2$ were equivalent in terms of 1 and 2 but that $B0$ and $Buff_2$ were not. However, $Buff_2$ and $B0$ would be equivalent in terms of 1 and 3. Our strong notion of equivalence uses ideas 1 and 2 while the weak notion uses ideas 1 and 3. These notions of equivalence are examples of bisimulations, which are relations that show that two processes may mimic each other's behaviour by relating pairs of equivalent states. We will first of all see how to define a bisimulation for the stronger form, as this is the more straightforward, and later see how to modify it to give us the weaker version.

9.2 Strong equivalence

The notion of equivalence which we are calling 'strong equivalence' does not make allowances for τ-actions and thus equates agents if their internal and external behaviours are equivalent.

Definition 9.1   A binary relation, $\mathbf{R} \subseteq \mathcal{E} \times \mathcal{E}$, is a bisimulation if, whenever $(E, F) \in \mathbf{R}$, then for all actions α the following is true:

$$1)\ E \xrightarrow{\alpha} E' \text{ implies } \exists F' \bullet F \xrightarrow{\alpha} F' \wedge (E', F') \in \mathbf{R}$$

$$2)\ F \xrightarrow{\alpha} F' \text{ implies } \exists E' \bullet E \xrightarrow{\alpha} E' \wedge (E', F') \in \mathbf{R}$$

Basically, definition 9.1 says that whatever actions E can perform then F must be capable of exactly the same actions. Furthermore, whatever state that F has a transition to, then E must have the same transition to a state which preserves the equivalence. Thus F must be able to mimic the behaviour of E, and this must also hold in reverse for E mimicking F.

Definition 9.2 $E \sim F$ (E and F are strongly equivalent) exactly when there is a strong bisimulation $\mathbf{R}$ with $(E, F) \in \mathbf{R}$.

Definition 9.3 $\sim = \bigcup \{\mathbf{R} : \mathbf{R} \text{ is a strong bisimulation}\}$

Definition 9.3 states that the relation $\sim$ is defined to be the distributed union of all the strong bisimulation relations.

Our definition of strong equivalence relates agents which can mimic each other's behaviour for all actions including the τ-action. The following are examples of relations which are bisimulations, and you should check them through to make sure you agree:

$$\{(\mathbf{0} \quad , \quad \mathbf{0})\}$$

$$\{(a.b.\mathbf{0} + a.c.\mathbf{0} \quad , \quad a.c.\mathbf{0} + a.b.\mathbf{0})$$
$$(b.\mathbf{0} \quad , \quad b.\mathbf{0})$$
$$(c.\mathbf{0} \quad , \quad c.\mathbf{0})$$
$$(\mathbf{0} \quad , \quad \mathbf{0})\}$$

$$\{(a.\mathbf{0} \mid b.\mathbf{0} \quad , \quad a.b.\mathbf{0} + b.a.\mathbf{0})$$
$$(\mathbf{0} \mid b.\mathbf{0} \quad , \quad b.\mathbf{0})$$
$$(a.\mathbf{0} \mid \mathbf{0} \quad , \quad a.\mathbf{0})$$
$$(\mathbf{0} \mid \mathbf{0} \quad , \quad \mathbf{0})\}$$

$$\{(send.X \quad , \quad Y)$$
$$(X \quad , \quad receive.Y)\}$$

where $X \overset{\text{def}}{=} receive.send.X$ and $Y \overset{\text{def}}{=} send.receive.Y$

The following are examples of relations that are not bisimulations:

$$\{(a.\mathbf{0} \quad , \quad a.\mathbf{0} + b.\mathbf{0})$$
$$(\mathbf{0} \quad , \quad \mathbf{0})\}$$

$$\{(a.\mathbf{0} \quad , \quad a.\mathbf{0})\}$$

The first is not a bisimulation because, although both pairs of states match up for the action a, the agent $a.\mathbf{0}$ cannot perform the action b whereas $a.\mathbf{0} + b.\mathbf{0}$ can. The second is not a bisimulation even though $a.\mathbf{0}$ should surely be considered equivalent to itself, the reason being that the additional pair $(\mathbf{0}, \mathbf{0})$ is needed to turn the relation into a bisimulation.

In chapter 2 we looked at a system, Mx, which exhibited a very simple form of mutual exclusion. A possible specification for that system could be expressed in the following manner:

$$Spec \overset{\text{def}}{=} \tau.c1.\tau.Spec + \tau.c2.\tau.Spec$$

The agent $Spec$ has a far simpler definition than the agent Mx but a closer examination of their transition graphs reveals striking similarities. They both seem to have the same possible sequences of actions and in addition the same sort of choices in equivalent states even though they do not appear to have the same number of states. We are now in a position to prove their equivalence by building a bisimulation relation which has, as an element, the pair $(Mx, Spec)$. Starting from this pair we can build the following bisimulation which proves their equivalence:

$$\{(\ (P1\mid P2\mid Sem)\backslash\{get,put\} \quad , \quad \tau.c1.\tau.Spec + \tau.c2.\tau.Spec)$$
$$(\ (c1.\overline{put}.P1\mid P2\mid put.Sem)\backslash\{get,put\} \quad , \quad c1.\tau.Spec)$$
$$(\ (P1\mid c2.\overline{put}.P1\mid put.Sem)\backslash\{get,put\} \quad , \quad c2.\tau.Spec)$$
$$(\ (\overline{put}.P1\mid P2\mid put.sem)\backslash\{get,put\} \quad , \quad \tau.Spec)$$
$$(\ (P1\mid \overline{put}.P2\mid put.Sem)\backslash\{get,put\} \quad , \quad \tau.Spec)\}$$

One interesting point to note is that, although strongly equivalent, Mx and $Spec$ do not have the same number of states in their transition graphs, which means that our definition of strong equivalence is doing more than simply comparing transition graphs.

EXERCISE 9.1

Prove which of the following are strongly equivalent by attempting to build strong bisimulations to relate pairs of agents: $Buff_2$, $B0$, $B0'$, $C\mid C$, and $C'\mid C'$ where

$$C \stackrel{\text{def}}{=} in.\overline{out}.C \quad C' \stackrel{\text{def}}{=} in.\tau.\overline{out}.C'$$

EXERCISE 9.2

Determine which of D_0, E_1, F, and G are strongly equivalent, given the following definitions:

$$D_0 \stackrel{\text{def}}{=} a.D_0 + b.D_1 + \tau.D_1$$
$$D_1 \stackrel{\text{def}}{=} a.D_1 + \tau.D_2$$
$$D_2 \stackrel{\text{def}}{=} b.D_0$$

$$E_1 \stackrel{\text{def}}{=} a.E_1 + \tau.E_2$$
$$E_2 \stackrel{\text{def}}{=} b.E_1$$

$$F \stackrel{\text{def}}{=} a.F + \tau.b.F$$

$$G \stackrel{\text{def}}{=} (G_1\mid G_2)\backslash\{c\}$$
$$G_1 \stackrel{\text{def}}{=} a.G_1 + \overline{c}.\mathbf{0}$$
$$G_2 \stackrel{\text{def}}{=} c.b.G_3$$
$$G_3 \stackrel{\text{def}}{=} G_1\mid G_2$$

Can you identify any problems in making your decisions?

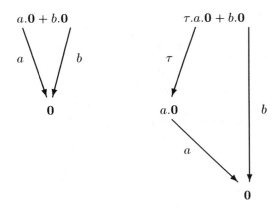

Figure 9.1. *Transition graphs for $a.0 + b.0$ and $\tau.a.0 + b.0$.*

9.3 Observational equivalence

We have already seen in the examples used in this chapter that strong equivalence is perhaps too strict and makes distinctions between agents that we might usefully wish to consider equivalent. A very good reason for this is that we might wish to prove whether or not two expressions, which represent a specification and its implementation respectively, are indeed equivalent in some sense. In particular we wish two such expressions to be considered equivalent if they can be seen to be equivalent in terms of their observable behaviour only. Thus, we would want to equate $Buff_2$ and $B0$ which differ only in terms of a single internal action. A first attempt might thus be to simply ignore τ-actions altogether. However, this will be too accommodating and would equate expressions which we definitely would regard as being different. An example of two such systems would be

$$a.0 + b.0 \quad \text{and} \quad \tau.a.0 + b.0$$

which can be seen to be different simply by studying figure 9.1.

We thus cannot ignore τ-actions altogether. In order to arrive at a suitable definition of 'observational equivalence', as we shall call it, we need to consider what we mean by an observable transition. Informally, an observable action should be any action $a \in \mathcal{A}$ preceded and succeeded by any number of τ-actions. We will build up a formal definition of this but first we will need some additional notation, beginning with a way of denoting a sequence of τ-actions:

$E \xrightarrow{\tau^n} E'$ if E can perform n τ-actions and become E'.

$E \xrightarrow{\tau^0} E$ for all processes E, e.g.

$$\tau.\tau.a.\tau.\mathbf{0} \xrightarrow{\tau^0} \tau.\tau.a.\tau.\mathbf{0}$$
$$\tau.\tau.a.\tau.\mathbf{0} \xrightarrow{\tau^1} \tau.a.\tau.\mathbf{0}$$
$$\tau.\tau.a.\tau.\mathbf{0} \xrightarrow{\tau^2} a.\tau.\mathbf{0}$$

$E \xRightarrow{\epsilon} E'$ exactly when there is an n such that $E \xrightarrow{\tau^n} E'$, e.g.

$$\tau.\tau.a.\tau.\mathbf{0} \xRightarrow{\epsilon} \tau.a.\tau.\mathbf{0}$$
$$\tau.\tau.a.\tau.\mathbf{0} \xRightarrow{\epsilon} a.\tau.\mathbf{0}$$

$E \xRightarrow{\epsilon} E$ for all agents E.

Using these ideas we can now define an observable transition in the following manner:

$$E \xRightarrow{a} E' \quad \text{means} \quad \begin{array}{ccc} E & \xRightarrow{\epsilon} & E_1, \\ E_1 & \xrightarrow{a} & E_2, \\ E_2 & \xRightarrow{\epsilon} & E' \end{array}$$

This means that E can initiate an unspecified number of τ-actions, followed by an a-action, followed by an unspecified number of τ-actions, e.g.

$$\tau.\tau.(a.\tau.\mathbf{0} + \tau.b.\mathbf{0}) \xRightarrow{a} \tau.\mathbf{0}$$
$$\tau.\tau.(a.\tau.\mathbf{0} + \tau.b.\mathbf{0}) \xRightarrow{a} \mathbf{0}$$
$$\tau.\tau.(a.\tau.\mathbf{0} + \tau.b.\mathbf{0}) \xRightarrow{b} \mathbf{0}$$

It is worth considering the meaning of $E \xRightarrow{\tau} E'$ which we will use later on. This transition means that E can become E' by performing at least one τ or internal action. The transition might involve more than one such action but it cannot be accomplished by no internal actions. We are almost ready to define weak bisimulations which are, not unexpectedly, at the heart of our new equivalence. We still need one extra piece of notation, however, to describe what we will call 'observable counterparts'. These are simply a means of replacing a single τ-transition, $\xrightarrow{\tau}$, with its observable counterpart $\xRightarrow{\epsilon}$ and in this way equating a single τ-transition with an unspecified number of τs.

Definition 9.4 An observable counterpart, $E \xRightarrow{\hat{a}} E'$, is defined to be a if $a \neq \tau$ else ϵ.

This definition assures that observable actions remain unaffected by observable counterparts. We can now define the required observational equivalence in terms of a *weak* bisimulation relation.

Definition 9.5 A binary relation $\mathbf{S} \subseteq \mathcal{E} \times \mathcal{E}$ over agents is a weak bisimulation if $(E, F) \in \mathbf{S}$ implies, for all actions α, the following is true:

1. $E \xrightarrow{\alpha} E'$ implies $\exists F' \bullet F \overset{\hat{\alpha}}{\Rightarrow} F' \wedge (E', F') \in \mathbf{S}$

2. $F \xrightarrow{\alpha} F'$ implies $\exists E' \bullet E \overset{\hat{\alpha}}{\Rightarrow} E' \wedge (E', F') \in \mathbf{S}$

Definition 9.6 $E \approx F$ (E and F are observationally equivalent) if there is a weak bisimulation $\mathbf{S}$ such that $(E, F) \in \mathbf{S}$.

Definition 9.7 $\approx = \bigcup \{\mathbf{S} : \mathbf{S}$ is a weak bisimulation$\}$

The following are examples of relations that are weak bisimulations:

$$\{(\tau.a.\mathbf{0} \quad , \quad a.\mathbf{0})$$
$$(a.\mathbf{0} \quad , \quad a.\mathbf{0})$$
$$(\mathbf{0} \quad , \quad \mathbf{0})\}$$

$$\{((a.\mathbf{0} \mid \bar{a}.\mathbf{0})\backslash\{a\} \quad , \quad \mathbf{0})$$
$$(\mathbf{0} \mid \mathbf{0})\backslash\{a\} \quad , \quad \mathbf{0})\}$$

$$\{(a.\tau.b.\mathbf{0} \quad , \quad a.b.\mathbf{0})$$
$$(\tau.b.\mathbf{0} \quad , \quad b.\mathbf{0})$$
$$(b.\mathbf{0} \quad , \quad b.\mathbf{0})$$
$$(\mathbf{0} \quad , \quad \mathbf{0})\}$$

$$\{(\tau.\tau.a.\tau.\mathbf{0} + \tau.b.\mathbf{0} \quad , \quad \tau.a.\mathbf{0} + \tau.\tau.b.\mathbf{0})$$
$$(\tau.a.\tau.\mathbf{0} \quad , \quad a.\mathbf{0})$$
$$(a.\tau.\mathbf{0} \quad , \quad a.\mathbf{0})$$
$$(\tau.\mathbf{0} \quad , \quad \mathbf{0})$$
$$(\mathbf{0} \quad , \quad \mathbf{0})$$
$$(b.\mathbf{0} \quad , \quad b.\mathbf{0})$$
$$(b.\mathbf{0} \quad , \quad \tau.b.\mathbf{0})\}$$

The following are examples of relations that are not weak bisimulations:

$$\{(\tau.a.\mathbf{0} + b.\mathbf{0} \quad , \quad a.\mathbf{0} + b.\mathbf{0}),$$
$$(\mathbf{0} \quad , \quad \mathbf{0})\}$$

$$\{(a.\mathbf{0} \quad , \quad \tau.(a.\mathbf{0} + b.\mathbf{0})),$$
$$(a.\mathbf{0} \quad , \quad a.\mathbf{0} + b.\mathbf{0})$$
$$(\mathbf{0} \quad , \quad \mathbf{0})\}$$

The first is not a weak bisimulation because the τ-action prevents the choice between a and b for the agent on the left of the first pair. The second is not a weak bisimulation because the agent on the left has no action b whereas the other has.

EXERCISE 9.3

Re-do exercises 9.1 and 9.2 but this time check for observational equivalence.

EXERCISE 9.4

$$Spec_1 \stackrel{\text{def}}{=} c1.Spec_1 + c2.Spec_2$$
$$Spec_2 \stackrel{\text{def}}{=} \tau.c1.Spec_2 + \tau.c2.Spec_2$$
$$Spec_3 \stackrel{\text{def}}{=} \tau.c1.\tau.Spec_3 + \tau.c2.\tau.Spec_3$$

1. Which of the above are strongly equivalent with Mx?
2. Which of the above are observationally equivalent with Mx?
3. What conclusions do you come to regarding the relationship between the two definitions of equivalence?

9.4 Equivalence and substitution

Let us be quite clear about the kinds of properties we will expect of the equivalences we have defined. Suppose we have proved $Buff_2$ weakly equivalent to $B0$ and $B0$ weakly equivalent to $B0'$. Are we able to infer that $Buff_2$ is weakly equivalent to $B0'$? The answer is 'yes' and the reason for it is because of a particular property of both the equivalences we have defined in this chapter. Both equivalences are in fact *equivalence relations* which we can characterise in the following manner:

Definition 9.8 A binary relation **R** over some set Λ is an equivalence relation when the following hold:

1. $(E, E) \in \mathbf{R} \ \forall E \in \Lambda$
2. $(E, F) \in \mathbf{R}$ and $(F, G) \in \mathbf{R}$ implies $(E, G) \in \mathbf{R}$
3. $(E, F) \in \mathbf{R}$ implies $(F, E) \in \mathbf{R}$

Both strong and observational equivalences are equivalence relations and allow us to infer the equivalences we required of the various definitions of the two-place buffer. However, full equality normally has an extra property that given some expression E with subexpression E' we can replace E' with some expression equivalent to it without affecting E itself. In the case of CCS, where expressions are agents, this would mean that replacing E' with an agent with equivalent behaviour does not change the behaviour of E itself.

Definition 9.9 A relation **R** over some set Λ is a congruence relation when the following hold:
1. **R** is an equivalence relation.
2. If $E \in \Lambda$ and E' is a subexpression of E and $E' \approx^c F'$ then $E \approx^c F$ where F is E with F' substituted for E'.

Strong equivalence is a congruence relation but observational equivalence is not. We will now see why the latter is so, and go on to refine observational equivalence into a congruence relation, which will in turn be the basis for a set of equational laws to manipulate agents which will be the subject of the next chapter.

We observed that strong equivalence is *too strong* and makes more distinctions than we would wish. By considering equivalence as a congruence relation we will see that weak equivalence conversely makes too few distinctions. To see why, let us, first of all, demonstrate why observational equivalence is not a congruence relation. Certainly, we can show that

$$\tau.a.\mathbf{0} \approx a.\mathbf{0} \approx a.\tau.\mathbf{0}$$

but is it true that we can substitute $\tau.a.\mathbf{0}$ for $a.\mathbf{0}$ or vice versa in more complex agent expressions and retain the same behaviour? In other words, is the following true?

$$\tau.a.\mathbf{0} + b.\mathbf{0} \approx a.\mathbf{0} + b.\mathbf{0}$$

The answer is 'no'! We cannot build a weak bisimulation that contains the pair $(a.\mathbf{0} + b.\mathbf{0}, \tau.a.\mathbf{0} + b.\mathbf{0})$ and so

$$a.\mathbf{0} + b.\mathbf{0} \not\approx \tau.a.\mathbf{0} + b.\mathbf{0}$$

is the true statement of the relationship, in terms of weak equivalence, between the two agents.

We cannot necessarily substitute weakly equivalent expressions for each other in more complex expressions. The problem is caused by the initial τ-action which is possible for $\tau.a.\mathbf{0} + b.\mathbf{0}$ and which makes a silent choice resulting in only the action a being possible next. However, $a.\mathbf{0} + b.\mathbf{0}$ can only attempt to match this behaviour by doing no τ-actions at all, but this preserves the choice between both a and b as possible next actions and the equivalence breaks down. This problem does not arise with $a.\mathbf{0}$ and $a.\tau.\mathbf{0}$ because the τ-action is guarded by the a and we can safely substitute the one for the other and preserve the equivalence. The following equivalence is indeed a true statement:

$$a.\mathbf{0} + b.\mathbf{0} \approx a.\tau.\mathbf{0} + b.\mathbf{0}$$

We can get over this problem by specifying conditions under which
weakly equivalent expressions may be considered congruent. We shall call
this relation *observational congruence* and it will be based on the definition
of observational equivalence but with added constraints on τ-actions.

We will say E and F are *obervationally congruent*, $E \approx^c F$, when the
following conditions hold:

1. $E \approx F$

2. $E \xrightarrow{\tau} E'$ implies $\exists F' \bullet F \xRightarrow{\tau} F' \wedge E' \approx F'$

3. $F \xrightarrow{\tau} F'$ implies $\exists E' \bullet E \xRightarrow{\tau} E' \wedge E' \approx F'$

First of all this means that E and F must be observationally equivalent.
Secondly it means that if E can do a non-empty sequence of τ-actions and
become E' then F must have a transition to an observationally equivalent
expression via a non-empty sequence of τ-actions. Thirdly, the same must
hold in reverse so that E can match the τ-actions of F. Therefore, the
following hold:

$$a.0 \not\approx^c \tau.a.0 \quad \text{but} \quad \tau.a.0 \approx^c \tau.\tau.a.0 \quad \text{and} \quad a.0 \approx^c a.\tau.0$$

Definition 9.10 $E \approx^c F$ exactly when the following hold:

1. $E \approx F$

2. If C is a CCS expression involving E and D is the CCS expression
   obtained by substituting E for F, then $C \approx D$.

EXERCISE 9.5

Repeat all the exercises in this chapter but attempt to prove observational congruence between the agents instead of observational equivalence.

9.5 Relating equivalences

We have now defined three forms of equivalence over CCS expressions. We
called them strong equivalence, observational equivalence and observational
congruence, and the exercises throughout this chapter have been designed,
not only to practise their application, but also to build up the reader's ideas
concerning the relationships between them. This is not only of academic
interest but will also be a matter of some practical use in the next chapter

when we study the use of systems of equations to add to our reasoning power over expressions.

In this chapter's exercises you should have proved the following equivalences:

$$Buff_2 \quad \sim \quad Buff0' \qquad Mx \quad \sim \quad Spec_3$$

$$Buff_2 \quad \approx \quad Buff0' \qquad Mx \quad \approx \quad Spec_2$$
$$Buff_2 \quad \approx \quad Buff0 \qquad Mx \quad \approx \quad Spec_3$$

$$Buff_2 \quad \approx^c \quad Buff0' \qquad Mx \quad \approx^c \quad Spec_2$$
$$Buff_2 \quad \approx^c \quad Buff0 \qquad Mx \quad \approx^c \quad Spec_3$$

Bearing in mind that we have already shown that $E \approx F$ does not guarantee $E \approx^c F$, we can suggest the following relationships between our various equivalences:

1. All strong equivalences are also weak equivalences.

2. All strong equivalences are also observational congruences.

3. All observational congruences are also weak equivalences.

4. It is *not* true that all weak equivalences are observational congruences.

5. It is *not* true that all weak equivalences are strong equivalences.

This in turn would seem to suggest the following:

$$E \sim F \text{ implies } E \approx^c F \text{ and } E \approx^c F \text{ implies } E \approx F$$

In other words:

$$\sim \; \subseteq \; \approx^c \; \subseteq \; \approx$$

With a little thought we should be able to see why this is indeed true. First of all, by examining the definitions for $\sim$ and $\approx$ we can establish that all strong equivalences also satisfy the definition for weak equivalence. Suppose $E \sim F$ then we have that $E \approx F$ and to establish $E \approx^c F$ we need to show that in addition E and F can match each other on initial τ-actions as demanded by the definition of observational congruence. That this is so is guaranteed by $E \sim F$ and therefore we can conclude $E \approx^c F$.

For the second part we assume $E \approx^c F$ and need to show that $E \approx F$ in the knowledge that if $E \xrightarrow{\alpha} E'$ and $F \xrightarrow{\alpha} F'$ then $E' \approx F'$ by the definition of $\approx^c$. We thus need to show that all the initial actions of E and F will respect the definition of $\approx$ in addition to that of $\approx^c$. The only difference between the two equivalences is their treatment of initial τ-actions. For weak equivalence we require that for each τ-action the other agent must be able to do zero or more τ-actions and reach an equivalent state. The definition for observational congruence is stronger than this and says that for every τ-action the other agent must also be able to do a τ-action and reach an equivalent state. Thus, we may safely conclude that $E \approx^c F$ implies $E \approx F$.

9.6 Equivalences for time and value passing

Strong equivalence may be defined for TCCS by extending the definitions so that agents must match up on delays as well as atomic transitions.

Definition 9.11 A binary relation, $\mathbf{R} \subseteq \mathcal{E}^T \times \mathcal{E}^T$, is a timed bisimulation if, whenever $(E, F) \in \mathbf{R}$, then for all actions α and delays t the following are true:

1) $E \xrightarrow{\alpha} E'$ implies $\exists F' \bullet F \xrightarrow{\alpha} F' \wedge E'\mathbf{R}F'$

2) $F \xrightarrow{\alpha} F'$ implies $\exists E' \bullet E \xrightarrow{\alpha} E' \wedge E'\mathbf{R}F'$

3) $E \overset{t}{\rightsquigarrow} E'$ implies $\exists F' \bullet F \overset{t}{\rightsquigarrow} F' \wedge E'\mathbf{R}F'$

4) $F \overset{t}{\rightsquigarrow} F'$ implies $\exists E' \bullet E \overset{t}{\rightsquigarrow} E' \wedge E'\mathbf{R}F'$

EXERCISE 9.6

Use arbitrary natural-number constants e_1 and e_2 to prove the equivalence of $Buff_2^{\mathbf{N}}$ and $Buff_{\mathbf{N}}^2(\langle\rangle)$ from chapter 5.

9.7 Summary and further reading

We have demonstrated that a number of equivalences for CCS can be defined and that they have a useful part to play in the development of specifications for concurrent and real-time systems. All the definitions of equivalence for basic CCS are taken from [Mil89] while those for value-passing CCS arise naturally from its semantics being given in basic CCS. The equivalences for TCCS can be found in [Tof89]. A number of other equivalences have been studied for process algebras, of which *failures* is perhaps the most interesting [Hoa85]. Hennessy develops this equivalence for a CCS-like language using *may* and *must* preorders. These latter are used by Baillie [Bai91] in CCS analysis of a safety-critical level-crossing system. In [HL94] equivalences for value-passing CCS may be found. In the next chapter we go on to study a set of equational laws, based on observational congruence, which can be used to manipulate CCS expressions in a variety of ways for a variety of purposes.

10

Equational laws

Now that we have established various theories of equivalence, and in particular observational congruence, we can consider general laws which will hold between classes of agents. These laws will be expressed in terms of equations which will allow us to restructure agents by substituting structurally different but congruent agents for each other. Remember that if two agents are observationally congruent then we can freely substitute one for the other without fear of changing the behaviour of the global system. The equational laws are divided into static and dynamic laws and an expansion law. The equational laws are used as an additional tool in the formal reasoning process and as a means of making more practical use of the equivalences. The set of laws presented is not exhaustive and some important laws have been left out in the interests of keeping the level of the book at a practical and introductory level. We give some justification for the correctness of the equational laws within the theory. Finally, various uses of the laws in building specifications and implementations are explored by applying the laws to CCS specifications from earlier chapters in the book.

10.1 Uses of equations

In the previous chapter we developed various theories of equivalence that allowed us to demonstrate whether or not particular agents were equivalent in terms of a particular theory. However, there may be cases where equivalence between processes is more general and can be expressed between classes of agent expressions. For instance, it seems reasonable to assume that $E + F$ should be equivalent to $F + E$ whatever expressions E and F represent.

In the last chapter we also established various equivalences which included pairs such as

$$(0 \mid 0, 0)$$

These expressions occur as an element of both weak and strong bisimulations and because they have no initial τ-actions, indeed no actions at all, then it should be true that

$$0 \mid 0 \approx^c 0$$

Another example of such an equivalence might be

$$0 + 0 \approx^c 0$$

We would like to generalise these types of equivalences into a set of laws that characterise general equivalences between processes. For instance, we might find it useful to establish a general law to the effect that $0 + E \approx^c E$. This law simply states that if an agent has a choice between any process E and the null process then the same set of behaviours would be possible for E on its own.

Another useful set of laws might tell us in general terms when we can safely remove τ-actions from agent expressions. Using our equivalence theories we have shown the following:

$$a.0 \approx^c a.\tau.0$$

So we might wish to generalise this information to the equation

$$a.E \approx^c a.\tau.E$$

and thus allow us to add or remove τ-actions in this general context. We cannot, however, introduce a law of the form $a.E \approx^c \tau.a.E$ because, although

$$a.0 \approx \tau.a.0$$

is certainly true, these two agents are not congruent,

$$a.0 \not\approx^c \tau.a.0$$

and all our equational laws are based on classes of agents which are congruent. Remember that not all observational equivalences are congruences whereas all strong equivalences are. With the exception of laws for τ-actions, for instance, most of the laws will be based on strong equivalence.

In previous chapters we have noted the relationships between concurrency and non-deterministic choice in CCS, for example, we can prove the equivalence

$$a.b.0 + b.a.0 \approx^c a.0 \mid b.0$$

and we might wish to establish a general law to show us when such equivalences are, in general, allowable. Such a law would allow us to transform an agent constructed from a number of simpler, concurrent agents into one defined only in terms of sequence and choice. We could thus transform a specification into an equivalent form which more closely resembled the kind of system we might wish to implement. In chapter 2 we developed a specification for $System2$ in terms of the parallel composition of a four-place buffer and various agents which either produced values for the buffer or consumed values from it. One solution to exercise 2.7 was to add an additional agent to act as a semaphore through which C and D could gain control of $Buff_4^2$. In this case the full system would have been

$$(A \mid B \mid Buff_4^2 \mid C \mid D \mid Sem)\backslash L$$

but, although meeting the requirement, this would produce a rather cumbersome implementation. We might be happier with simply two parallel processes and a buffer. *Producer* would be a single sequential agent replacing both A and B, and *Consumer* would be a single agent replacing C, D and *Sem*. We would then require the following congruence

$$System2 \approx^c (Producer \mid Buff_2^2 \mid Consumer)\backslash L'$$

We have changed the restriction set to L' because some restricted actions may disappear or apply only to particular sub-agents. One way of achieving this type of objective would be to define expressions for *Producer* and *Consumer* which looked correct and then prove observational congruence. The other, perhaps more satisfactory, method would be to transform components from our initial specification into observationally congruent forms using laws which would guarantee to preserve this equivalence.

In the following sections we define a set of useful equations which will allow us to prove observational congruence by general equational reasoning rather than building appropriate bisimulations for particular pairs of expressions. We will introduce these equational laws as we need them but you will find all those introduced in this chapter collected in Appendix B along with other useful laws which we did not have the space to illustrate.

10.2 Basic transformations on agents

To illustrate the way we are going to use our equational laws let us state those for the choice operator, which are fairly intuitive and present some example transformations. In all the laws stated in this chapter E, F and G, etc. are elements of the set $\mathcal{E}$ and thus range over the set of all basic-CCS expressions.

Laws for choice

CH1 $E + F \approx^c F + E$

CH2 $E + (F + G) \approx^c (E + F) + G$

CH3 $E + E \approx^c E$

CH4 $E + \mathbf{0} \approx^c E$

Remember that $E + F + G$ is actually $E + (F + G)$ according to the precedence rules introduced in chapter 3. The laws CH1 and CH2 simply say that the order of agents related by the choice operator is immaterial to the behaviour of the agent as a whole. The law CH3 says that a choice between two identical agents is behaviourally the same as a single copy of the agent. The law CH4 says that the behaviour of an agent defined as the choice between some agent E and the null agent is just the behaviour of E itself.

Now let us use these laws to prove the observational congruence of two agents by showing that we can transform the one into the other by repeated applications of just the choice laws. At each state we will use the law identified to the right of each line to transform the subexpression underlined. We wish to prove the following congruence true:

$$((E + F) + ((E + F) + G)) + (0 + (F + 0)) \approx^c (E + F) + G$$

$$
\begin{array}{lll}
 & ((E + F) + ((E + F) + G)) + (0 + \underline{(F + 0)}) & \text{(CH4)} \\
\approx^c & ((E + F) + ((E + F) + G)) + \underline{(0 + F)} & \text{(CH1)} \\
\approx^c & ((E + F) + ((E + F) + G)) + \underline{(F + 0)} & \text{(CH4)} \\
\approx^c & \underline{((E + F) + ((E + F) + G)) + F} & \text{(CH2)} \\
\approx^c & \underline{(((E + F) + (E + F)) + G) + F} & \text{(CH3)} \\
\approx^c & \underline{((E + F) + G) + F} & \text{(CH1)} \\
\approx^c & \underline{(G + (E + F)) + F} & \text{(CH2)} \\
\approx^c & G + \underline{((E + F) + F)} & \text{(CH2)} \\
\approx^c & G + \underline{(E + (F + F))} & \text{(CH3)} \\
\approx^c & G + \underline{(E + F)} & \text{(CH1)} \\
\approx^c & (E + F) + G &
\end{array}
$$

Of course this is not the only proof of the correctness of this congruence. There are many more sequences of applications of the choice laws that would have given us the required transformation. We could for example have expanded the right hand side of the equation instead of simplifying the left. Simplification is usually simpler, however, and is also a useful technique in its own right in the process of building and reasoning about specifications.

We will now introduce some laws for the prefixing operator, all of which are concerned with τ-actions.

Laws for prefix

PRE1 $\alpha.\tau.E \approx^c \alpha.E$

PRE2 $E + \tau.E \approx^c \tau.E$

PRE3 $\alpha.(E + \tau.F) + \alpha.F \approx^c \alpha.(E + \tau.F)$

The first prefix law, PRE1, says that we can delete or introduce a τ-action if it occurs inside a sequence of actions and is not active in making a choice between next states. The second law states that any agent, E, is equivalent to an agent defined as the choice between E and E prefixed by τ. Draw transition graphs for simple examples of such agents if you are not convinced. The third prefix law is not quite so obvious and we will build a weak bisimulation to demonstrate its correctness and then check for initial τ-actions:

$$\{(\alpha.(E + \tau.F) + \alpha.F \quad , \quad \alpha.(E + \tau.F)),$$
$$(E + \tau.F \quad , \quad E + \tau.F),$$
$$(E \quad , \quad E),$$
$$(F \quad , \quad F)\}$$

Obviously E is weakly equivalent to itself, as is F, and so it is true that $\alpha.(E + \tau.F) + \alpha.F \approx \alpha.(E + \tau.F)$ and, because there are no initial τ-actions, congruence must be true also. We observed earlier that the equation $E \approx^c \tau.E$ is *not* a valid prefix law for CCS because these two expressions are not congruent although they are observationally equivalent.

A valid law which will be of considerable use to us just says that constants are congruent with their defining expressions. We can always replace a constant with its definition or vice versa.

CON1 If $A \overset{\text{def}}{=} E$ then $A \approx^c E$.

As a further example of equational reasoning for CCS we will use the laws introduced to date to prove

$$E \approx^c \tau.((a.\tau.C + \tau.b.\tau.C) + (a.\tau.C + b.\tau.\tau.C)) + (a.C + \tau.b.C)$$

where

$$C \overset{\text{def}}{=} a.C + \tau.b.C \quad \text{and} \quad E \overset{\text{def}}{=} \tau.C$$

It is probably easier to simplify the right hand side rather than expand the left hand side:

$$
\begin{array}{lll}
& \tau.((a.\tau.C + \tau.b.\tau.C) + (a.\tau.C + b.\tau.\tau.C)) + (\underline{a.C + \tau.b.C}) & \text{(CON1)} \\
\approx^c & \tau.((\underline{a.\tau.C} + \tau.\underline{b.\tau.C}) + (\underline{a.\tau.C} + b.\underline{\tau.\tau.C})) + C & \text{(PRE1)} \\
\approx^c & \tau.(\underline{((a.C + \tau.b.C) + (a.C + b.C))} + C & \text{(CH2)} \\
\approx^c & \tau.(((((a.C + \tau.b.C) + a.C) + b.C) + C & \text{(CH2)} \\
\approx^c & \tau.((a.C + \underline{(\tau.b.C + a.C)}) + b.C) + C & \text{(CH1)} \\
\approx^c & \tau.((a.C + \underline{(a.C + \tau.b.C)}) + b.C) + C & \text{(CH2)} \\
\approx^c & \tau.(((\underline{a.C + a.C}) + \tau.b.C) + b.C) + C & \text{(CH3)} \\
\approx^c & \tau.(\underline{(a.C + \tau.b.C) + b.C}) + C & \text{(CH2)} \\
\approx^c & \tau.(a.C + \underline{(\tau.b.C + b.C)}) + C & \text{(PRE2)} \\
\approx^c & \tau.(\underline{a.C + \tau.b.C}) + C & \text{(CON1)} \\
\approx^c & \underline{\tau.C} + C & \text{(PRE2)} \\
\approx^c & \underline{\tau.C} & \text{(CON1)} \\
\approx^c & E &
\end{array}
$$

EXERCISE 10.1

Prove the following using the laws introduced so far:

1. $\alpha.(P + \tau.\tau.P) \approx^c \alpha.P$

2. $P + S \approx^c S$

3. $\tau.(P + T) \approx^c \tau.(P + T) + \alpha.R$

where

$$S \overset{\text{def}}{=} \tau.(P + Q)$$
$$T \overset{\text{def}}{=} \alpha.(Q + \tau.R)$$

10.3 Laws for restriction and composition

Sometimes it is useful to be able to use the equational laws to transform expressions involving restrictions. In the introduction to this chapter we considered the agent $System2$ from chapter 2 and suggested that we might wish to transform it into an agent of the form

$$(Producer \mid Buff_4^2 \mid Consumer)\backslash L'$$

which more closely resembles a possible implementation. Remember that the restricted actions get, put only apply to the expression $C \mid D \mid Sem$, so it would simplify the overall expression a little further if we could push this subset of L inside the parallel compositions so that it formed part of the consumer only. We defined $Buff_2^2$ in this manner from the outset. The following congruence is the one we are after:

$$System2 \approx^c (Producer \mid Buff_4^2 \mid Consumer\backslash\{get, put\})\backslash L'$$

where

$$L' \overset{\text{def}}{=} \{in0, in1, \overline{out0}, \overline{out1}\}$$

To make this translation we need to introduce some laws that allow us to manipulate expressions involving restrictions. However, due to the definition of the restriction operator, in chapter 3, we will often need to know whether or not the set restricted on has any effect on the agent expression it is applied to. In other words, we will need to know if some restriction set L intersects the set of actions which some agent expression E will be capable of at some time in the future. To this end we will define a function $sort$ which will return such a set when given an expression E as an argument.

Definition 10.1

$$
\begin{aligned}
sort(\mathbf{0}) &= \{\} \\
sort(l.E) &= \{l\} \cup sort(E) \\
sort(\tau.E) &= sort(E) \\
sort(E + F) &= sort(E) \cup sort(F) \\
sort(E \mid F) &= sort(E) \cup sort(F) \\
sort(E \backslash L) &= sort(E) \backslash (L \cup \overline{L})
\end{aligned}
$$

In addition, for any agent definiton $P \stackrel{\text{def}}{=} E$ it must be true that $sort(P) \subseteq sort(E)$.

We now introduce the equations we are going to need.

RES1 $E \backslash L \approx^c E$ if $sort(E) \cap (L \cup \overline{L}) = \{\}$

RES2 $E \backslash K \backslash L \approx^c E \backslash (K \cup L)$

RES3 $(E \mid F) \backslash L \approx^c E \backslash L \mid F \backslash L$ if $sort(E) \cap \overline{sort(F)} \cap (L \cup \overline{L}) = \{\}$

The first restriction law, RES1, simply says that a restriction set L which does not affect an agent E can be added or removed as required. Notice the side condition using the *actions* function. The second law, RES2, is equally simple and says any restriction set may be considered as two separate restrictions and vice versa.

The third law requires a little more thought. The basic intuition behind the law is that we would, on occasions, like to distribute a restriction across parallel compositions or vice versa. We have to be careful when we do this and make sure that we do not prevent possible synchronisations from taking place. Applying such a law in the other direction might introduce new synchronisations that were not possible before. The side condition on RES3 ensures that these undesirable transformations are prevented. First of all, $sort(E) \cap \overline{sort(F)}$ checks to see if E and F can synchronise at some time in the future. If this returns the empty set then the whole side condition will evaluate to true otherwise we must consider the intersection with this set and the union of L and its complement. If this set is empty then L will not affect any synchronisations between E and F and the side condition evaluates to true, otherwise problems might occur and the side condition will return false and we cannot apply the law in this particular case.

We will now return to $System2$ and illustrate the use of these laws. First of all, we state two laws for parallel composition which state that the ordering and bracketing of expressions composed in parallel is immaterial.

COM1 $E \mid F \approx^c F \mid E$

COM2 $E \mid (F \mid G) \approx^c (E \mid F) \mid G$

We may thus conclude that

$$System2 \approx^c ((A \mid B \mid Buff_2^4) \mid (C \mid D \mid Sem)) \backslash L$$

and apply the restriction laws in the following manner.

$$\frac{((A \mid B \mid Buff_2^2) \mid (C \mid D \mid Sem))\backslash L}{((A \mid B \mid Buff_2^2) \mid (C \mid D \mid Sem))\backslash\{get, put\}\backslash L'} \qquad \text{(RES2)}$$
$$\approx^c \quad \overline{((A \mid B \mid Buff_2^2) \mid (C \mid D \mid Sem))\backslash\{get, put\}\backslash L'} \qquad \text{(RES3)}$$
$$\approx^c \quad \overline{((A \mid B \mid Buff_2^2)\backslash\{get, put\} \mid (C \mid D \mid Sem)\backslash\{get, put\})\backslash L'} \quad \text{(RES1)}$$
$$\approx^c \quad ((A \mid B \mid Buff_2^2) \mid (C \mid D \mid Sem)\backslash\{get, put\})\backslash L'$$

where

$$L' \equiv \{in0, in1, out0, out1\}$$

10.4 The expansion law

We saw in chapter 3 that the two agents $Spec3$ and Mx were not only weakly equivalent but were also observationally congruent as well. The next law we introduce will demonstrate, in conjunction with other laws such as the τ-laws, how we can begin to demonstrate the behavioural equivalence of such structurally different agents as $Spec3$ and Mx. It is called the *expansion law*, and we will develop and make use of it first before formally defining it.

Consider the initial actions the agent Mx can perform. There are two of them and they are both τ-actions. After performing one of the τ-actions Mx would be in the state

$$(c1.\overline{put}.P1 \mid P2 \mid put.Sem)\backslash\{get, put\}$$

However, by performing the other τ-action Mx would evolve to the state

$$(P1 \mid c2.\overline{put} \mid put.Sem)\backslash\{get, put\}$$

There are no other actions possible for Mx in its initial state and so there is a choice between two next states depending upon which τ-action is performed. We could write out an equivalent expression for Mx in the following manner:

$$\begin{aligned} Mx \quad \approx^c \quad & \tau.(c1.\overline{put}.P1 \mid P2 \mid put.Sem)\backslash\{get, put\} \\ & +\tau.(P1 \mid c2.\overline{put} \mid put.Sem)\backslash\{get, put\} \end{aligned}$$

For this equivalence to be valid we must make sure that all possible next actions and resulting states are represented. It is now clear why we called this new law the 'expansion law' (EX). Notice that what is really going on here is that we are beginning to define in a formal way the generation of an agent's transition graph.

If we apply this new law several times to the agent

$$(c1.\overline{put}.P1 \mid P2 \mid put.Sem)\backslash\{get, put\}$$

we get the following equivalence:

$$(c1.\overline{put}.P1 \mid P2 \mid put.Sem)\backslash\{get, put\} \quad \text{(EX)}$$
$$\approx^c \quad c1.\overline{(put}.P1 \mid P2 \mid put.Sem)\backslash\{get, put\} \quad \text{(EX)}$$
$$\approx^c \quad c1.\tau.(P1 \mid P2 \mid Sem)\backslash\{get, put\} \quad \text{(CON1)}$$
$$\approx^c \quad c1.\tau.\overline{MX} \quad \text{(PRE1)}$$
$$\approx^c \quad c1.Mx$$

By a similar line of reasoning we can derive the following equivalence:

$$(P1 \mid c2.\overline{put}.P2 \mid put.Sem)\backslash\{get, put\} \approx^c c2.Mx$$

Substituting back into our first expansion of Mx we obtain the following congruence:

$$Mx \approx^c \tau.c1.Mx + \tau.c2.Mx$$

which now bears a striking resemblance to the definition of $Spec2$. By using the expansion law in conjunction with some of the other laws, we have demonstrated by equational reasoning what we had already shown through building transition graphs, namely that although defined in very different ways the two agents $Spec_2$ and Mx have identical behaviour patterns up to weak equivalence. This result is in fact stronger because we have now shown them to be congruent and not just observationally equivalent. Before using the new law further let us give it a formal definition so there can be no arguments as to what it means or how to apply it.

The first point to note is that the expansion law applies to agent expressions of the following form:

$$P \equiv \prod_{i \in I} E_i \backslash L \equiv (E_1 \mid \ldots \mid E_n)\backslash L \quad (I = \{1, \ldots, n\})$$

In other words the agent P must consist of the parallel composition of a number of agent subexpressions with a restriction set L which might be the empty set. We will say that agents of this type are in Standard Concurrent Form. The law must state that we have to take all possible next actions of such an agent and construct a new agent expression which gives the choice between all these actions prefixing the agent expressions which represent the resulting states that will be reached after performing them. There will obviously be two types of actions which might be possible from an agent such as P. There will be a possible choice between a number of observable actions and a number of τ-actions. We will define both types separately and then put them together to form the whole definition. The definitions make use of indexed sums as defined and used in the traffic lights chapter. The sum of each observable transition can be stated in the form

$$\sum\{\alpha.(E_1 \mid \ldots \mid E_i' \mid \ldots \mid E_n)\backslash L : E_i \xrightarrow{\alpha} E_i', \alpha \notin L \cup \overline{L}\}$$

and we thus have a choice for all i such that E_i satisfies the condition $\alpha \notin L \cup \overline{L}$. All together this simply says that if E_i can perform an action

α which is not restricted then we must build an expression $\alpha.E_i'$ such that $E_i \xrightarrow{\alpha} E_i'$. The possible expressions resulting from synchronisations require a slightly more complex definition:

$$\sum\{\tau.(E_1 \mid \ldots \mid E_i' \mid \ldots \mid E_j' \mid \ldots \mid E_n)\backslash L :$$
$$E_i \xrightarrow{l} E_i', \ E_j \xrightarrow{\bar{l}} E_j', i < j\}$$

This time we do not refer to the restriction set L because both restricted and unrestricted actions may engage in synchronisations resulting in a τ-action.

The completed definition, which we will call **EX**, states that an agent in concurrent form may be transformed using the expansion law into an agent which consists of the sum of all the possible transitions

The expansion law
EX

If $P \ \equiv \ \prod_{i \in I} E_i \backslash L$

then $P \ \approx^c \ \sum\{\alpha.(E_1 \mid \ldots \mid E_i' \mid \ldots \mid E_n)\backslash L : E_i \xrightarrow{\alpha} E_i', \alpha \notin L \cup \overline{L}\}$
$+$
$\sum\{\tau.(E_1 \mid \ldots \mid E_i' \mid \ldots \mid E_j' \mid \ldots \mid E_n)\backslash L :$
$E_i \xrightarrow{l} E_i', \ E_j \xrightarrow{\bar{l}} E_j', i < j\}$

EXERCISE 10.2

Use the expansion law, among others, to show that $G \ \approx^c \ a.G + \tau.b.G$. Exercise 9.2 gives the definitions for G.

10.5 Solving equations

If we successively apply the expansion law to the agent $Buff_2$ which we have used in previous chapters we get the following sequence of transformations:

	$Buff_2$	(CON1)
$\approx^c$	$(C1 \mid C2)\backslash\{m\}$	(CON $\times$ 2)
$\approx^c$	$(in.\overline{m}.C1 \mid m.\overline{out}.C2)\backslash\{m\}$	(EX)
$\approx^c$	$in.(\overline{m}.C1 \mid m.\overline{out}.C2)\backslash\{m\}$	(EX)
$\approx^c$	$in.\tau.(C1 \mid \overline{out}.C2)\backslash\{m\}$	(PRE1)
$\approx^c$	$in.(C1 \mid \overline{out}.C2)\backslash\{m\}$	(CON1)
$\approx^c$	$in.(in.\overline{m}.C1 \mid \overline{out}.C2)\backslash\{m\}$	(EX)
$\approx^c$	$in.(in.(\overline{m}.C1 \mid \overline{out}.C2)\backslash\{m\} + \overline{out}.(in.\overline{m}.C1 \mid C2)\backslash\{m\})$	(CON1)
$\approx^c$	$in.(in.(\overline{m}.C1 \mid \overline{out}.C2)\backslash\{m\} + \overline{out}.(C1 \mid C2)\backslash\{m\})$	(EX)
$\approx^c$	$in.(in.\overline{out}.(\overline{m}.C1 \mid C2)\backslash\{m\} + \overline{out}.(C1 \mid C2)\backslash\{m\})$	

If we now look at the definitions for our sequential version of the buffer we can see the same behavioural patterns emerging:

$$B0 \stackrel{\text{def}}{=} in.B1$$
$$B1 \stackrel{\text{def}}{=} \overline{out}.B0 + in.B2$$
$$B2 \stackrel{\text{def}}{=} \overline{out}.B1$$

Applying CON1 a few times to B_0 gives us the following congruence:

$$\begin{array}{ll} \underline{B0} & \text{(CON1)} \\ \approx^c \quad in.\underline{B1} & \text{(CON1)} \\ \approx^c \quad in.(\overline{out}.B0 + in.\underline{B2}) & \text{(CON1)} \\ \approx^c \quad in.(\overline{out}.B0 + in.\overline{out}B1) & \text{(CON1)} \end{array}$$

An obvious question now arises. If we can demonstrate that two agents possess the same behavioural patterns can we consider them to be congruent? In particular, are the following congruences true?

$$Mx \approx^c Spec_2 \qquad Buff_2 \approx^c B0$$

The answer is 'yes' to both questions but the basis for this requires a little more thought. If we consider the two congruences

$$Mx \approx^c \tau.c1.Mx + \tau.c2.Mx$$

and

$$Spec_2 \approx^c \tau.c1.Spec_2 + \tau.c2.Spec_2$$

it is easy to see that the only difference is the constant names we have used, despite the fact that their defining expressions appear quite different. We can build a general pattern of behaviour out of these congruences if we introduce a variable into the equation.

$$X \approx^c \tau.c1.X + \tau.c2.X$$

We intend X to be a variable which ranges over agent expressions. If we substitute first Mx for X and then $Spec2$ for X it is obvious from our previous calculations that they both satisfy the equation for X, and it is for this reason that we may conclude $Mx \approx^c Spec_2$. $Spec3$ also satisfies this equation and we have the following statement of observational congruence:

$$Mx \approx^c Spec_2 \approx^c Spec_3$$

What we seem to have established here is that any expression which satisfies the equation for X has a unique behaviour up to observational congruence. We have to be a little careful because there are equations which do not guarantee unique solutions. The following equation is a good example:

$$Y \approx^c \tau.Y$$

Now consider the two agents $Spec_1$ and $Spec_2$. It is certainly true that $Spec_1 \not\approx Spec_2$ and it is therefore also true that $\tau.Spec_1 \not\approx^c \tau.Spec_2$. Check back on the definition of observational congruence in chapter 9 (page 162) to see why. Yet it is easy to prove that both expressions satisfy the equation $Y \approx^c \tau.Y$. If we substitute $\tau.Spec_1$ for Y and $Spec_2$ for Y we then have the following equations to prove correct:

$$\tau.Spec_1 \quad \approx^c \quad \tau.\tau.Spec_1$$
$$\tau.Spec_2 \quad \tilde{\approx}^c \quad \tau.\tau.Spec_2$$

If we apply PRE1 to the right hand sides of both equations we achieve the desired results immediately. In this particular case the problem is that the variable is prefixed only by a τ-action and we therefore do not have to explore the behaviour of the agent itself at all. In fact any agent of the form $\tau.E$ will satisfy this equation for Y. The equation $X \approx^c X$ is even more general, for any agent E will satisfy it.

In order to ensure that our equations yield unique solutions we have to place restrictions on the position of the variable in the right hand side of the equation. These restrictions are captured by the following definition:

Definition 10.2 Let E be any agent expression.

1. An agent variable X is *sequential* in E if it only occurs within the scope of prefix or choice operators in E.

2. An agent variable X is *guarded* in E if each occurrence of X in E is within some subexpression of the form $l.F$ of E.

Both conditions are necessary to ensure that an observational action occurs before the variable on the right hand side of an equation. The guardedness condition is obvious. The sequentiality condition is there to ensure that the observable action is not lost as the result of a synchronisation. In the equation

$$X \approx^c (\bar{a}.X \mid a.\mathbf{0})\backslash\{a\}$$

X is certainly prefixed by an observable action on the right hand side but the action is restricted and the only possible action is a τ-action. The same set of agents that satisfied the equation for Y above will satisfy this equation. It is important, therefore, that we ensure that all variables are guarded and sequential in the equations we use.

Before stating the second constant law (CON2) we should return to the $Buff_2$ and $B0$ example which we were using as a working example. There is a difference between this example and Mx in that we cannot reduce the sequential version of the buffer $B0, B1, B2$ to a single equation. It requires at least two or three and in this case they could be

$$X \quad \approx^c \quad in.Y$$
$$Y \quad \approx^c \quad \overline{out}.X + in.Z$$
$$Z \quad \approx^c \quad \overline{out}.Y$$

although we could do away with the need for the equation for Z altogether by replacing Z in the equation for Y by $\overline{out}.Y$. Notice that we could do the same for the reference to X in the equation for Y, in which case Y takes on a very simple pattern indeed. This only applies because this is a two place buffer.

Of course, we will need two substitutions as in the case for Mx and $Spec3$, but each substitution must have values for X, Y and Z and the proof will, in effect, solve simultaneous equations – one for each variable. One set of substitutions is easily established:

$$Sub1 \stackrel{\text{def}}{=} \{B0/X, B1/Y, B2/Z\}$$

The other can be gained from the expansion of $Buff_2$ constructed above and results in a second substitution:

$$Sub2 \stackrel{\text{def}}{=} \{Buff_2/X, (C1 \mid \overline{out}.C2)\backslash\{m\}/Y, (\overline{m}.C1 \mid \overline{out}.C2)\backslash\{m\}/Z\}$$

If you apply both substitutions to the equations for X, Y, Z we get two sets of three equations to solve:

$$
\begin{aligned}
B0 &\approx^c in.B1 \\
B1 &\approx^c \overline{out}.B0 + in.B2 \\
B2 &\approx^c \overline{out}.B1
\end{aligned}
$$

and

$$
\begin{aligned}
Buff_2 &\approx^c in.(C1 \mid \overline{out}.C2)\backslash\{m\} \\
(C1 \mid \overline{out}.C2)\backslash\{m\} &\approx^c \overline{out}.Buff_2 \\
&\quad + \\
&\quad in.(\overline{m}.C1 \mid \overline{out}.C2)\backslash\{m\} \\
(\overline{m}.C1 \mid \overline{out}.C2)\backslash\{m\} &\approx^c \overline{out}.(C1 \mid \overline{out},.C2)\backslash\{m\}
\end{aligned}
$$

The proofs themselves are not difficult and are left to the reader as an exercise. In the next section of this chapter we will give a detailed account of the solution to a similar problem to reinforce the ideas presented here. The full definition for the second constant law follows from the current example, but first let us state the simple form of it where the behaviour can be captured in a single equation.

SimpCON2 If $P \approx^c E\{P/X\}$ and $Q \approx^c E\{Q/X\}$ and X is guarded and sequential in E then $P \approx^c Q$.

The more general form of the law is required to cope with mutually recursive behaviour patterns.

CON2 If

$$
\begin{aligned}
\tilde{P} &\equiv P_1, \ldots, P_n \\
\tilde{Q} &\equiv Q_1, \ldots, Q_n \\
\tilde{X} &\equiv X_1, \ldots, X_n
\end{aligned}
$$

and if $\tilde{P} = \tilde{E}\{\tilde{P}/\tilde{X}\}$ and $\tilde{Q} = \tilde{E}\{\tilde{Q}/\tilde{X}\}$ then $\tilde{P} \approx^c \tilde{Q}$, where $\tilde{X}$ is guarded and sequential in $\tilde{E}$.

Although perhaps formidable in aspect, CON2 is a reasonably straightforward law to apply once a little practice has been gained. In a similar way to the expansion law, its notational complexity arises from the need to define it for an arbitrary number of variables, all of which will require a single equation. CON2 can be interpreted in the following way; for a set of equations $X_i \approx^c E_i$ with $i \in I$, start by finding a set P_i of expressions which can systematically replace all variables X_i. The substitution will be of the form $\{P_i/X_i : i \in I\}$ and applying it to the set of equations will generate equations of the form

$$P_i \approx^c E_i\{P_i/X_i : i \in I\}$$

The task is then to prove whether or not all of these equations can be satisfied, in other words that the left hand side can be translated into the right hand side purely by the application of the equational laws given in this chapter. If we can find another substitution of the form $\{Q_i/X_i : i \in I\}$ and use this to satisfy the same set of equations then we will have established the following congruences:

$$P_i \approx^c Q_i \quad : i \in I$$

In the next section we will go through this process again in the context of a slightly larger example.

EXERCISE 10.3

Use the equational laws to prove that $E_1 \approx^c G$ using the definitions for E and G given in exercise 9.2.

Why can't you prove $D_0 \approx^c G$?

EXERCISE 10.4

Given the following definitions prove $System \approx^c Spec_1$.

$$
\begin{aligned}
System &\stackrel{\text{def}}{=} (Sender \mid Medium \mid Receiver)\backslash\{s, r, ok\} \\
Sender &\stackrel{\text{def}}{=} ok.\overline{send}.\overline{s}.Sender \\
Medium &\stackrel{\text{def}}{=} \overline{ok}.s.\overline{r}.Medium \\
Receiver &\stackrel{\text{def}}{=} r.\overline{receive}.Receiver \\
Spec_1 &\stackrel{\text{def}}{=} \tau.send.Spec_2 \\
Spec_2 &\stackrel{\text{def}}{=} receive.Spec_1 + \tau.Spec_3 \\
Spec_3 &\stackrel{\text{def}}{=} receive.\overline{send}.Spec2 + \overline{send}.receive.Spec_2
\end{aligned}
$$

10.6 A larger example

Buffers are excellent examples of systems which cannot be reduced to a single equation for the simple reason that a two place buffer currently holding one value always has the choice of reading another value. In this new state it will have to output the first value it received and be left holding a single value again. The buffer may constantly alternate between holding one value and holding two and may never be empty again. In a similar fashion the buffer may never become full. In this section we will consider two versions of a two place buffer that can store zeros or ones. We will use the equational laws to show that the two systems are observationally congruent. First of all we will give the definitions for the two versions of the buffer:

$$
\begin{aligned}
Buff_2^2 &\stackrel{\text{def}}{=} (Cell_1 \mid Cell_2)\backslash\{o, z\} \\
Cell_1 &\stackrel{\text{def}}{=} in0.\bar{z}.Cell_1 + in1.\bar{o}.Cell_1 \\
Cell_2 &\stackrel{\text{def}}{=} z.\overline{out0}.Cell_2 + o.\overline{out1}.Cell_2
\end{aligned}
$$

$$
\begin{aligned}
Sbuff &\stackrel{\text{def}}{=} in0.Sbuff_0 + in1.Sbuff_1 \\
Sbuff_0 &\stackrel{\text{def}}{=} in0.Sbuff_{00} + in1.Sbuff_{10} + \overline{out0}.Sbuff \\
Sbuff_1 &\stackrel{\text{def}}{=} in0.Sbuff_{01} + in1.Sbuff_{11} + \overline{out1}.Sbuff \\
Sbuff_{00} &\stackrel{\text{def}}{=} \overline{out0}.Sbuff_0 \\
Sbuff_{10} &\stackrel{\text{def}}{=} \overline{out0}.Sbuff_1 \\
Sbuff_{01} &\stackrel{\text{def}}{=} \overline{out1}.Sbuff_0 \\
Sbuff_{11} &\stackrel{\text{def}}{=} \overline{out1}.Sbuff_1
\end{aligned}
$$

The basic problem is to use the equational laws at our disposal to prove the following equation correct:

$$ Buff_2^2 \approx^c Sbuff $$

First of all we can use the first constant law to simplify the equations for $Sbuff$. We then have only the following three definitions:

$$
\begin{aligned}
Sbuff &\approx^c in0.Sbuff_0 + in1.Sbuff_1 \\
Sbuff_0 &\approx^c in0.\overline{out0}.Sbuff_0 + in1.\overline{out0}.Sbuff_1 + \overline{out0}.Sbuff \\
Sbuff_1 &\approx^c in0.\overline{out1}.Sbuff_0 + in1.\overline{out1}.Sbuff_1 + \overline{out1}.Sbuff
\end{aligned}
$$

To prove the equation $Buff_2^2 \approx^c Sbuff$ correct we must find a set of equations and two substitutions such that both substitutions solve the set of equations and $Buff_2^2$ and $Sbuff$ are substituted for the same agent variable in their respective substitutions. We will use the set of definitions for $Sbuff$ to give us the equations we require:

$$X \quad \approx^c \quad in0.Y + in1.Z$$
$$Y \quad \approx^c \quad in0.\overline{out0}.Y + in1.\overline{out0}.Z + \overline{out0}.X$$
$$Z \quad \approx^c \quad in0.\overline{out1}.Y + in1.\overline{out1}.Z + \overline{out1}.X$$

It should be obvious that we can solve these equations trivially with the substitution

$$Sub1 \equiv \{Sbuff/X, Sbuff_0/Y, Sbuff_1/Z\}$$

Applying the substitution yields the following congruences:

$$Sbuff \quad \approx^c \quad in0.Sbuff_0 + in1.Sbuff_1$$
$$Sbuff_0 \quad \approx^c \quad in0.\overline{out0}.Sbuff_0 + in1.\overline{out0}.Sbuff_1 + \overline{out0}.Sbuff$$
$$Sbuff_1 \quad \approx^c \quad in0.\overline{out1}.Sbuff_0 + in1.\overline{out1}.Sbuff_1 + \overline{out1}.Sbuff$$

all of which may be proved correct by a single application of the first constant law. To prove $Buff_2^2 \approx^c Sbuff$ we will need a second substitution of the form:

$$Sub2 \equiv \{Buff_2^2/X, B0/Y, B1/Z\}$$

Our task is to find suitable expressions for $B0$ and $B1$ which will enable us to solve the equations for X, Y and Z. The way to do this is to use the equational laws, and in particular the expansion law, to transform $Buff_2^2$ into a form which begins to resemble the right hand side of the equation for X. As additional practice the subexpressions to which particular laws apply will not be underlined in this section but left for the reader to identify:

	$Buff_2^2$	(CON1)
$\approx^c$	$(Cell_1 \mid Cell_2)\backslash\{o, z\}$	(CON1)
$\approx^c$	$(in0.\overline{z}.Cell1 + in1.\overline{o}.Cell_1 \mid Cell_2)\backslash\{o, z\}$	(EX)
$\approx^c$	$in0.(\overline{z}.Cell_1 \mid Cell_2)\backslash\{o, z\}$	
	$+$	
	$in1.(\overline{o}.Cell_1 \mid Cell_2)\backslash\{o, z\}$	(CON1 × 2)
$\approx^c$	$in0.(\overline{z}.Cell_1 \mid z.\overline{out0}.Cell_2 + o.\overline{out1}.Cell_2)\backslash\{o, z\}$	
	$+$	
	$in1.(\overline{o}.Cell_1 \mid z.\overline{out0}.Cell_2 + o.\overline{out1}.Cell_2)\backslash\{o, z\}$	(EX × 2)
$\approx^c$	$in0.\tau.(Cell_1 \mid \overline{out0}.Cell_2)\backslash\{o, z\}$	
	$+$	
	$in1.\tau.(Cell_1 \mid \overline{out1}.Cell_2)\backslash\{o, z\}$	(PRE1 × 2)
$\approx^c$	$in0.(Cell_1 \mid \overline{out0}.Cell_2)\backslash\{o, z\}$	
	$+$	
	$in1.(Cell_1 \mid \overline{out1}.Cell_2)\backslash\{o, z\}$	

We can now make an informed guess that the substitution for Y should be $(Cell_1 \mid \overline{out0}.Cell_2)\backslash\{o, z\}$ and the substitution for Z should be $(Cell_1 \mid$

$\overline{out1}.Cell_2)\backslash\{o, z\}$. We therefore make the following definitions:

$$
\begin{aligned}
B0 & \overset{\text{def}}{=} (Cell_1 \mid \overline{out0}.Cell_2)\backslash\{o, z\} \\
B1 & \overset{\text{def}}{=} (Cell_1 \mid \overline{out1}.Cell_2)\backslash\{o, z\}
\end{aligned}
$$

We now have values for $B0$ and $B1$, and $Sub2$ is thus complete and can be applied to the equations for X, Y and Z to gain the following set of congruences:

$$
\begin{aligned}
Buff_2^2 & \overset{\text{def}}{=} in0.B0 + in1.B1 \\
B0 & \overset{\text{def}}{=} in0.\overline{out0}.B0 + in1.\overline{out0}.B1 + \overline{out0}.Buff_2^2 \\
B1 & \overset{\text{def}}{=} in0.\overline{out1}.B0 + in1.\overline{out1}.B1 + \overline{out1}.Buff_2^2
\end{aligned}
$$

We have virtually proved the first of these equations in our search for values for $B0$ and $B1$. Two applications of the first constant law will complete the proof. It remains for us to prove the correctness of the second and third equations. We will prove the equation for $B0$ and leave the other as an exercise for the reader.

$$
\begin{array}{lll}
& B0 & \text{(CON1)} \\
\approx^c & (Cell_1 \mid \overline{out0}.Cell_2)\backslash\{o, z\} & \text{(CON1)} \\
\approx^c & ((in0.\overline{z}.Cell_1 + in1.\overline{o}.Cell_1 \mid \overline{out0}.Cell_2)\backslash\{o, z\} & \text{(EX)} \\
\approx^c & in0.(\overline{z}.Cell_1 \mid \overline{out0}.Cell_2)\backslash\{o, z\} & \\
& + & \\
& in1.(\overline{o}.Cell_1 \mid \overline{out0}.Cell_2)\backslash\{o, z\} & \\
& + & \\
& \overline{out0}.(in0.\overline{z}.Cell_1 + in1.\overline{o}.Cell_1 \mid Cell_2)\backslash\{o, z\} & \text{(CON1)} \\
\approx^c & in0.(\overline{z}.Cell_1 \mid \overline{out0}.Cell_2)\backslash\{o, z\} & \\
& + & \\
& in1.(\overline{o}.Cell_1 \mid \overline{out0}.Cell_2)\backslash\{o, z\} & \\
& + & \\
& \overline{out0}.(Cell_1 \mid Cell_2)\backslash\{o, z\} & \text{(CON1)} \\
\approx^c & in0.(\overline{z}.Cell_1 \mid \overline{out0}.Cell_2)\backslash\{o, z\} & \\
& + & \\
& in1.(\overline{o}.Cell_1 \mid \overline{out0}.Cell_2)\backslash\{o, z\} & \\
& + & \\
& \overline{out0}.Buff_2^2 & \text{(EX} \times 2)
\end{array}
$$

$\approx^c$ $in0.\overline{out0}.(\overline{z}.Cell_1 \mid Cell_2)\backslash\{o,z\}$
$+$
$in1.\overline{out1}.(\overline{o}.Cell_1 \mid Cell_2)\backslash\{o,z\}$
$+$
$\overline{out0}.Buff_2^2$ (EX $\times$ 2, CON1 $\times$ 2)
$\approx^c$ $in0.\overline{out0}.\tau.(Cell_1 \mid \overline{out0}.Cell_2)\backslash\{o,z\}$
$+$
$in1.\overline{out1}.\tau.(Cell_1 \mid \overline{out1}.Cell_2)\backslash\{o,z\}$
$+$
$\overline{out0}.Buff_2^2$ (PRE1 $\times$ 2)
$\approx^c$ $in0.\overline{out0}.(Cell_1 \mid \overline{out0}.Cell_2)\backslash\{o,z\}$
$+$
$in1.\overline{out1}.(Cell_1 \mid \overline{out1}.Cell_2)\backslash\{o,z\}$
$+$
$\overline{out0}.Buff_2^2$ (CON1 $\times$ 2)
$\approx^c$ $in0.\overline{out0}.B0 + in1.\overline{out1}.B1 + \overline{out0}.Buff_2^2$

Assuming the proof for $B1$, we are finally in a position to apply CON2 to demonstrate the following congruences:

$$Buff_2^2 \approx^c Sbuff \qquad B0 \approx^c Sbuff_0 \qquad B1 \approx^c Sbuff1$$

EXERCISE 10.5
Write out the proof for $B1$.

EXERCISE 10.6
Given the following definitions prove, using the equational laws, that $Proc1 \approx^c Proc2$.

$$
\begin{aligned}
Proc1 &\stackrel{\text{def}}{=} (A \mid B \mid C)\backslash\{m,n\} \\
A &\stackrel{\text{def}}{=} \overline{m}.a.n.A \\
B &\stackrel{\text{def}}{=} m.\overline{n}.b.B \\
C &\stackrel{\text{def}}{=} \overline{n}.c.m.C \\
Proc2 &\stackrel{\text{def}}{=} \tau.a.((p.\mathbf{0} + \overline{q}.b.Proc2) \mid (q.\mathbf{0} + \overline{p}.c.Proc2))\backslash\{p,q\}
\end{aligned}
$$

10.7 Summary and further reading

The equational system for CCS is developed in [Mil89] where proofs to justify some of the equational laws are also given. In particular, we shall see in chapter 15 that the expansion law is of particular importance when we come to consider implementing systems from CCS specifications. Another interesting practical application of the equational laws can be found in [Par87] where solutions to equations of the form $(A \mid X) \backslash R \approx^c B$ are solved for unknown X as a form of process refinement. In other words, given an abstract specification and a partial implementation, also in CCS, then the missing agent definition for X can be found. The function *sort* which was required for some of the laws is called $\mathcal{L}$ by Milner and I have renamed it only so as not to confuse it with the set $\mathcal{L}$ of observable actions. Equational laws for TCCS can be found in [MT89].

11

Properties of specifications

An important aspect of the use of formal methods in systems development is to be able to express properties that systems are required to possess and then to prove whether or not a system does indeed possess or satisfy such properties. When using formal specification languages such as Z or VDM a crucial early activity in building any specification is the identification and specification of invariants for the system we are starting to reason about. An invariant is a property or set of properties that must always be true for any state which the system may evolve to. We would like to do the same for the CCS family of languages we have been considering. In this chapter we are going to look at a logic and an associated proof system which allows us to express and verify the particular types of properties that are important in real-time systems. Modal action logics are introduced as a vehicle for expressing such properties. These logics extend propositional logic to include concepts such as the possibility and necessity of performing particular actions. The logic defined is decidable for agents which are image-finite, ie. those with finite transition graphs. We consider required properties of systems such as the traffic lights and home heating system and show that in its basic form the logic is not expressive enough for this task. It is left to the following chapter to extend the logic so that it can handle such properties.

11.1 Properties of concurrent systems

In general invariants or properties of real-time systems are behavioural in that they model, in some abstract way, patterns of behaviour which we do or do not wish a system to be capable of. In particular, we wish to reason about such things as livelock, deadlock, safety, and so on, which were introduced in chapter 1 and generally encountered throughout Part One of the book. We would also like to have some means of formally establishing whether or not a particular system possesses or satisfies a property and, if possible, we would like to automate this process. Logic is the natural language for expressing such properties and formal proof is the natural means of verifying whether or not agents satisfy properties expressed as formulae in a particular logic. However, as we are principally interested in behavioural properties which talk about the evolution of a system over time the logics used in Z and VDM are not going to express in a natural way all the things we wish to say about real-time systems.

Before considering the definition of the logic we require let us consider the nature of the behavioural properties we are interested in. In the traffic lights, for instance, we are really concerned with the safety of the control system. In other words, whether there is only ever one set of green lights on or, perhaps in a stronger sense, always at least one set of red lights on. In the case of the home heating system we want to be sure that errors detected in the furnace cause the system to shut down quickly enough. It would seem that we have to make a great leap from such properties expressed in English to their formal specification in some logic. Let us begin by considering a number of very simple agents and comparing their behaviours. We can then establish the nature of the required properties and thus make the definition of the required logic far easier to understand. Later in this chapter we will consider such systems as the home heating system.

$$D \stackrel{\text{def}}{=} a.(b.\mathbf{0} + c.\mathbf{0})$$
$$E \stackrel{\text{def}}{=} a.b.\mathbf{0} + a.c.\mathbf{0}$$
$$F \stackrel{\text{def}}{=} e.b.\mathbf{0} + e.c.\mathbf{0}$$
$$G \stackrel{\text{def}}{=} e.b.\mathbf{0} + a.(b.\mathbf{0} + d.\mathbf{0})$$

Certainly none of the agents defined above are equivalent under any of the equivalences studied in chapter 9 but they do appear to possess similar behaviours. For instance, they can all perform the action b or c as their second action regardless of their first action. This property would be true of all the four agents. It is possible therefore that all of these agents might satisfy a requirement which just said '*the choice of second actions must include b or c*'.

We might wish to be more specific. We might wish to say that if an agent can perform the action a then afterwards it must then be able to do b or c. The agent F does not satisfy this property but the other three do. We can imagine other properties which would identify various subsets of the agents specified above.

EXERCISE 11.1

1. Try to express informally in English properties that would distinguish each of the agents D, E, F and G from each other.

2. Can you identify one or two properties that would be true of all four of the agents?

11.2 Hennessy–Milner logic (HML)

The next step in this process is to express such properties formally. You might have noticed in the preceding discussion that we often used words such as *necessary* or *possible* to capture some of our ideas about evolving behaviours. We are going to extend basic propositional logic with a new operator which expresses the idea that a certain property will hold after an agent performs a particular action. First of all we will look at the syntax of the logic and its semantics. We will then return to the agents we have already looked at in this chapter and see how we can express such properties formally. The syntax of the logic is defined in the following manner and all the operators except one will be quite familiar:

$$P ::= tt \mid \neg P \mid P \wedge P \mid [a]P$$

In the syntax, P is, of course, any formula in the logic and a is any action from the set Act. The first definition says simply that a formula can be the atomic formula tt. We use tt instead of $true$ because we will make use of the latter in the definitions of the logic. The second two definitions say that a formula may be the negation of a formula or the conjunction of two formulae. The fourth definition says that it is necessary that after performing the action a the formula P must hold. It is easier to see how to use this logic if we refer directly to its semantics, and we will present this now.

We wish to know whether or not a CCS agent E satisfies a particular property A, where A is any well formed formula of HML. In other words, is it true that $E \models A$. A traditional model-theoretic semantics can be given in the following manner:

$$E \models tt$$
$$E \models \neg A \quad \text{iff} \quad E \not\models A$$
$$E \models A \wedge B \quad \text{iff} \quad E \models A \text{ and } E \models B$$
$$E \models [a]A \quad \text{iff} \quad \forall E' \in S \bullet E \xrightarrow{a} E' \text{ implies } E' \models A$$

Every process has the property tt. A process has the property $\neg A$ when it fails to have the property A. A process has the property $A \wedge B$ when it satisfies both A and B. The final definition is more subtle in that it says that E satisfies $[a]A$ if after every performance of the action a the resulting state has the property A. Notice that if E cannot perform the action a at all then the property is trivially satisfied because the implication then must evaluate to true. We will return to this again in more detail a little later.

There is another way in which we can establish satisfaction for Hennessy–Milner logic. We can assert that $E \models A$ if the agent E is an element of the set of agents which satisfy the property A. This may sound somewhat circular but is actually very practical. Our second semantics will thus map formulae in the logic to sets of agents expressed as CCS expressions. To do this we will define a semantic function which takes a formula as an argument and returns a set of agents as a result. We will say E satisfies A, $E \models A$, iff $E \in \|A\|$ where $A, B \in P$ and $\|\_\| \colon P \to \mathbf{P}\mathcal{E}$ has the following definition:

$$
\begin{aligned}
\|tt\| &= S \\
\|\neg A\| &= S \setminus \|A\| \\
\|A \wedge B\| &= \|A\| \cap \|B\| \\
\|[a]A\| &= \{E \in S \mid \forall E' \in S \bullet E \xrightarrow{a} E' \text{ implies } E' \in \|A\|\}
\end{aligned}
$$

This alternative semantic interpretation maps a formula in the logic to a set of agents all of which satisfy the property expressed by the formula. The formula tt holds for all agents and makes no distinctions between agents and is thus just the set S of all agents. The formula $\neg A$ should give us the set of all agents which do not satisfy the property A and thus $\|\neg A\|$ denotes the set S less all the agents that do satisfy A. The formula $A \wedge B$ should identify the set of agents which satisfy both the property A and the property B. We must thus find the set denoted by $\|A\|$ and the set denoted by $\|B\|$ and take their intersection.

The final formula, $[a]A$, requires a little more thought. A first tentative interpretation could be expressed as 'it is necessary that whenever an agent performs the action a then A will be true for all resulting states'. A more subtle and accurate interpretation of $\|[a]A\|$ would be that it denotes the set of those agents which cannot fail to satisfy the property A after any performance of the action a. Consider an agent E which can perform at least one action a. There are two possibilities. First, for all E' such that $E \xrightarrow{a} E'$ and $E' \models A$ then E satisfies $[a]A$. On the other hand, if there is at least one E' which does not satisfy A then $E \not\models [a]A$. We must also consider an agent F which cannot perform the action a at all. In this case F cannot fail to satisfy $[a]A$ and we will still say $F \models [a]A$. The semantic interpretation of the formula makes this clear. Thus the set denoted by $\|[a]A\|$ contains not only all agents that definitely satisfy the property $[a]A$ but also all those agents that cannot perform the action a at all and this is the reason for the subtlety with which we approached our intuitive interpretation of the operator.

This set-theoretic semantics for HML is of value because we can use it to *calculate* whether or not $E \models A$. Before we put this into practice there are some useful derived operators which we can define:

$$ff \stackrel{\text{def}}{=} \neg tt$$
$$\langle a \rangle A \stackrel{\text{def}}{=} \neg [a] \neg A$$

The first of these just says that ff is the opposite of tt, which is confirmed by the semantic interpretation of ff for

$$\|\neg tt\| = S \setminus \|tt\| = S \setminus S = \{\}$$

The second derived operator states the possibility that after performing the action a then A will be true. The semantic interpretation of this operator gives us the equivalence

$$\|\langle a \rangle A\| = \{E \in S \mid \exists E' \bullet E \stackrel{a}{\to} E' \wedge E' \in \|A\|\}$$

which says first of all that if an agent E cannot perform the action a then it does not satisfy the property. However, if E is capable of at least one action a and at least one of the resulting states, E', satisfies A then $E \models \langle a \rangle A$. In other words, if there is at least one E' such that $E \stackrel{a}{\to} E'$ and $E' \models A$ then $E \models \langle a \rangle A$. This obviously means that there might be other states to which E can evolve by performing a which do not satisfy the property A. If no state to which E can evolve by performing the action a satisfies A then E does not satisfy the property, $E \not\models A$.

We will now see how to use this logic in the context of the simple agents D, E, F, G introduced earlier in this section. We will use the set-theoretic semantics of the logic and calculate the sets of agents which satisfy certain properties. We can consider the system as comprising the four transition graphs for the four agents. Therefore the set S of all states of our system is

$$\{D, E, F, G, b.\mathbf{0} + c.\mathbf{0}, b.\mathbf{0}, c.\mathbf{0}, b.\mathbf{0} + d.\mathbf{0}, \mathbf{0}\}$$

and the set of all possible actions is

$$\{a, b, c, d, e\}$$

With these in mind we can consider some simple properties. The simplest formulae are the two atomic formulae tt and ff:

$$\|tt\| = S$$
$$\|ff\| = \{\}$$

Every agent has the property tt and no agent has the property ff. From these two simple formulae we can construct more complex ones using the syntax defined above. The following are examples of well-formed formulae:

$$\langle a \rangle tt, \quad \langle a \rangle ff, \quad [a]tt, \quad [a]ff$$

We have to be careful as to the usefulness of some of these formulae. The formula $\langle a \rangle tt$ has the denotation

$$\{E \in S \mid \exists E' \in S \bullet E \overset{a}{\to} E' \wedge E' \in S\}$$

which evaluates to the set $\{D, E, G\}$ because these are the only agents to satisfy the condition $E \overset{a}{\to} E'$ and every agent is in the set S. In contrast the property $\langle a \rangle ff$ denotes the set

$$\{E \in S \mid \exists E' \in S \bullet E \overset{a}{\to} E' \wedge E' \in \{\}\}$$

and we conclude that if an agent can perform the action a its resulting state must be in the set $\{\}$, which it cannot be. Conversely, if an agent cannot perform the action a then the condition $E \overset{a}{\to} E'$ fails and the agent also does not have that property. Therefore, no agent has the property $\langle a \rangle ff$. The two properties involving necessity have similar surprises in store. $[a]tt$ is denoted by the following set:

$$\{E \in S \mid \forall E' \in S \bullet E \overset{a}{\to} E' \text{ implies } E' \in S\}$$

The surprise here is that every agent has this property in that every agent that can perform an a reaches a state which must be in the set S. Every agent that cannot do an a is also in the set because if $E \overset{a}{\to} E'$ is false then the implication evaluates to true regardless of whether $E' \in S$. The final property, $[a]ff$, denotes the set of all agents which cannot perform the action for similar reasons to those in the previous argument. We can thus establish the sets denoted by these four agents:

$$
\begin{aligned}
\|\langle a \rangle tt\| &= \{D, E, G\} \\
\|\langle a \rangle ff\| &= \{\} \\
\|[a]tt\| &= S \\
\|[a]ff\| &= \{F, b.\mathbf{0} + c.\mathbf{0}, b.\mathbf{0}, c.\mathbf{0}, b.\mathbf{0} + d.\mathbf{0}, \mathbf{0}\}
\end{aligned}
$$

From this we can easily conclude that some of these very simple formulae contribute nothing extra to the properties we can express in the logic.

$$
\begin{aligned}
\|\langle a \rangle ff\| &= \{\} &= \|ff\| \\
\|[a]tt\| &= S &= \|tt\|
\end{aligned}
$$

and are thus equivalent to ff and tt respectively. However $\|\langle a \rangle tt\|$ returns the set of those agents that can perform the action a and $[a]ff$ returns the set of all agents which cannot perform the action a. We can now assert that the agents D, E, G satisfy the property that they can perform the action a:

$$D \models \langle a \rangle tt, \quad E \models \langle a \rangle tt, \quad G \models \langle a \rangle tt$$

The agent F does not satisfy this property and we write

$$F \not\models \langle a \rangle tt, \quad F \models [a]ff$$

The property $\langle e \rangle tt \wedge [a]ff$ is only satisfied by F and no other agent in S. The property $[a](\langle b \rangle tt \wedge \langle c \rangle tt)$ is true of D because it has the choice of b and

c as next actions after performing the action a. The agent F also satisfies this property because it cannot perform the action a and does not fail to satisfy the property. The agents E and G can both perform the action a but neither has the choice between both b and c afterwards and thus do not satisfy the property.

We can extend this property slightly to further distinguish D from F. The formula $\langle a \rangle tt \wedge [a](\langle b \rangle tt \wedge \langle c \rangle tt)$ expresses the property that it must be possible to perform the action a and that it is necessary that after having done so then there must be a choice between both b and c. This formula is satisfied by D but not F and is a general technique for distinguishing between agents that definitely satisfy a *necessary* property and those that do so by default.

EXERCISE 11.2

Reconsider exercise 10.1 and formally specify four properties which will distinguish D, E, F and G from each other. Try to think of new properties in addition to those which have already been formalised above in this section.

EXERCISE 11.3

$$Start \stackrel{\text{def}}{=} forward.Position1 + stop.0$$
$$Position1 \stackrel{\text{def}}{=} forward.back.back.Start + right.left.back.Start$$

Express the following properties in HML:

1. After the action *forward* another *forward* is immediately possible.
2. After the action *forward* followed by the action *right*, both the action *left* is possible and the action *back* impossible.
3. *forward* is the only possible first action.
4. After any two actions *forward* is not possible.

11.3 Useful extensions to HML

So far we have used HML to express properties concerned with allowable patterns in which actions may occur. There are occasions when HML formulae can become quite clumsy if sets of actions or choices from a set of actions have to be considered. In this section we will look at these issues and see how we can adapt HML without too much trouble to cope with

them. We will also return to such systems as the traffic lights which moti-
vated this chapter in the first place and look at the kinds of property they
require and think about how to specify them.

One very useful extension to, in fact a generalisation of, HML is to allow modalities to range over sets of actions instead of a single action. We
replace the formula $[a]A$ with the formula $[K]A$ where $K \subseteq T$ for the set
T of possible actions in the system. Satisfaction is defined in the following
manner:

$$E \models [K]A \text{ iff } \forall E' \in S \bullet \forall a \in K \bullet E \xrightarrow{a} E' \text{ implies } E' \models A$$

where the only change to the meaning of such a formula is that we have to
check that the property holds for all $a \in K$ and not just the single action
a as was previously the case. The set-theoretic view is changed in a similar
manner. Let us call this new logic HML$^+$. As is often the case, this simple
extension proves to be of great benefit to us when specifying properties
of systems. Before discussing the benefits gained we will introduce three
simple, but useful, abbreviations:

$$[a_1, \ldots, a_n] \equiv [\{a_1, \ldots, a_n\}]$$
$$[-K] \equiv [T - K]$$
$$[-] \equiv [T]$$

Let us return to the agents D, E, F, G which we investigated earlier in
this chapter and consider an apparently simple property which proves very
clumsy in HML. Suppose we wished to specify a property that says we
are not worried what the first action is as long as it is an a or an e and
that after either of these there is a choice between b or c but no other
action. Properties which restrict allowable actions are difficult in HML.
Remember that when we specify the property $\langle a \rangle A$ we are simply saying
that the action a must be possible, we are not saying it is the only action
possible. To say that we would then have to add in formulae of the form

$$[b]ff \wedge [c]ff \wedge \ldots$$

for all actions we do not want from the set T. A further complication
for HML is that if we are offering a choice of actions then we have to
specify them individually. In the case we are now looking at we would have
to separate properties for both a and e and take their disjunction. The
resulting specification would be along the following lines:

$$\langle a \rangle tt \wedge \langle e \rangle tt \wedge$$
$$((([a](\langle b \rangle tt \vee \langle c \rangle tt \wedge [d]ff \wedge \ldots)$$
$$([e](\langle b \rangle tt \vee \langle c \rangle tt \wedge [d]ff \wedge \ldots))$$

Using HML$^+$ both of these problems disappear. By making good use of
the set modalities and abbreviations we can specify the whole property,

thus:
$$\langle a, e \rangle tt \wedge [a, e][-b, c] ff$$

The interpretation of this is that either a or e or both are possible and that performing either will mean that all actions except b and c are impossible. There is no need to point out the advantages of HML^+ in this instance despite the fact that it does not add to the expressive power of HML.

It is also possible to express properties which refer explicitly to time rather than just patterns of behaviour. We can extend HML^+ with the formulae of the form $\{t\}.A$ where t ranges over some time-domain $\mathcal{T}$. The implication of this is that there will be a logic for each time domain. The intended meaning of this formula is that it is possible for E to satisfy the property A at some point within the next t units of time. We can extend the satisfaction relation in the following way:

$$E \models \{t\}A \text{ iff } E \models A \vee$$
$$(\exists E' \in S, t' \in \mathcal{T} \bullet E \overset{t'}{\leadsto} E' \wedge t' \leq t \wedge E' \models A)$$

As usual there is a dual to this operator, which in this case represents the property that A must be satisfied at every point for the next t units of time:

$$\lfloor t \rfloor A \overset{\text{def}}{=} \neg\{t\}\neg A$$

Expressive as it is, HML^+ cannot express all properties that one might wish to verify a CCS specification against. If we consider the mutual exclusion example Mx from chapter 2 we can express the property that after a τ-action it is not possible that both $c1$ and $c2$ are available:

$$[\tau]\neg(\langle c1 \rangle tt \wedge \langle c2 \rangle tt)$$

But this obviously deals only with the first two actions of the system. If we wish to check for all future behaviours we would need to endlessly nest this property inside itself. These types of properties are very important and in order to express them we will have to consider some substantial extensions to HML.

EXERCISE 11.4
  User HML^+ to answer questions 3 and 4 from exercise 11.3

EXERCISE 11.5
  Refer back to exercise 2.6 and express the following properties:

1. Define in HML^+ the property that expresses the manner in which Twb^2 deadlocks.

2. Express a property that captures the idea that if communication in Twb^2 is always unidirectional then no deadlock occurs.

11.4 Summary and further reading

We have defined a modal logic which can express abstract behavioural properties of systems [Mil89]. We have also shown that there is a decidable proof system which will check whether or not a particular agent satisfies a given property or not [Sti91]. Stirling bases his definitions on labelled transition systems, which were alluded to at the end of chapter three but not studied in this book. The problem of properties involving values and the extension of HML to include set modalities is also discussed in that reference. The model operator for time is defined in [Tof89]. At this stage we should return to our initial intentions from the beginning of this chapter and begin to reconsider systems such as the traffic lights and the home heating system and the kinds of properties required for them. This will turn out to be no simple matter as they invariably involve properties which are *infinite* in the sense identified above for Mx. We will continue our investigations of these and related matters in the next chapter and for this reason we will also defer references to relevant case studies.

12

Safety and CCS

In the previous chapter we studied a logic which allowed us to express required properties of systems which we were specifying. We were then able to prove whether or not an agent satisfied a particular property. We also saw that the logic could be extended to include properties on values and time. Just as important was the realisation that the logic could be easily generalised to include modalities on sets of atomic actions rather than just single actions. At the end of the last chapter we posed the question: How useful is HML in the development of real-time specifications? Obviously this is something of an open-ended question but we can make some attempt to answer it by considering what kinds of properties we might wish to satisfy and, indeed, what kinds of properties we might have to satisfy in order to meet the requirements of standards and/or certification authorities. So before we take another look at HML let us first take a more general view of what we are trying to do and see what is required of us.

12.1 Classifying properties

In the systems analysis phase of systems development a variety of desirable or necessary properties may be produced. These constitute what are often called the 'non-functional requirements' of the system. Such properties are often concerned with such issues as efficiency, security, data integrity, safety, and so on. In building specifications in model-based languages such as Z and VDM we would attempt to express such properties as system invariants and thus constrain the possible reachable states of the system. However, some properties such as efficiency and security may be difficult to express as data invariants because they are dependent on patterns of behaviour or speed of execution which cannot be measured against sets of variable bindings. Of course this is one of the reasons for wishing to use a language such as CCS in the first place. Some things are best expressed as behaviours rather than as data spaces. When building specifications in CCS we are considering concurrent and/or real-time systems which are often control systems. The behaviour patterns of such systems have to be correct in order to prevent loss of life, damage to the environment, etc. We would obviously like to know what contribution CCS and HML could make to the development of such systems. In general, it is in the area of safety-critical systems that formal methods are going to find their greatest range of applications.

12.2 Adding temporal properties to HML^{+}

The logic we have already studied allows us to express important properties of behavioural systems. We can formulate properties to do with the necessity and possibility of named actions occurring. We can also express properties to do with the ordering of such actions. At the end of the last chapter we pointed out an important limitation on the usefuless of HML in that we are constrained to expressing properties on finite sequences of actions. Often, however, we will be dealing with agents with possibly infinite behaviours and wish to know if a property is *always* true or, alternatively, *sometime* true in the future.

We can illustrate these kinds of ideas by redefining the simple agents D, E, F and G which acted as our basic examples in the last chapter:

$$D^r \;\stackrel{\text{def}}{=}\; a.(b.D^r + c.D^r)$$
$$E^r \;\stackrel{\text{def}}{=}\; a.b.E^r + a.c.E^r$$
$$F^r \;\stackrel{\text{def}}{=}\; e.b.F^r + e.c.F^r$$
$$G^r \;\stackrel{\text{def}}{=}\; e.b.G^r + a.(b.G^r + d.G^r)$$

The types of property we would like to prove are often of the form

$$Always \; \langle a \rangle true$$

which we will take to mean it is always possible to perform the action a. Another way of saying this is that a is possible now and will also be possible in every future state of the system. In the context of our simple example agents it should be obvious that none of the four possesses the property that it can always perform the action a. However, we will expect the property

$$Sometime \; \langle a \rangle true$$

to hold for D^r, E^r and G^r. Our intended meaning for this expression will be that the action a will be possible in some future state of the system. The property that the action b will always be possible sometime in the future has the following specification:

$$Always \; Sometime \langle b \rangle$$

This property is possessed by all agents in our example set.

We must be careful about the way we wish these new temporal operators and our original modal formulae to interact. Consider the temporal property

$$Always \ \langle a \rangle true \land [a](\langle b \rangle true \land \langle c \rangle true)$$

The modal subformula is quite familiar to us but the effect of applying the *Always* temporal operator to it gives rise to a number of possibilities. We might wish the interpretation to be that in every state the action a is possible followed by the possibility of both b and c, and that having performed an a all this would be true again, and again, etc. However, this would also mean that in the second and subsequent states a and b and c would all be possible – which is perhaps not quite what we intended. This would in fact be equivalent to the formula

$$\langle a \rangle true \land [a] \ Always \ (\langle a \rangle true \land \langle b \rangle true \land \langle c \rangle true)$$

which looks rather different. The confusion arises from the fact that our modal properties do indeed express finite temporal properties themselves and the above meaning just given for the temporal operators seems to override this.

If what we mean to say is that whenever the action a is performed then there will be a choice of both b and c in the next state, then the property we require is

$$Always \ [a]\langle b,c \rangle tt$$

Another interpretation is that it is always true that an a can be performed now and after the a there must then be a choice between both b and c but not a. Furthermore, after performing either b or c then the modal property must once again become true. Another way of saying this is to imagine the states numbered, starting with 1 for the initial state. In this case all odd-numbered states will be expected to possess the stated property. In this way we get a sensible interaction between the temporal operators and the finite modal properties which are expressed by the modal formulae:

$$Always \ ((\langle a \rangle tt \land [-]\langle b,c \rangle tt) \lor (\langle b,c \rangle tt \land [-]\langle a \rangle tt))$$

The question of how to formalise all this should by now be uppermost in our thoughts. It all looks very nice, but how can we be precise about the meaning of it all?

EXERCISE 12.1

Use our new temporal operators to specify properties which distinguish D^r, E^r, F^r and G^r from one another.

12.3 A temporal logic for CCS

Obviously we wish to extend the syntax of HML$^+$ with temporal operators to represent such constructions as *Always* and *Sometime*. We will call this extended logic Temporal HML$^+$ (THML$^+$) and then show how the satisfaction relation from the previous chapter can be extended to include these new operators. First, we give a note on the nature of time, or rather temporal evolution, necessary in order to model such properties as safety and liveness. Time, in the context of temporal logic, can be discrete or continuous, meaning essentially that we work with the natural numbers or the reals as a time domain; our logic assumes the former. Time in this context can also be either linear or branching. In the former case system states can be totally ordered, giving each state a unique successor and predecessor. Branching time makes no such assumption but allows for multiple successor states. Obviously this complicates what we mean by concepts such as *Always A*, by which we might mean the property A is true for all future states or that there is an infinite sequence of states for which A is always true. Because we are defining a temporal logic for CCS we will have to use branching time because for states of a given system there may not be a unique next state. However, we will start by defining a logic based on linear time first for two reasons. First, such logics are simpler than branching time logics and thus easier to learn and use; we can use the ideas to build up to the required logic. Secondly, by working with a linear time logic we can identify its particular deficiencies and thus demonstrate the practical need for the branching time version. With these ideas in mind we start to define THML$^+$:

$$P::=\ \ tt \mid \neg P \mid P \wedge P \mid [K]P \mid \{t\}P \mid \mathbf{G}P \mid P \,\mathcal{U}P$$

Traditionally the *Always* operator is represented in temporal logic by $\square$ or $\mathbf{G}$, and so to avoid confusion with necessity we use $\mathbf{G}$. The *Sometime* operator is usually given the symbol $\Diamond$ or $\mathbf{F}$, and we have used the latter for the same reason. In fact $\mathbf{F}$ is the dual of $\mathbf{G}$ in the usual way:

$$\mathbf{F} \stackrel{\text{def}}{=} \neg\mathbf{G}\neg$$

The formula $A \,\mathcal{U}B$ represents the general property that A must be true in all states until some state in which B is true is reached. It is usual to extend the expressive power of temporal logics with this operator.

The satisfaction relation given for HML$^+$ can be extended to yield one for THML$^+$, but first we need some extra notation. For a given transition system with states S and actions T we define the set of execution paths or traces to be T^*, the set of all strings over T. The empty trace is represented by $\langle\rangle$ and concatenation of traces by st for all s and t in T^*. We define a prefix ordering on strings in the following manner:

$$\forall s, s' \in T^* \bullet s \leq s' \; iff \; \exists s'' \in T^* \bullet ss'' = s'$$

With this new notation we can extend the satisfaction relation as required:

$$E \ \models \ \mathbf{G}A \ \ iff \ \ \forall s \in T^*, \ E' \in S \bullet E \xrightarrow{s} E' \ implies \ E' \models A$$
$$E \ \models \ A \ \mathcal{U}B \ \ iff \ \ \exists s \in T^*, \ E' \in S \bullet (E \xrightarrow{s} E' \wedge E' \models B)$$
$$\wedge \ \ \forall s' \in T^*, E'' \in S \bullet (s' \leq s \wedge E \xrightarrow{s'} E'' \ implies \ E'' \models A$$

A set-theoretic semantics may also be given in the manner of the previous chapter. Although $\mathbf{F}$ is the dual of $\mathbf{G}$ its satisfaction relation may be separately defined in the following way:

$$E \models \ \mathbf{F}A \ \ iff \ \exists s \in T^*, \ E' \in S \bullet E \xrightarrow{s} E' \wedge E' \models A$$

Another useful operator, essential in the definition of temporal logics, is the next-time operator, $\bigcirc A$, which requires that the property A becomes true in the next state. We can define this as a derived operator of HML$^+$:

$$\bigcirc A \overset{\mathrm{def}}{=} \langle - \rangle tt \wedge [-]A$$

There must be at least one next state and whatever action is performed the state reached must satisfy the property A. A weaker definition would have required that $\bigcirc A$ be true in at least one next state but not necessarily all.

We can return now to our plan to investigate safety properties of some of our example systems. For example, the purpose of the traffic lights is to try and prevent traffic flows in two directions at once. Of course, the lights only provide signals which attempt to control the behaviour of drivers but cannot physically prevent a vehicle jumping a red light. Our prime concern is making sure that the lights themselves function as expected. With this in mind we can recommence the formulation of such properties, which were identified on page 188 of the previous chapter. We have already identified the requirement that there should only ever be one set of green lights on. The difference between those two properties is that the former expresses the fact that a hazardous condition should never occur while the latter makes a positive statement about the nature of the system's safe behaviour. The former might well arise from some form of safety analysis performed on the CCS model. For this reason safety properties are often of the form

$$\mathbf{G} \ \neg A$$

that is, it is always true that not A. Let us tackle this property first.

First of all we need to know when a green light is on. Our temporal logic considers states in terms of their potential for action and does not record the current state of a light in terms of a boolean value, for instance. Basically the only way we can tell if a light is on is if we are able to turn it off at some time in the future without, in the meantime, turning it on. A slight complication is that we might wish to allow τ-actions in this interval. The major lights in their green state is a case in point because the turning off of their green light is guarded by a τ-action. With this in mind we can express the fact that the major green lights are on in the following manner:

$$[-\tau]ff\,\mathcal{U}\langle maGoff\rangle tt$$

The minor green lights being on will be expressed in a similar fashion. We can now specify the hazard we are wishing to prevent:

$$\neg(([-\tau]ff\,\mathcal{U}\langle maGoff\rangle tt)\wedge([-\tau]ff\,\mathcal{U}\langle maGoff\rangle tt))$$

The final property should state that it is always true that the hazard is not a property of the specification in question:

$$\mathbf{G}\neg(([-\tau]ff\,\mathcal{U}\langle maGoff\rangle tt)\wedge([-\tau]ff\,\mathcal{U}\langle maGoff\rangle tt))$$

We now have a classic safety property in the form identified above. Using $\Rightarrow$, the observable transition version of THML$^+$, we get an even simpler specification:

$$\mathbf{G}\neg(\langle\langle maGoff\rangle\rangle tt\wedge\langle\langle maGoff\rangle\rangle tt)$$

Although having two sets of green lights on is an obvious hazard, and one that would almost certainly have been identified through a safety review, this might become very cumbersome if we had an n-way junction. The problem now would be that a number of hazards could give rise to an accident caused by more than one flow of traffic through the junction at any one time. In this case each two green lights being on would be a different hazard requiring a new safety property to be expressed. If we were to say in the simple case that there must always be at least one red light on then we would only need a single property. It is tempting to specify this in a similar manner to the one above:

$$\mathbf{G}\langle\langle maRoff, maRoff\rangle\rangle tt$$

However, there is a complication in that the occurrence of the next $maRoff$, for instance, might not be guarded by a, possibly empty, sequence of τ-actions but a whole set of actions from the minor lights and none from the major lights. So we will have to work a little harder to get this property. We have to separate out the actions we wish to allow when a major red light is on from those we wish to allow when a minor red light is on. In the former case only τ-actions and actions from the minor road are allowed and in the latter case only τ-actions and major road actions. Using the set modalities offered by THML$^+$ this is not a great problem:

$$Mi \stackrel{\text{def}}{=} actions(Major)\setminus\{s, ma, mi, \ldots\}\cup\{\tau\}$$
$$Ma \stackrel{\text{def}}{=} actions(Minor)\setminus\{ma, min, \ldots\}\cup\{\tau\}$$

The property that a major red light is now on thus becomes

$$MaR \stackrel{\text{def}}{=} [Ma]ff\,\mathcal{U}(\langle maRoff\rangle tt\wedge\langle maAoff\rangle tt)$$

A similar property, MiR, to represent the minor red being on is also specified; and we can then specify the general property that there must always be one red light on:

$$\mathbf{G}(MaR \vee MiR)$$

We can now turn to the fairness property we identified that if the sensor detects a vehicle then it will eventually get a green light. Basically, we need to say that it is always true that after the action *press* it is necessary that the system will reach a state where $miGoff$ is the next possible action. In the light of this we might suggest the following specification of the property:

$$\mathbf{G}[press](\mathbf{F}\langle miGoff\rangle tt))$$

This is not a strong enough property, however, because it only says that if the sensor is pressed then it will be possible for the minor green lights to be turned on. It certainly does not say that a green light will be guaranteed. Another possibility is to use the until operator in the following way:

$$\mathbf{G}[press](\langle-\rangle tt \ \mathcal{U}\langle miGoff\rangle tt))$$

This property suffers from the same problem in that our version of until is *weak* in the same sense as $\mathbf{F}$; it talks about a possible future, not all futures. In fact the logic we have specified is not expressive enough to give us this property. In the next section we will extend THML$^+$ so that we can complete our task.

EXERCISE 12.2
Formally express the properties you developed for exercise 12.1.

12.4 A branching time logic for CCS

We have already encountered the cause of our problem when trying to define the next-time operator, $\bigcirc$, for which there were two possible versions, depending on whether the property A was required to be true in all next states or only at least one. The reason is that we require a branching time temporal logic and need two versions of all the operators depending on whether or not we wish them to be true in all futures or just one or more. For this reason it is usual to introduce trace or path quantifiers A and E, for *all traces* and *there exists* a trace respectively. As usual these two operators are the duals of each other. In fact, our problem is slightly more complicated than this because we are not restricted to infinite traces but have to allow for finite, or bounded, traces caused by deadlocks, and this in turn will cause us a little extra complication.

The syntax of our amended temporal logic, BTHML$^+$, is as follows:

$$P::= \quad tt \mid \neg P \mid P \wedge P \mid [K]P \mid \{t\}P \mid \mathbf{G}P \mid P\,\mathcal{U}P \mid \mathbf{A}P$$

The new formulae we are particularly interested in are

$$\mathbf{AG}P \quad \text{and} \quad \mathbf{EG}P$$

which constitute the property P always being true in all futures and always being true in at least one future respectively. The definition of $\mathbf{AG}P$ is the same as for $\mathbf{G}P$ in THML$^+$ but the definition of $\mathbf{EG}P$ requires a little more subtlety because we have to make explicit the way we handle finite traces. So, before giving the new definitions we have to define what we mean by a trace which constitutes a complete computation. We call traces *maximal* if they are either infinite, or finite and lead to a deadlock state. Assuming $T^F \subset T^*$ to be the set of all finite traces we make the following definitions:

$$
\begin{aligned}
T^\omega &= T^* \setminus T^F \\
T^\bullet &= \{s \in T^F \mid \exists E \in S \bullet \forall s' \in T \bullet \xrightarrow{s} E \wedge \neg E \xrightarrow{s'} \} \\
T^{max} &= T^\omega \cup T^\bullet
\end{aligned}
$$

where we take $\xrightarrow{s} E$ and $E \xrightarrow{s}$ to mean that we do not need to know respectively what the source and target states for E are. With this in mind, we can now redefine the satisfaction relation to cope with trace quantifiers:

$$
\begin{aligned}
E &\models \mathbf{AG}P \;\; iff \;\; \forall s \in T^*, \, E' \in S \bullet E \xrightarrow{s} E' \text{ implies } E' \models P \\
E &\models \mathbf{EG}P \;\; iff \;\; \exists s \in T^{max}, \forall s' \in T^*, \, E' \in S \bullet \\
&\quad (E \xrightarrow{s'} E' \wedge s' \le s) \text{ implies } E' \models P
\end{aligned}
$$

The first property means that property P is true in all states for all traces of E, while the second property states there is at least one maximal trace which has P true in all states it passes through. Notice that the definition for $\mathbf{AG}P$ is exactly the definition for the always operator, $\mathbf{G}P$, of THML$^+$. Notice also that the definition for $\mathbf{EG}P$ makes explicit the possibility that a finite but maximal trace might establish satisfaction.

Let us look at some simple agents and the way their behaviours relate to these new temporal operators. We also define a very simple property which says that a and b cannot both be possible at the same time:

$$
\begin{aligned}
Q_1 &\stackrel{\text{def}}{=} a.b.(b.a.\mathbf{0} + c.a.\mathbf{0} + b.Q_1) \\
Q_2 &\stackrel{\text{def}}{=} a.b.(c.(a.\mathbf{0} + b.\mathbf{0}) + c.Q_2 \\
\phi &\stackrel{\text{def}}{=} \neg(\langle a \rangle tt \wedge \langle b \rangle tt)
\end{aligned}
$$

$$Q_1 \models \mathbf{EG}\phi$$
$$Q_2 \models \mathbf{EG}\phi$$
$$Q_1 \models \mathbf{AG}\phi$$
$$Q_2 \not\models \mathbf{AG}\phi$$

Notice that in the final case Q_2 does not satisfy the property $\mathbf{AG}\phi$ because there is a trace abc which leads it to the state $a.0 + b.0$ which of course does not satisfy ϕ. This is so even though there is an identical trace which does satisfy ϕ. In fact there are an infinite number of traces which cause Q_2 to fail to satisfy the property in question.

We can define the duals of these operators in the usual way:

$$\mathbf{AF}P = \neg\mathbf{E}\neg\mathbf{G}P$$
$$\mathbf{EF}P = \neg\mathbf{A}\neg\mathbf{G}P$$

Notice that the weaker version of *Sometime*, $\mathbf{F}P$ of THML$^+$, is the dual of the stronger version of *Always*. Likewise, the stronger version of *Sometime* is the dual of the weaker version of *Always*. The formula $\mathbf{AF}P$ states that P must become true in all traces, while its weaker partner $\mathbf{EF}P$ states that there is a trace in which P becomes true. With these operators we are now in a position to solve our problem with the liveness property for the traffic lights. The formula $\mathbf{AF}P$ can be read as *Eventually* and is the one we need to express our liveness property, which now becomes

$$\mathbf{AG}[press](\mathbf{AF}\langle miGoff\rangle tt))$$

An informal translation would be: it is always true that if the sensor is pressed then eventually there must be a green light on the minor road.

EXERCISE 12.3

What version of $\mathcal{U}$ have we actually defined for THML$^+$ in section 12.3, i.e. $\mathbf{A}P\mathcal{U}P$ or $\mathbf{E}P\mathcal{U}P$? Complete the satisfaction relation by defining the other versions of $\mathcal{U}$.

EXERCISE 12.4

Express the following temporal properties for the agent *Start* introduced in exercise 11.3 in the previous chapter:

1. Moving *back* will be possible sometime in the future.

2. It will always be possible to go *forward* sometime in the future.

3. It will always be possible not to perform both *left* and *right*.

4. In all traces it will be possible to go *right*.

5. It is always true that after *left*, *left* is not possible again before a *right* has occurred, and similarly for *right*.

6. There is a trace in which *right*, *left* and *back* are never possible.

EXERCISE 12.5

Which of the properties expressed in answer to the previous exercise are actually satisfied by *Start*?

EXERCISE 12.6

Suggest and formally express some safety properties for the home heating system of chapter 8 and decide whether the basic CCS version given in that chapter satisfies your properties. You really need tool support in the form of the Edinburgh Concurrency Workbench to verify these properties satisfactorily.

12.5 Summary and further reading

The subject of determining whether or not agents satisfy properties, such as safety, liveness, and so on, is an important one for real-time systems specification. We have done no more than introduce the reader to the subject and hope he/she will pursue it through the further reading suggestions in this section. The extensions of HML with temporal operators used in this chapter were developed by the author for teaching purposes, and are based on well established work. The literature on temporal logic in general is comprehensive and a good starting point is [Bar86]. By comparison the literature on the application of temporal logics to process algebra is restricted to papers on the modal μ-calculus which is the actual temporal logic for CCS. A lucid and detailed introduction to the modal μ-calculus is given by Colin Sterling [Sti91] which is a must for any further study of the subject. Another interesting case study in the application of temporal logics to CCS specifications is [Wal89] in which classic mutual exclusion algorithms are analysed. Hazard and operability studies for CCS and requirements models in general are discussed in [FH94].

III

Tools, Methods, and Lifecycles

13

Tool support

Putting formal methods to real practical use means being able to use them in the development of large-scale systems. We established quite early in this book that verifying the behaviour of all but fairly simple CCS specifications is not a practical proposition either mentally or on paper. As you gain experience with CCS and its related formalisms your intuitions become stronger and you can mentally check through larger specifications. Pen and paper exercises, such as the Verification Game, are helpful here but soon become unmanageable. Transition graphs, bisimulations and proofs suffer the same limitations when conducted on a similar basis. The obvious solution is to provide some sort of tool support to allow the specification and analysis of realistically large systems.

A variety of tools to support the development of formal specifications of concurrent and real-time systems are now available or in the process of development. In this chapter we will briefly consider what we expect to gain from tool support for a language such as CCS. By way of illustration we will look at some of the features of the Concurrency Workbench (CWB), a prototype tool developed at Edinburgh University, which supports the development of CCS specifications. In ths manner we can identify some of the actual benefits and problems of tool support. This chapter should not, however, be seen as a user guide for CWB. For this type of information the user should consult the Summary and Further Reading section at the end of this chapter.

13.1 Expectations

The main problem encountered in verifying CCS specifications is concerned with the size of the state space. If this is relatively small, a few tens of states, then some form of mental or paper-based verification can be undertaken. If the specification is even remotely large, 100 or so states or more, then some form of tool support becomes essential if any verification activities are to be at all successful. Many people think that verification for formal methods means proof and that the reason for using formal methods is because we can prove things about specifications expressed in them. This in turn leads to the idea that tools to support formal methods will thus be proof assistants or automated theorem provers. Proof, however, is not as important as is often supposed and many of the benefits to be gained from the use of formal methods arise from the clarity of insights gained through the modelling of requirements in such an unambiguous way. Just as it is not true to say that the ability to prove is the sole motivation behind formal methods so it is not true to say that simply building a formal specification to meet the stated requirements is enough. Useful tool support for a language such as CCS should both facilitate the building of specifications and make their verification more effective. Proof support may or may not be part of the latter.

Formal methods are very often weak in helping users to build specifications. Many incorporate mechanisms for structuring and decomposing problems etc. whilst not providing support for moving from systems analysis to specification and design. In other words, they offer support for the technical aspects of the task without supporting its creative aspects. This is very much the subject of the next chapter which looks at the integration of structured and formal methods. We will now move on to the verification issue.

Having arrived at a formal specification the first things we wish to do are to check that it is syntactically correct and then to go on to use the formal semantics of the methods to check whether or not what we have specified correlates with our understanding of the system requirements. We would then go on to test our specification more rigorously before perhaps attempting to construct proofs to find out whether or not the specification satisfies certain properties. So, syntax checking, animation, tests, walkthroughs, and so on are all very much part of the *method* of a formal method and will sensibly be conducted before proof is even considered.

When a formal specification is deemed acceptable the process of implementation will typically begin. This may mean transforming the formal specification directly into code but does not necessarily have to mean that. The formal specification may serve as some kind of prototype to be discarded once we have learnt all we can from it. The final chapter of this book looks briefly at such implementation issues. This chapter focuses mainly on support for verification of CCS specifications.

Verification exercises, such as testing and proving, arise of course from the semantics of the language in question and will thus be more or less appropriate to the type of system under consideration. For CCS this should mean being able to easily investigate patterns of behaviour and behaviour properties. In turn this essentially means analysing transition graphs as these are the basis of the semantics for CCS.

13.2 The Concurrency Workbench

The Concurrency Workbench (CWB) is a tool that offers a variety of analyses and verification techniques for basic-CCS and some of the variations on it we studied in the first two parts of this book. In fact, wherever possible, all examples and exercises used in this book have been analysed on the workbench. All the analyses mentioned above may be conducted, along with checking the various equivalences and a certain amount of equational reasoning. In addition the workbench syntax checks specifications as it attempts to enter them, thus identifying typographical errors or misconceptions concerning allowable expressions. The tool has a simple command line interface which makes it relatively easy to learn and sometimes frustrating once you know what you want to do with it. In general, the tool does not support systems analysis or systems refinement, as is the case for CCS itself.

The following is a record of a simple, interactive session with the workbench. Agents can be defined using the command bi which prompts the user for an identifier (agent constant) and an agent (CCS expression). The workbench action 'm is the action $\overline{m}$, while the other standard CCS symbols can be readily found on any keyboard. When we have defined some agents the command pe lists all definitions in the current environment. The session then goes on to demonstrate some simple animation techniques made available by CWB. The vs command takes as input an agent and a natural number n and prints out the visible sequences of length n. The rest of the session is occupied with the animation of Buff2 via the command sim which essentially allows the user to choose particular paths through the transition graph for a given agent. At any stage the simulator provides the user with a list of next actions for the current agent it is holding. The user chooses an action by typing the number for a particular choice and causing the simulator to change the agent it is holding to the one resulting from the performance of the chosen transition. Assuming the reader is only too aware of the expected behaviour of $Buff_2$, the simulation should offer no surprises.

The Edinburgh Concurrency Workbench
(Version 6.0, August 15, 1991)

```
Command: bi
Identifier: C1
Agent: in.'m.C1

Command: bi
Identifier: C2
Agent: m.'out.C2
```

```
Command: bi
Identifier: Buff2
Agent: (C1 | C2) \ {m}

Command: pe

  Buff2 = (C1 | C2)\m
  C1 = in.'m.C1
  C2 = m.'out.C2

Command: vs
Number: 4
Agent: Buff2
=== in in 'out in ===>
=== in in 'out 'out ===>
=== in 'out in in ===>
=== in 'out in 'out ===>

Command: sim
Agent: Buff2

Simulated agent: Buff2
Transitions:
     1: --- in ---> ('m.C1 | C2)\m

Sim> 1
  --- in --->

Simulated agent: ('m.C1 | C2)\m
Transitions:
     1: --- t ---> (C1 | 'out.C2)\m

Sim> 1
  --- t --->

Simulated agent: (C1 | 'out.C2)\m
Transitions:
     1: --- in ---> ('m.C1 | 'out.C2)\m
     2: --- 'out ---> (C1 | C2)\m

Sim> 2
  --- 'out --->

Simulated agent: (C1 | C2)\m
```

```
Transitions:
    1: --- in ---> ('m.C1 | C2)\m
```

```
Sim> quit
```

```
Command: quit
```

It can thus be seen that syntactic checking, animation, and more rigorous testing are all made possible with just the features we have already presented.

13.3 Formal analyses

Before considering a more general evaluation of CWB and tools like it in the context of concurrent systems specification let us briefly consider some of the other features offered. We have seen that we can use CWB to check equivalences for us. It will also generate bisimulations for pairs of agents on which equivalences are based. As we saw in chapter 9, the calculation on paper of equivalences is no simple matter, but the workbench makes them a very practical technique indeed. In the chapters on temporal logic we saw that the specification of safety and liveness properties and the demonstration whether or not they were satisfied by particular agents were of great importance. Once again, however, successfully carrying out this activity on paper is not realistic, and the workbench once again comes to our rescue.

For instance, suppose we enter into the workbench the definitions for the sequential version of the two place buffer, $B0$, $B1$ and $B2$. In chapter 9 we established, by building strong and weak equivalences, that $Buff_2 \not\sim B0$ but $Buff_2 \not\approx B0$. We can use the Concurrency Workbench to check these equivalences mechanically for us:

```
Command: bi
Identifier: B0
Agent: in.B1
```

```
Command: bi
Identifier: B1
Agent: 'out.B0 + in.B2
```

```
Command: bi
Identifier: B2
Agent: 'out.B1
```

Command: pe

```
Buff2 = (C1 | C2)\m
C1 = in.'m.C1
C2 = m.'out.C2
B0 = in.B1
B1 = 'out.B0 + in.B2
B2 = 'out.B1
```

Command: strongeq
Agent: Buff2
Agent: B0
false

Command: eq
Agent: Buff2
Agent: B0
true

CWB supports temporal logic, BTHML$^+$, and provides a tableau-based proof procedure for the satisfaction relation. In fact, the workbench supports a more general logic, called the 'μ-calculus', in which BTHML$^+$ may be defined. As with many other facilities offered by the workbench, proofs of BTHML$^+$ properties only terminate, in general, if the agent under consideration is image-finite. As with agents, propositions may be defined, and there is also a facility for defining generic macro propositions which we will make use of in our next demonstration. We can illustrate this by checking that the agents Q_1 and Q_2 of chapter 12 do actually satisfy the properties stated on page 205. Comments are given in brackets to the right of CWB command lines.

```
Command: clear               (remove all definitions}
Command: if
Filename: bthml+             (input the BTHML$^+$ definitions)
done.
Command: if
Filename: Q1Q2.ccs           (input the Q1, Q2 definitions)
done.
Command: pe

  Q1 = a.b.(b.a.nil + c.a.nil + b.Q1)
  Q2 = a.b.(c.(a.nil + b.nil) + c.Q2)

  proposition Phi = ~(<a>T & <b>T)
```

```
macro AF P = min(Z.P | ([-]Z & <->T))

macro AG P = max(Z.P & [-]Z)

macro EF P = min(Z.P | <->Z)

macro EG P = max(Z.P & (<->Z | [-]F))
```

```
Command: cp
Agent: Q1
Proposition: EG Phi
true
Command: cp
Agent: Q2
Proposition: EG Phi
true
Command: cp
Agent: Q1
Proposition: AG Phi
true
Command: cp
Agent: Q2
Proposition: AG Phi
false
Command: quit
```

13.4 Summary and further reading

CWB is very much a prototype tool to support the formal specification
of concurrent systems. Many other tools have been developed for other
process algebras such as LOTOS. It is not the intention to indulge in a
detailed critique of CWB in this book. It is the intention to demonstrate
the very real benefits to be gained by employing such a tool. What we will
do now is to examine, in general terms, the benefits and problems found in
using tools to support formal, concurrent systems specification.

One problem with CWB is that if such things as equivalence or temporal
logic proofs fail then we are not given much help as to why. A very real problem encountered in characterising the behaviour of such systems is state
explosion. For instance, using the size operation of CWB we quickly ascer-
tain that TWB2 and NewTWB2 have 9 and 17 states respectively. Getting TWB2
to behave correctly meant almost doubling the state space. In contrast, applying the same operation to the completed specification for *System*, the
producer–consumer problem from chapter 2, yields 917 states. This is a

graphic example of the power of concurrent composition as a specification technique. The home heating system has a state space running into several thousands, with the result that commands such as fd, find deadlock, and cp, check proposition, require a lot of runtime memory and a lot of time. Some agents have infinite state spaces and thus cannot be analysed by many of the CWB commands. It is possible to minimise agents, in the manner of Mx and $Spec_2$ in the equational reasoning chapter, and thus cut down the amount of work required. Sometimes there are great savings to be made here and sometimes not.

All the analyses supported by CWB are outlined in [Mol92] which is the user manual supplied with the workbench. A general introduction to the construction of the CWB can be found in [RCS89].

14

Lifecycles, methods and CCS

One of the aims of this book from the outset was not just to provide a text-book for formal methods for concurrency but to demonstrate the practical relevance of such techniques to real problem solving. This was one of the reasons why we tried to adopt *awkward* case studies. In this chapter we are going to reflect a little on what we mean by the term 'method' and then begin to compare CCS, and its family of languages, against this notion and against other methods of real-time systems design such as structured methods. We will adopt a particular view of what we mean by a 'method' and assess the strengths and weaknesses of CCS on its own and when integrated into a particular development lifecycle. The particular development lifecycle will be Ward and Mellor structured analysis for real time. The technique used to do this will be *methods integration* and our aim will be to show how CCS can be firmly placed within a wider context of practical systems development. The chapter is only intended to serve as an introduction to these ideas but should help the interested reader to place the CCS family of languages within a broad software engineering context.

14.1 Methods

We are going to start by considering what we mean by the term 'method', but first of all we will highlight some confusions, ambiguities and obstacles which make such a consideration necessary. We list these in no particular order:

- The word 'method' is used widely in software engineering in a variety of different ways and can refer variously to notations, techniques, rules for utilising the first two, and so on.

- Equally confusing is the common use of the word 'methodology' in a particular but inappropriate way. This word, which should refer to the study of methods, usually refers to meta-methods, methods which incorporate other methods.

- In a software engineering context the term 'process model' is used to denote the means by which a particular system development is carried out and not the definition of a behavioural component within a real-time system.

- The term 'formal method' is a generic name given to notations, languages with a formal semantics, which are often manifestly lacking in methods.

- Very often different communities, or groupings of practitioners, within systems engineering use the same terminology in quite different ways. The term 'completeness' is an example. In structured methods it tends to refer to some sort of consistency check on the components in a diagram, for instance, while in discrete mathematics it refers to a general property possessed by the underlying language.

- The division of methods, whatever they may be, into structured, formal, object-oriented, and so on, also causes problems and indeed hinders the development of good working practices.

Before going any further let us consider what we mean by the term 'method'. A method should consist of, at least, the following features:

1. An underlying model
2. A language
3. A process model
4. Heuristics

Briefly, the first is essentially an abstract conceptualisation of the nature of the process and product of the method. This is important for methods integration because it abstracts away from the practical view of a method and allows clearer insights into the way in which a particular method may be categorised; this in turn aids in the identification of compatible methods. The language of a method consists of the textual, diagrammatic and tabular notations, etc. in which the product of the method is expressed. It serves to document decisions that have been made as a result of applying the method. The language should also include the semantic definitions for the method's notations in whatever form they may take. The process model should consist of a series of stages or activities and clearly stated ordering on their application; its purpose is to structure the process of generating the intended product of the method and to make sure that particular activities are carried out at the appropriate point in the systems development lifecycle. Guidance, in the form of heuristics, should be available to help the user undertake the various activities in the most profitable manner so as to make best use of the method.

The obvious question arises: how does CCS rate as a method?

One way of considering the underlying model of CCS is as a behavioural system where states record the potential to perform various actions and their actual performance results in the system switching to a new state. In a sense we are talking about systems that could be understood in terms of a labelled transition system, however informally expressed. With regard to 2, we should be satisfied that CCS is well endowed with notations to build systems models with respect to concurrency, value passing, and time. Of course, the language component of CCS also consists of a formal semantics. Remember, we also have a notation, temporal logic, to express non-functional requirements such as safety, liveness, and so on. The picture is not so good when we consider point 3. Reflecting on the way we went about building models in the first half of this book you should notice that we adopted a highly pragmatic approach and used a variety of ad hoc techniques because they seemed to work. We might sum up the approach as *try it and see*. Certainly, techniques such as parallel decomposition, re-labelling, and non-determinism are important techniques to help in the generation of models.

There are no prescribed techniques for analysing requirements and guiding the construction of an initial model and non-functional requirements. To date we have no means of moving from specification to design and implementation, although the next chapter will specifically consider this. In terms of verification CCS is quite well off, both formally and informally. We have the Verification Game and the Concurrency Workbench with which to perform informal analyses, tests, and we have the equivalences, equational laws, and temporal logic and its proof system to carry out formal analyses. However, there is no explicit process model which guides us through the systems development lifecycle and relates the various activities in a practical way. With regard to 4, the picture is somewhat uneven. There are a number of good case studies available to which intending users could refer but the knowledge inherent in them has not been synthesised and represented. In summary, we might consider CCS as very well endowed with regard to 2, largely lacking with regard to 3, and potentially, at least, well endowed with regard to 4.

It is thus not true that CCS fails as a method but there are significant gaps, particularly when large-scale, awkward, systems are under consideration. In fact, experience has shown that modelling all but simple systems in CCS is a difficult exercise whereas building a model of the same system in a structured method for real-time, such as Ward and Mellor (W/M) [WM85], is far less so [PCFT92]. Indeed, Ward/Mellor has a far stronger claim to the title 'method' than CCS does for the simple reason that it has an explicit process model and well organised heuristics whereas CCS largely does not. Notice also that in our modelling activities we did not hesitate to use diagrams and non-formal information, such as state tables, when we thought it to be helpful. It is very important to remember that our business is real-time systems modelling and not the application of CCS for its own sake.

The interesting thing is that, far from being incompatible, notations such as CCS and W/M are highly complementary and between them can generate a far more powerful method for systems development. Comparisons have shown that structured methods, such as W/M, quite successfully supply the missing pieces of the process model, such as analysis techniques, for CCS. On the other hand, CCS is very strong in the area of verification and complements W/M admirably in this respect. There is a growing belief that the long-standing debate over the pre-eminence of structured or formal methods for systems development is being superseded by a desire to integrate such methods. These integrations are of immense value in the teaching of specification methods for information systems as well as in their application. It is a strongly held belief that the outcome of the current interest in methods integration will be a set of powerful, expressive and practical methods which will find favour with those involved in the development of large-scale systems.

Referring to the characterisation of method, given above, we can informally define an 'integrated method' as one which combines some or all of the features of two or more methods to produce a new method. In other words, an integrated method is itself a method but, hopefully, with enhanced capability and effectiveness. We are going to consider the integration of W/M and CCS both in terms of how the integration can be accomplished and in terms of the benefits to be gained. In the next section we will give some idea as to the nature of W/M, and follow that with a section outlining its integration with CCS. We then discuss the practical advantages of such integrated methods in more detail as well as setting out criteria which we believe should guide those involved in methods integration.

14.2 Aspects of Ward and Mellor

We will not give a complete description of W/M nor of its integration with CCS but will just point to enough of the method to demonstrate its potential usefulness. W/M combines a set of notations, mainly diagrammatic, for documenting ideas and/or decisions, together with rules and advice on how to construct systems models. There is also a process model which gives details of how to move through to design and implementation. We will consider some of the notational techniques available and to a lesser extent the rules and heuristics put forward to guide this process.

In essence, W/M is an extension of Yourdon structured analysis for information systems but with the inclusion of techniques for modelling control aspects of real-time systems. Yourdon, primarily, makes use of data flow diagrams (DFDs) to build systems models and we assume most readers will be familiar with these in some form or other. In addition, W/M makes use of state transition diagrams (STDs) to make behavioural aspects of

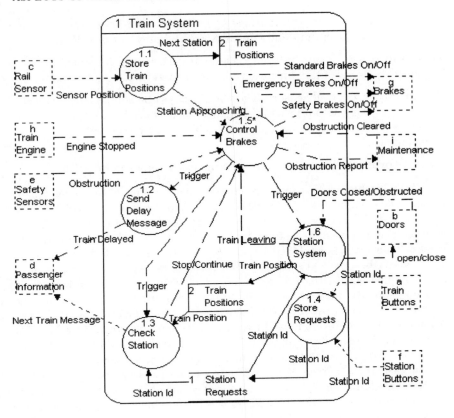

Figure 14.1. *Top level W/M DFD of automated transit system*

the system explicit, and again we assume readers will have encountered at least the idea of these. In any case, we will introduce these and other principal features by using them to model some features of the automated transit system from chapter 1. At this stage it might well be useful if the reader reread section 1.2 so as to refresh his/her memory of the system's description.

Figure 14.1 is a typical example of a W/M DFD and models a possible top-level decomposition of the automated transit system. Such DFDs have the following basic components:

Control Transforms eg. Control Brakes – These essentially determine the flow of control within a model but have no interaction whatsoever with data.

Control Flows eg. Station Approaching – These are essentially control signals which provide flow of control within the DFD.

Data Transforms eg. Station System – These essentially process data. They receive both data and control flows and may initiate either.

Data Flows eg. Train Position – These are the means by which data is passed between data transforms and possibly terminators as well.

Terminators eg. Rail Sensor – These are devices and components external to the system actually being modelled but which interact with it by means of data and/or control flows. The flows are the only aspects of terminators which are modelled.

Data Stores eg. Train Positions – Database components of a DFD.

A DFD is hierarchical and its components now need to be modelled by so called 'explosions'. Data transforms may be modelled as either a further nested DFD which itself must be exploded or, in the case of simple subsystems, as pre- and post-conditions on its event and data flows. Each control transform is exploded (modelled) by an STD such as figure 14.2 which describes the behaviour of Control Brakes. An STD consists of a set of named states, the boxes, and a set of transitions. Transitions have two components: above the bar is a single condition which permits the transition to fire, below the bar are a number of actions which take place when the input condition is satisfied. A transition occurs when the STD is in a particular state and a condition on one of its transitions is satisfied; at this point the actions are performed and the STD changes state appropriately. In this case, if the current state of Control Brakes is Train Moving and the control signal Station Approaching is received then the control flow 'Trigger Check Station' is sent and the STD moves into the new state, Approaching Station.

Thus, a W/M model consists of a hierarchical DFD whose leaf nodes are either data transforms, specified by pre- and post-conditions, or control transforms, specified by STDs. In addition there must be a data dictionary which details types for data flows etc. There is also a collection of somewhat ad hoc checks which can be applied to models by way of verification. There is tool support for much of this, eg. [LG89] which also allows animation of DFDs.

The W/M process model actually prescribes a series of models which describe the system at different levels of abstraction in conjunction with techniques for building the various models. First of all there is the Environmental Model which is concerned with determining the system's boundary with its environment and the interactions that can take place across that boundary. The Essential Model uses DFDs etc. to build an idealised logical model of the system identified by the Environmental Model. The Implementation Model is, as its name suggests, at a far lower level of abstraction and is essentially a system design built from the Essential Model but from which an implementation may be built. A particular characteristic of all

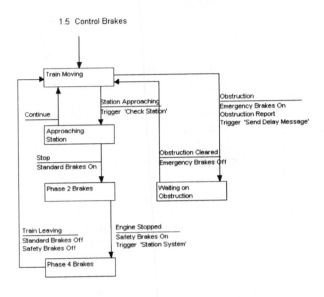

Figure 14.2. *W/M STD for Control Brakes*

these models is their semantics which are informally and often incompletely expressed.

It is interesting to consider whether we would have modelled the home heating system, in chapter 8, differently if we had been using W/M, for we might have assigned some of the subsystems, such as the sensor, to the environment rather than model them explicitly. Of course, our intention there was to specify a complex system in its entirety.

If we compare W/M and CCS in the context of the characterisation of method adopted above we can begin to see that, despite the fact that the former is a so-called structured method and the latter a so-called formal method, they are in fact complementary in many respects. W/M has an explicit and detailed process model supported by heuristics and covers much of the lifecycle. It is also strong on analysis and offers great help to the system's builder early in the lifecycle when interpreting requirements. CCS on the other hand is strong on formal notation and semantics, and very strong on formal verification techniques. Both have a very similar underlying model which is based on the system model as consisting of a set of states which are interconnected by the performing of actions which may or may not pass values.

14.3 Integrating W/M and CCS

In this section we outline some aspects of the W/M and CCS integration.
We first of all present a general view of a possible process model for the
integrated method and then give a brief outline of the nature of the W/M
to CCS translation for control transforms and data transforms. We then
discuss the potential benefits of employing such techniques in systems development.

Figure 14.3 gives a general view of a possible process model for an integration between W/M and CCS. It is intended to illustrate the way in
which the given activities of the two methods may contribute to effective
real-time systems building. Below we have enumerated a brief description
of each of the stages:

1. Derive the Context Diagram (Environmental Model). In the case of real-
   time systems the externals will tend to be devices which are controlled by
   the system rather than people who interact with the system. Externals
   may also, of course, include other systems.

2. Derive System Properties in English. In order to (automatically) check
   the formal model against the requirements it is necessary to formalise
   the requirements themselves. To achieve this, desirable properties of the
   required system are identified from the user and user requirements.

3. Specify System Properties Formally. The required properties are then
   translated into a Hennessy–Milner-based logic, see chapter 12, which is
   supported by the Concurrency Workbench. This step also continues to
   define the vocabulary for the intercommunication components which was
   begun in step 2.

4. Derive DFD Explosions. Break the transforms down into as many levels
   as necessary. It is helpful if the data and control aspects of the system
   can be separated without compromising the model. The behaviour of
   the data transforms can be defined during either this step or the next
   one.

5. Derive State Transition Diagrams. There should in fact be two STDs for
   each control transform, one for the active state initiated by the enable
   action and the other for the inactive state initiated by the disable. NB:
   the latter is not modelled in our example above. In practice the inactive
   state is defined by implication.

6. Convert STDs to CCS. This is done automatically but some constructs
   produce complex alternative behaviours. It may be necessary to manually refine some agents; ideally this would be done via the STDs to
   maintain the continuity and revisability of the entire model.

7. Check Functioning of Model. Ensure that the model can behave in the
   desired manner. This entails using the Concurrency Workbench to find
   deadlocks and to animate the model in various ways.

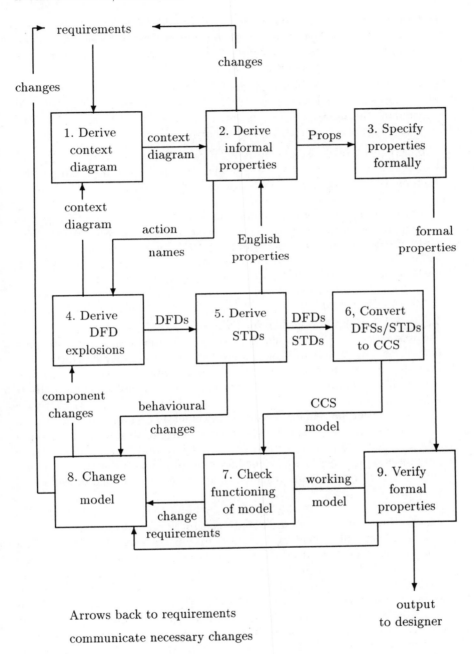

Arrows back to requirements
communicate necessary changes

Figure 14.3. *A process model for W/M CCS integration*

8. Change Model. Any changes required to get the model to function as required must be performed on the structured model. At best this means changing the flow in an STD (step 5) and at worst soliciting new requirements from the customer (step 1).

9. Check Properties against Model. When it has been established that the model can behave as required, use the Concurrency Workbench to validate the model against the properties expressed formally in HML. Changes may again result from this step.

It should be obvious that both W/M and CCS benefit from being embedded in this integrated process model. However, this does assume that there is some integration at the language level of the two methods, and this is what we now go on to discuss.

The relationship between the languages of Ward/Mellor and CCS is most obvious in two respects. First, there is a strong link between W/M DFDs and CCS flow graphs and thus the formal CCS notions of parallel composition and restriction. For instance, the W/M DFD train system (fig. 14.1) can actually be defined in terms of the CCS expression

$$Train\_System_{CCS} \stackrel{\text{def}}{=} (STP \mid SDM \mid CB \mid SS \mid SR) \backslash R$$

where STP is an abbreviation for Store Train Positions, for instance, and the restriction set R contains the names of all flows which do not have links with any terminators, ie. devices in the environment. Notice that because CCS communication is via complementary actions the arrowed control flows in the DFD have to be replaced by complementary pairs of actions, eg. Station Approaching, which we might abbreviate to sa for CCS purposes, would be replaced by the complementary $\overline{sa}$ and sa to give both the name of the flow and its direction, ie. output to input. In a similar way data flows can be translated with the addition of appropriately typed parameters, the types being gleaned from the W/M data-dictionary entries. Notice that any data transforms which are exploded will also be defined in the same way.

Next, we will discuss the relationship between W/M STDs and CCS agents. First, all flows in an STD are control flows and therefore parameterless. There will be one CCS agent definition for each state in the STD and one for the STD itself. This latter agent is required to handle the *enable* signal (the unlabelled arrow) which every control transform must have. We then need to specify the body of each agent constant in terms of a choice over its possible transitions. Conditions enabling transitions will be modelled by CCS input actions and the resulting actions as CCS output actions. If we wish to use basic CCS then we need to impose some ordering on the CCS actions. We have chosen to prefix the condition onto an interleaving of the output actions and thus arrive at a definition, in basic CCS, for our example, Control Brakes. Note that, again, we have abbreviated the action names used in the W/M STD to minimise the CCS specification, eg. o for Obstruction, and $\overline{ebo}$ for Emergency Brakes On, etc.:

$$
\begin{aligned}
CB &\stackrel{\text{def}}{=} enable.TM \\
TM &\stackrel{\text{def}}{=} o.(\overline{ebOn} \updownarrow \overline{or} \updownarrow \overline{tsdm}).WoO \\
WoO &\stackrel{\text{def}}{=} oc.\overline{ebOff}.TM \\
AS &\stackrel{\text{def}}{=} c.TM + s.\overline{stbOn}.P2B \\
P2B &\stackrel{\text{def}}{=} es.(\overline{sabOn} \updownarrow \overline{tcd}).P4B \\
P4B &\stackrel{\text{def}}{=} tl.(\overline{stbOff} \updownarrow \overline{saBoff}).TM
\end{aligned}
$$

Thus it seems that translation in either direction is a simple process – states equate to agents, conditions equate to input actions, and actions equate to output actions (the clash of terminology once again is unfortunate). However, there are other considerations which concern the fact that W/M STDs are something of a shorthand. First of all, the informally stated semantics of W/M actually says that from every state in an STD it can be disabled; in other words, on receipt of the action *disable* it will be switched back to its initial, disabled, state, in our case CB. Secondly, the informal semantics demand that unexpected signals should be accepted but not responded to. In other words, the signal is received but the STD remains in its current state. This means that for all states except CB we have to add the extra choice to cope with these two eventualities. For the former it is sufficient to add one extra choice and thus WoO would be redefined as

$$ WoO' \stackrel{\text{def}}{=} oc.\overline{ebOff}.TM + disable.CB $$

The second extra case requires a little more thought. Basically we have to identify for each state the set of actions which we regard as unexpected and then add these in as extra choices that simply keep the agent in the same state. First of all, we need to know all actions which an STD in its CCS form is capable of. This is straightforward, as we already have the function *sort* from chapter 10. In our case $sort(CB)$ will return the set we require. We now need to identify the set of actions which an agent is immediately capable of, and this can be accomplished by the new function *actions* which has the same type as *sort* but is defined by the following equation:

$$ actions(E) = \{\alpha \mid E \stackrel{\alpha}{\to} E'\} $$

Therefore the set of unexpected actions of any state of a CCS representation of an STD will be

$$ sort(E) \setminus actions(E_i) $$

where we assume E is the initial or disabled state of an STD and E_i is some intermediate state. We can gather together all these additional transitions using an indexed sum over the unexpected actions. For the state WoO of our current example the completed form WoO_{comp} would be as follows:

$$WoO_{comp} \stackrel{\text{def}}{=} oc.\overline{ebOff}.TM + disable.CB + \sum_{\alpha \in A} \alpha.WoO_{comp}$$

where

$$A = sort(CB) \setminus actions(WoO')$$

All states except for CB will need to be *completed* in this way. In its disabled state an STD can respond only to the action *enable* and no other. It is interesting that W/M forces the engineer to think of unexpected as well as expected behaviours.

We will not consider how to translate data transforms but they will essentially take the form of an interleaving of inputs followed by an interleaving of outputs with functions determining the required output parameters.

The important point to note is that integrating a well known and well liked structured technique with CCS makes it far easier to build formal specifications which can then be subjected to the available formal analyses. The resulting formal specification, in this case, also seems to be more complete.

14.4 Summary and further reading

The integration of structured and formal methods has a vital role to play in the future of software engineering and the pace of research continues to grow as this book goes to press. However, experience shows that any method must be fully accepted by its users if it is to be truly successful. The integrated method discussed in this chapter has evolved from the way users wish to specify systems and should thus match their problem solving intuitions. In the light of this a set of criteria can be set out to assess the practicality of any method, whether structured, formal, integrated, or whatever:

- Practitioners should feel comfortable with the method and freely choose to use it.

- Practitioners should feel that the notations and techniques match their intuitions and help in the process of problem solving.

- The integrated method should use tried and trusted techniques which should remain as little changed as possible by the process of integration.

- The method should not only enhance the specification of systems but should also enhance their validation and the ability of developers to provide information concerning the developmental state of the system.

This type of integration of structured and formal techniques may well provide a means of gaining acceptance for formal methods by those in industry who might benefit from them but are at present wary. We have found the use of integrated methods of great benefit to students in the application of formal methods to realistically sized systems. Structured and formal methods foster differing views of a system and prompt the software engineer to ask different questions of the system. This can only help in the process of validation and the generation of trust in the acceptability of the final implementation. For similar reasons a fully integrated method allows the software engineer to produce radically different information from the current state of the system as required by a variety of interested parties, eg.

1. Management information in the form of diagrams and statistics,

2. Formal views and proofs for standards compliance etc.

We are naturally led to ask some more general questions concerning the relationships between such methods. Certainly, it would seem that the translation between structured and formal specification is a reification, an adding of detail. This STD to CCS translation represents only one possible interpretation of the STD–CCS relationship. Thus although there is some overlap between the two it would appear that structured methods might, in general, be more 'abstract' than formal methods. It seems certain that synthesised or integrated methods will have a central role to play in the future of software engineering in both education and commerce. There are very encouraging signs that the structured vs formal methods debate may be giving way to a more pragmatic approach to the problems of building and learning to build large software systems.

The Ward/Mellor structured method is described in [WM85], while the basic ideas on integration introduced in this chapter are discussed in [PCFT92]. The standard reference for the Yourdon structured method is [You89]. A good general set of methods-integration case studies can be found in [CK93]. A rather deeper analysis of the integration of Ward/Mellor and CCS, or rather W/M Essential Models and SCCS, can be found in [PCFP94]. Finally, structured methods can provide the initial context for formal specification in languages such as Z and VDM which are best suited to modelling information systems [Sem91].

15

Implementation issues

The main objective of this book has been to introduce readers to the use of process algebra, and in particular CCS-based languages, for the formal specification of concurrent and real-time systems. We have also looked at verification techniques for CCS specifications with the emphasis on formal verification via equivalences, and temporal logic. An obvious question which will have occurred to readers would be: How does all this help me to construct implementations which meet requirements? Certainly, the whole point of methods, whether formal, structured, or whatever, is to help us in the realisation of systems. It lies outside the scope of this book to present a detailed account of the refinement or reification process, as it is variously called, but on the other hand such a book would be incomplete without some discussion of this important subject. What we will do is to take a general look at the relationship between CCS and working systems and then to take a more detailed look at the relationship between CCS and software control systems. We will first look at a specific translation between CCS and program code, by way of an example, and then point the reader in the direction of more detailed discussions of the topic.

15.1 CCS and systems implementation

It is worthwhile reflecting on the scope we have allowed ourselves in applying the various versions of CCS to formal systems specification. To date we have not asked ourselves whether or not we were specifying software, hardware, or devices such as sensors and so on. We have simply taken requirements and proceeded to build CCS models of them. Given the basic specification philosophy of considering the *what* and not the *how*, this seems to make good sense. It is, I believe, a measure of the applicability of languages such as CCS to the specification of concurrent and real-time systems that the classification of subsystems into software or hardware, etc. is not demanded and is unnecessary. Certainly, in terms of safety-critical systems this type of general model is often mandatory prior to safety analysis and the allocation of safety integrity levels to subsystems.

However, when it comes to the design and implementation of the type of systems we have been considering, the question obviously arises. Usually, but not always, software components will have to be written but hardware components may well pre-exist the specification process and may also be specifically identified in the requirements document. Our principal concern in this book will be with the implementation of software subsystems. This in general will be concerned with control, safety management, and provision of run-time monitoring information. Typically, we would wish such software subsystems to be implemented by a sequential program written in a third-generation language (3GL) such as C, though there are other possibilities such as ladder logic for programmable logic controllers. In the case of safety-critical systems, safety management may be specifically required to be implemented electro-mechanically. Thus the CCS specification, from which we are to construct an implementation, and which itself consists of a number of top-level subsystems composed in parallel with some appropriate restriction set to control the interface, actually models a variety of subsystems some of which we assume are to be software-implemented. It should be the goal, whenever possible, that each such software subsystem should be sequential in structure for reasons of efficiency and maintainability. Interestingly, the techniques we looked at in the chapter on equational reasoning, chapter 10, demonstrated how to achieve this. We were able to rearrange restriction sets, and so on, in order to separate out a group of components, composed in parallel, into a coherent subsystem and apply the expansion law and the second constant law, among others, to derive a congruent but sequential version.

It is the translation of such sequential specification components into C that will be the principal concern of the rest of this chapter. Despite its lack of concurrent and real-time features C is a reasonable choice for our target language for several reasons. First of all, C, in conjunction with Unix, does allow concurrent and real-time programs to be written. Secondly, C is widely used for implementing real-time systems and suchlike because of the natural way in which it allows such programming problems to be solved. A further, more pragmatic, reason is that much of the research into refinement techniques for process algebras, such as CCS, has concentrated on C as the target language, and so there is a larger body of material on which we can draw. However, we will also see how to extend this technique to allow software prototypes of complete systems, hardware and software, to be constructed. In many ways the more obvious target language for implementing CCS specifications would be a language such as Ada which incorporates many of the CCS-style constructions for concurrency and, importantly, time, without recourse to external facilities provided by an operating system. For this reason we will also look at the way in which

Ada may be derived from CCS specifications. We assume the reader is familiar with a 3GL such as Pascal but not necessarily C or Ada themselves. Interestingly, it seems that an understanding of a language such as CCS and the basic concepts of 3GL programming make it very easy to learn to use concurrent programming languages such as the ones we have mentioned.

15.2 CCS to C

We will now look at the relationship between CCS and C, or rather a subset of C, referred to as C′, which is sufficient for our purposes. In particular, we are interested in translating value-passing CCS into C. We have already referred the reader to the chapter on equational reasoning which demonstrates how to formally derive a sequential version of a concurrently defined system. Our task is thus to show how a sequential, value-passing CCS specification may be translated into executable C code. In this section we will explore a particular translation in an informal manner by way of an example. In the following section we will demonstrate the way in which this translation may be formally expressed. With this in mind let us return to an example subsystem from the chapter on value passing in order to focus our attention on the problem before us. Below, you will find the definitions for the agent $ConVal$ from the data-manager–converter which you might like to reconsider for a moment. In order to make our discussions clearer three extra definitions have been added which make no changes whatsoever to the behaviour specified for $ConVal$ in previous chapters.

$Conv$	waiting for a request
$Conv1$	waiting for the first bit
$Conv2$	waiting for the second bit
$Conv3$	waiting for the third bit

$$ConVal \stackrel{\text{def}}{=} req.\overline{write}.ConVal1$$

$$ConVal1 \stackrel{\text{def}}{=} out(x).ConVal1'$$
$$ConVal1' \quad if\ x \neq 0\ then\ \overline{send}(odd).\overline{end}.ConVal$$
$$else\ ConVal2$$

$$ConVal2 \stackrel{\text{def}}{=} out(x).ConVal2'$$
$$ConVal2' \quad if\ x \neq 0\ then\ \overline{send}(even).\overline{end}.ConVal$$
$$else\ ConVal3$$

$$ConVal3 \stackrel{\text{def}}{=} out(x).Conval3'$$
$$ConVal3' \quad if\ x \neq 0\ then\ \overline{send}(even).ConVal$$
$$else\ \overline{send}(zero).ConVal$$

Having refreshed your memory as to the behaviour of $ConVal$ let us try to imagine what it would look like as a program. Basically we have a control loop which waits until the input *req* is received, after which *ConVal* attempts to gain the attention of the data-manager, *DMVal*, from which it needs to read the current bit pattern stored. *ConVal* then proceeds to read enough of the current bit pattern to be able to decide which result it should transmit via the action $\overline{send}$. At a glance this would, perhaps, not seem to present too many problems. We might observe that we are in need of at least the following:

- A loop construct to implement the recursion of CCS
- A conditional statement
- The ability to define typed variables
- A means of defining I/O routines to match the actions of CCS

Of these, the first three are all present in C while the last is provided by Unix as a means for programs to interact with externally defined *pipes*. So it would seem that we have the basic facilities we need. There are various ways in which we could now proceed with the translation process. The first of these would be to construct a translation function in the manner of the one we specified to translate value-passing expressions into basic CCS. The other way is to take a more abstract view and simply translate the behaviour patterns as represented by transition graphs. We are going to explore the latter and so it is helpful at this stage to consider the transition graph for *ConVal*, figure 15.1.

Notice that we have numbered each of the states in the graph. The reason for this is that we are going to interpret the transition graph as an infinite loop over a switch statement, known as a case stetement in most other 3GLs. We use the number of the nodes in the graph to tell the program which state has been reached. Thus in this case the main body of the program will be of the form:

```
main()
{
    for(;;)
    {
        switch (state)
            case(0); ...  break;
            ...
            case(6); ...  break;
    }
}
```

The line `main()` simply signals the beginning of the program's main block, the scope of which is given by the outermost braces. The line `for(;;)` sets up an infinite for loop over the statement bounded by the inner braces.

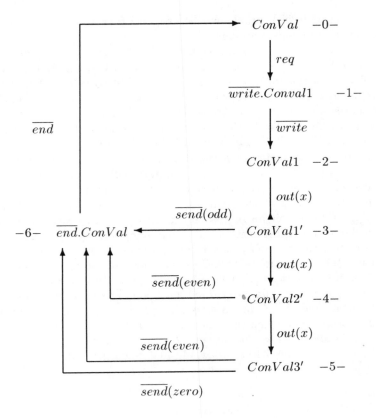

Figure 15.1. *Transition graph for ConVal*

The parameter `state` of the `switch` statement is a type which will have to be declared before the main body of the program is encountered. Following this are a number of `case` statements which are triggered according to the current value of `state`, which in this case should be in the range $0 \ldots 6$. Thus the current value for `state` tells the program which state the system is in, and from this it should be able to determine which actions are possible and which values are to be input or output as a result of an action being selected. The `break` which terminates each `case` statement tells the program to jump back to the top of the loop and begin again. Almost all CCS specifications can be implemented as C programs with this general structure. Specifications that cannot be implemented in this manner may well have infinite state-spaces or states with infinite transitions. For the present purposes actions of the form $a(x)$ are considered to generate a single transition. The vast majority of specifications we encounter will not present us with such problems. We can now turn to the structure of the code inside the `case` statements.

Again let us return to the transition graph for *ConVal* and consider how to interpret this in terms of program code. Looking first at the node labelled 2, for instance, we see that it is the first transition that involves a parameter. In this case we will require a value for x to be provided when the action $\overline{out}$ is performed. We must first consider how to implement CCS actions within C. To do this we will have to define functions which act as I/O routines. These functions will take as their parameter either the value to be transmitted or a variable for which a value to be input may be substituted. Each of these I/O routines will return a `true` or `false` depending on whether the interaction with the program's environment has been successful. In C this will require defining a type `bool`. Returning a value of `true` will mean that the connection has been made and will have the effect of instantiating an input parameter to a specific value or of recording the transfer of an output parameter to the environment. We will use the convention that CCS expressions of the form $out(x)$ will be defined in C as `out_r(&x)` where `&x` will be replaced by some value of the correct type when `true` is returned. CCS actions of the form $\overline{send}(y)$ will be implemented by a C function `send_s(y)` where y must be given a value of the correct type when the function is *called*.

All I/O routines must be declared before the main body of the program and for *ConVal* the definitions would look like this:

```
bool req_r()            bool write_s()
bool out_r(bit*)        send_s(result)
typedef enum result {odd, even, zero}
typedef enum bool {0,1}
int state = 0
bit x;                  bit value
```

Notice that some functions, such as `req_r`, require no parameters and that the function `out_r(bit*)` requires a *name* parameter of type `bit`. If a node in the graph was labelled by a τ action then we would implement it with the function `bool tau()`. All such function definitions will require function bodies to be defined after the main body of the program is completed.

Now that we know how to declare functions to implement actions we can implement the body of the `case` statement for node 2. Because there is only one possible action we will use a conditional statement to check if the connection has been made, in other words that the function `out_r(&x)` evaluates to `true`. If it does then we use the variable `value` to record the value of x and reset `state` to be 3. The break causes execution to jump out of the `switch` statement and return control to the top-level loop:

```
case(2);
   if (out_r(x))
   {
      value = x;
      state = 3;
   }
   break;
```

Now take a look at the node labelled 3. Notice that there are two possible actions which can be performed, but both depend on the evaluation of the condition. This first checks to see if the value input for x and held in `value` is 0 or 1. If `value` is not equal to 0 then the action $\overline{send}$ is enabled with the parameter odd. If `value` is equal to 0 then the action out is performed, again to input a second bit value. The code inside this `case` statement will thus consist of a conditional statement with one branch for each possible available action. The `case` statement for node 3 will be implemented in the following manner:

```
case(3);
   if ((value = 0) && send_s(odd))
   {
      state = 0;
   }
   break;
   if ((value = 1) && out_r(&x))
   {
      value = x;
      state = 4;
   }
   break;
```

We can now see how to put these various bits and pieces together to build the complete program minus the definitions of the function bodies:

```
bool req_r()            bool write_s()
bool out_r(bit*)        send_s(result)
typedef enum result {odd, even, zero}
int state = 0
int x;                  int value
```

```
main()
{
   for(;;)
   {
      switch (state)
         case(0);
            if (req())
            {
               state = 1;
            }
            break;
         case(1);
            if (write_s())
            {
               state = 2;
            }
            break;
         case(2);
            if (out_r(x))
            {
               value = x;
               state = 3;
            }
            break;
         case(3);
            if ((value = 0) && send_s(odd))
            {
               state = 0;
            }
            break;
            if ((value = 1) && out_r(&x))
            {
               value = x;
               state = 4;
            }
            break;
         ...
   }
}
```

We have shown, in an informal way, that there is a fairly natural relationship between sequential specifications expressed in value-passing CCS
and C programs which appear to implement them. It would obviously be
interesting to know more about this relationship, but to do so the reader

will have to pursue the further reading suggestions offered below.

EXERCISE 15.1

Complete the implementation of *ConVal* by writing C code for states
4 . . . 6.

15.3 Summary and further reading

The subject of refinement, reification, implementation, for formal methods
– call it what you will – could be and indeed has been the subject of whole
books. These have usually been devoted to the translation of Z or VDM
into 3GL code or rather the guarded command language; [Mor90] is a good
example. In this chapter we have simply demonstrated a working relationship between the languages of C and CCS without attempting to specify
the relationship formally or even presenting an algorithm for making the
translation. More than this, we would like to know that a CCS specification
and its C implementation are equivalent in some sense. Given that this is
a formal methods book we should, at least, attempt to demonstrate the
nature of the formal relationship between the two. The approach used in
this chapter is an informal version of that developed in [Sch93] where the
relationship between CCS and C is developed formally using bisimulation
equivalences. In fact, Schreiber does not concern himself specifically with
CCS but with a general mechanism for capturing the behavioural meaning of expressions given in process algebras with value passing. Another
approach which we have not been able to pursue here is to specify a concurrent programming language such as Ada in value-passing CCS. Milner
[Mil89] demonstrates this for a shared-variable-style language.

IV

Appendices

A

Solutions

Solutions to all exercises except those marked with an asterisk * are given below.

A.1 Chapter 2

Exercise 2.1

The action sequences for D_3 are exactly those for D_4 and consist of sequences consisting of the action in alternating with either $\overline{out0}$ or $\overline{out1}$. In terms of sequences of actions the two agents have the same behaviour. However, there are ways of comparing agents other than using possible sequences of actions. These are considered in chapter 9.

Exercise 2.2

CCS has no notion of data or abstract datatypes defined within it but we can give the impression of data by naming actions appropriately, eg. $in0$ to stand for inputting the value 0 when the action in is performed. We can then build up patterns of communications which mimic the input and output of data:

$$NewC_1 \stackrel{\text{def}}{=} in0.\overline{m0}.NewC_1 + in1.\overline{m1}.NewC_1$$
$$NewC_2 \stackrel{\text{def}}{=} m0.\overline{out0}.NewC_2 + m1.\overline{out1}.NewC_2$$
$$NewBuff_2 \stackrel{\text{def}}{=} (NewC_1 \mid NewC_2)\backslash\{m0, m1\}$$

Notice that we must restrict now on both $m0$ and $m1$ because CCS treats these as two separate actions and not the single action m with a value parameter of either 0 or 1.

Exercise 2.3

CCS can be used to build sequential as well as concurrent specifications of systems. In the latter case a specification consists of a number of definitions, one for each potential state of the system. There are thus three potential states of the buffer, as far as the environment is concerned, with the initial state being $B0$:

$$B0 \overset{\text{def}}{=} in.B1$$
$$B1 \overset{\text{def}}{=} in.B2 + \overline{out}.B0$$
$$B2 \overset{\text{def}}{=} \overline{out}.B1$$

Exercise 2.4

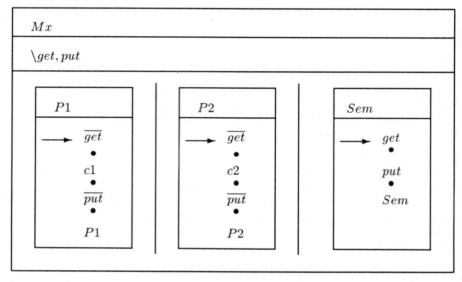

Exercise 2.5

$$B^{2\prime}_{ack} \overset{\text{def}}{=} (Ba'_1 \mid Ba'_2)\backslash\{ai, ao\}$$
$$Ba'_1 \overset{\text{def}}{=} in.\overline{ackin}.\overline{ao}.ai.Ba'_1$$
$$Ba'_2 \overset{\text{def}}{=} ao.\overline{ai}.\overline{out}.ackout.Ba'_2$$

Exercise 2.6

The two-place version of Twb should look like the following:

$$Twb^2 \overset{\text{def}}{=} (T1 \mid T2)\backslash\{l, r\}$$
$$T1 \overset{\text{def}}{=} inleft.\overline{l}.T1 + r.\overline{outleft}.T1$$
$$T2 \overset{\text{def}}{=} l.\overline{outright}.T2 + inright.\overline{r}.T2$$

Whether you used the Verification Game or the Concurrency Workbench you should have found that in certain circumstances Twb^2 can deadlock. If Twb^2 is empty and the next two actions are *inleft* and *inright*, in either order, then $T1$ and $T2$ will be offering the actions $\bar{l}$ and $\bar{r}$ respectively. This of course leaves Twb^2 deadlocked because both actions are restricted. In fact, the behaviour patterns of this little agent are quite complicated. Twb^2 can pass signals in one direction at a time and can also change direction if it becomes empty before attempting to do so. It thus can only hold a maximum of two signals in a single direction and never two in each direction at the same time as expected. The problem occurs because Twb only ever holds a pulse in one direction at a time and not both as required.

Exercise 2.7

The easiest way to use a semaphore to prevent Twb^2 deadlocking is to force $T1$ and $T2$ to gain control of the semaphore before each input:

$$
\begin{aligned}
Twb^{2\prime} &\stackrel{\text{def}}{=} (T1 \mid T2)\backslash\{l, r\} \\
T1 &\stackrel{\text{def}}{=} \overline{get}.inleft.\bar{l}.\overline{put}.T1 + r.\overline{outleft}.T1 \\
T2 &\stackrel{\text{def}}{=} l.\overline{outright}.T2 + \overline{get}.inright.\bar{r}.\overline{put}.T2 \\
Sem &\stackrel{\text{def}}{=} get.put.Sem
\end{aligned}
$$

This solution works but is not very efficient. We can make it more efficient by allowing $T1$ or $T2$ to gain control of the semaphore for an unspecified number of inputs. We specify $T1$ as being in a passive state, $T1P$, in which it can only pass on signals from $T2$ if it gains control of the semaphore, in which case it moves to an active state, $T1A$, in which it can accept input and pass it on or give up the semaphore and move to its passive state:

$$
\begin{aligned}
T1P &\stackrel{\text{def}}{=} \overline{get}.T1A + r.\overline{outleft}.T1P \\
T1A &\stackrel{\text{def}}{=} inleft.\bar{l}.T1A + \overline{put}.T1P
\end{aligned}
$$

Of course, $T2$ and $Twb^{2\prime}$ will have to be redefined as well.

Neither of these solutions is fair in the sense that both $T1$ and $T2$ are given equal access to the semaphore. It is quite possible that one or the other will never gain control of the semaphore because the choice is a non-deterministic one over the two τ actions. This is also true of the Mx system described earlier in chapter 1.

Exercise 2.8

The two-way buffer was presented in a rather peculiar way in that there is no need for the left→right channel to communicate with the right→left channel. We could have specified Twb in the following manner:

$$Twb' \stackrel{\text{def}}{=} LeftRight \mid RightLeft$$
$$LeftRight \stackrel{\text{def}}{=} inleft.\overline{outright}.LeftRight$$
$$RightLeft \stackrel{\text{def}}{=} inright.\overline{outleft}.RightLeft$$

The sequential version of this has four states:

$$STwb' \stackrel{\text{def}}{=} inleft.STwb'_l + inright.STwb'_r$$
$$STwb'_l \stackrel{\text{def}}{=} \overline{outright}.STwb' + inright.STwb'_{lr}$$
$$STwb'_r \stackrel{\text{def}}{=} \overline{outleft}.STwb' + inleft.STwb'_{lr}$$
$$STwb'_{lr} \stackrel{\text{def}}{=} \overline{outright}.STwb'_r + \overline{outleft}.STwb'_l$$

It is now necessary to construct the fully functioning two-place, two-way version of Twb^2 by composing two, appropriately edited, versions of either of the above in parallel.

Exercise 2.9

We can use a semaphore to achieve the mutual exclusion property required as we have already done on several occasions. We will leave this to the reader and only consider the respecification of C and D. The only real problem is when to instruct the two agents to gain control of the semaphore. We define the new version of C in the following way:

$$C \stackrel{\text{def}}{=} out0.out0.out0.\overline{get}.\overline{mod3}.\overline{put}.C$$

D will be respecified in a similar manner, thus ensuring that mutual exclusion applies only to the output actions $\overline{mod3}$ and $\overline{mod4}$ and not to the reading of values from $Buff_4^2$, which would have caused deadlock.

Exercise 2.10

The new modifications required for C and D are more difficult to meet and will require them to gain control of the semaphore before any synchronisations with $Buff_4^2$ are allowed. Having gained control of the semaphore C, for instance, will have to be able to read both zeros and ones from the buffer and discard those it does not want:

$$C' \stackrel{\text{def}}{=} \overline{get}.C_1$$
$$C_1 \stackrel{\text{def}}{=} out0.C_2 + out1.C_1$$
$$C_2 \stackrel{\text{def}}{=} out0.C_3 + out1.C_2$$
$$C_3 \stackrel{\text{def}}{=} out0.\overline{mod3}.\overline{put}.C' + out1.C_3$$

D will be respecified in a similar manner. It is possible to achieve the same effect by respecifying $Cell_4$ of the buffer so that it acts both as a semaphore and an output process. This solution is left for the reader to consider.

A.2 Chapter 3

Exercise 3.1

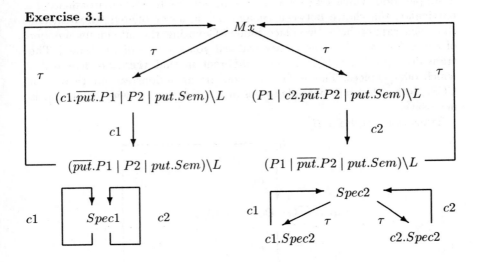

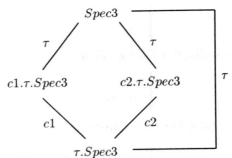

Comparing the transition graphs you might come to the following conclusions:

- Mx and $Spec_3$ are very similar indeed, $c1$ and $c2$ are always preceeded and succeeded by τ-actions.

- Mx and $Spec_2$ are also similar. The mutual exclusion property is preserved because the critical sections are only one action and the trailing τ-actions are not strictly necessary. This would not be the case if the critical actions were two or more actions in length.

- $Spec_1$ does not preserve the mutual exclusion property because it offers both $c1$ and $c2$ from the same state.

Exercise 3.2

In the following two transition graphs we see that the one for B_{ack}^2 is a simple loop which offers no choices of actions to the environment. In particular, the choice between *in* and $\overline{out}$ is never offered which means that this cannot be a two-place buffer. Counting the maximum number of *in*s before an $\overline{out}$ is necessary will tell you the size of the buffer. The transition graph for $B_{ack}^{2\prime}$ is quite different in that there are five states which offer choices. This is because concurrent actions are interleaved in CCS. Notice that it is possible to perform the action *in* twice before $\overline{out}$ is necessary.

Transition graph for B_{ack}^2

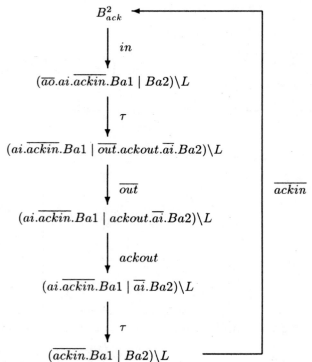

Transition graph for $B_{ack}^{2'}$

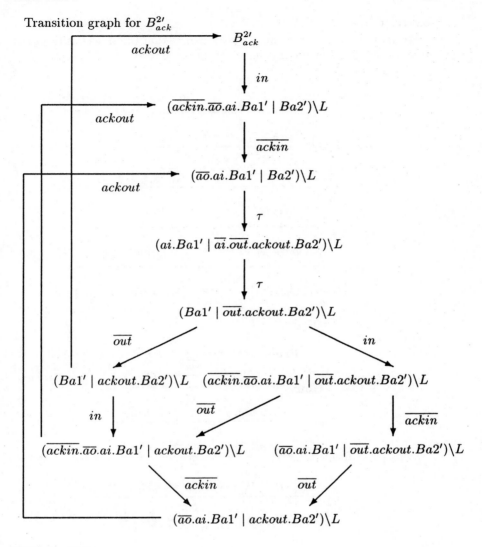

Exercise 3.3

The transition graphs for the two agents differ in that $Twb2$ has a deadlock state resulting from performing the action $inleft$ followed by $inright$ or vice versa. $Twb2'$ does not have the deadlock state and in general has a more complex transition graph as a result of this.

Exercise 3.4

We give two of the three proofs here. Notice that the side consitions have often been left off in the inference trees that follow.

$$
\textbf{Pre} \;\overline{\rule{4cm}{0pt}}
$$

$$
\textbf{Con}_1 \; \frac{in.\overline{m}.C_1 \xrightarrow{\;in\;} \overline{m}.C_1}{}
$$

$$
\textbf{Com}_1 \; \frac{C_1 \xrightarrow{\;in\;} \overline{m}.C_1}{}
$$

$$
\textbf{Brac}_2 \; \frac{C_1|\overline{out}.C_2 \xrightarrow{\;in\;} \overline{m}.C_1|\overline{out}.C_2}{}
$$

$$
\textbf{Res} \; \frac{(C_1|\overline{out}.C_2) \xrightarrow{\;in\;} (\overline{m}.C_1|\overline{out}.C_2)}{}
$$

$$
(C_1|\overline{out}.C_2)\backslash\{m\} \xrightarrow{\;in\;} (\overline{m}.C_1|\overline{out}.C_2)\backslash\{m\}
$$

$$
\textbf{Pre} \;\overline{\rule{4cm}{0pt}}
$$

$$
\textbf{Com}_2 \; \frac{\overline{out}.C_2 \xrightarrow{\;\overline{out}\;} C_2}{}
$$

$$
\textbf{Brac}_2 \; \frac{C_1|\overline{out}.C_2 \xrightarrow{\;\overline{out}\;} C_1|C_2}{}
$$

$$
\textbf{Res} \; \frac{(C_1|\overline{out}.C_2) \xrightarrow{\;\overline{out}\;} (C_1|C_2)}{}
$$

$$
\textbf{Con}_1 \; \frac{(C_1|\overline{out}.C_2)\backslash\{m\} \xrightarrow{\;\overline{out}\;} (C_1|C_2)\backslash\{m\}}{}
$$

$$
(C_1|\overline{out}.C_2)\backslash\{m\} \xrightarrow{\;\overline{out}\;} Buff_2
$$

Exercise 3.5

The first two proofs are straightforward with the first being correct and the second incorrect. The latter fails when an attempt is made to introduce the restriction set and the side condition fails, $put, \overline{put} \notin \{get, put\}$ is false. We will only give the solution to the third which is slightly more complicated:

$$\text{Pre} \frac{\rule{4cm}{0.4pt}}{get.put.Sem \xrightarrow{\;get\;} put.Sem}$$

$$\text{Con}_1 \frac{\rule{4cm}{0.4pt}}{Sem \xrightarrow{\;get\;} put.Sem}$$

$$\text{Pre} \frac{\rule{4cm}{0.4pt}}{\overline{get}.c1.\overline{put}.P1 \xrightarrow{\;\overline{get}\;} c1.\overline{put}.P1}$$

$$\text{Con}_1 \frac{}{P1 \xrightarrow{\;\overline{get}\;} c1.\overline{put}.P1}$$

$$\text{Com}_1 \frac{}{P1 \mid P2 \xrightarrow{\;\overline{get}\;} c1.\overline{put}.P1 \mid P2}$$

$$\text{Com}_3 \frac{}{P1 \mid P2 \mid Sem \xrightarrow{\;\tau\;} c1.\overline{put}.P1 \mid P2 \mid put.Sem}$$

$$\text{Brac}_2 \frac{}{(P1 \mid P2 \mid Sem) \xrightarrow{\;\tau\;} (c1.\overline{put}.P1 \mid P2 \mid put.Sem)}$$

$$\text{Res} \frac{}{(P1 \mid P2 \mid Sem)\backslash L \xrightarrow{\;\tau\;} (c1.\overline{put}.P1 \mid P2 \mid put.Sem)\backslash L}$$

$$\text{Con}_1 \frac{}{Mx \xrightarrow{\;\tau\;} (c1.\overline{put}.P1 \mid P2 \mid put.Sem)\backslash L}$$

$$L = \{get, put\}$$

Exercise 3.6

All the transitions are correct and the proofs straightforward. Be careful to use the constant laws correctly. In the first two you have to use Con_1 to establish R as the left hand side of the transition. In the third you have to use Con_2 to establish R on the right hand side of the transition.

Exercise 3.8

We give a proof of the third transistion. The others follow similar patterns.

$$\text{Pre} \ \overline{\rule{4cm}{0pt}}$$
$$[p].P \ \xrightarrow{[p]} \ P \qquad\qquad \text{Pre} \ \overline{\rule{4cm}{0pt}}$$
$$[q].Q \ \xrightarrow{[q]} \ Q$$

$$\text{Sum}_2 \ \overline{\rule{4cm}{0pt}}$$
$$[a].P + [p].P \ \xrightarrow{[p]} \ P \qquad\qquad \text{Sum}_2 \ \overline{\rule{4cm}{0pt}}$$
$$[b].Q + [q].Q \ \xrightarrow{[q]} \ Q$$

$$\text{Con}_1 \ \overline{\rule{4cm}{0pt}}$$
$$P \ \xrightarrow{[p]} \ P \qquad\qquad \text{Con}_1 \ \overline{\rule{4cm}{0pt}}$$
$$Q \ \xrightarrow{[q]} \ Q$$

$$\text{Com}_3 \ \overline{\rule{6cm}{0pt}}$$
$$P \mid Q \ \xrightarrow{[p,q]} \ P \mid Q$$

$$\text{Com}_1 \ \overline{\rule{6cm}{0pt}}$$
$$P \mid Q \mid R \ \xrightarrow{[p,q]} \ P \mid Q \mid R$$

$$\text{Brac}_2 \ \overline{\rule{6cm}{0pt}}$$
$$(P \mid Q \mid R) \ \xrightarrow{[p,q]} \ (P \mid Q \mid R)$$

$$\text{Perm} \ \overline{\rule{6cm}{0pt}}$$
$$(P \mid Q \mid R)\backslash\{a,b\} \ \xrightarrow{[p,q]} \ (P \mid Q \mid R)\backslash\{a,b\}$$

$$\text{Con}_1 \ \overline{\rule{6cm}{0pt}}$$
$$PQR \ \xrightarrow{[p,q]} \ (P \mid Q \mid R)\backslash\{a,b\}$$

$$\text{Con}_2 \ \overline{\rule{6cm}{0pt}}$$
$$PQR \ \xrightarrow{[p,q]} \ PQR$$

Exercise 3.9

The transition which is not possible for the agent PQR when reconsidered as an agent is $PQR \ \xrightarrow{[p,q]} \ PQR$. This is because the agent R has no observable actions and therefore must synchronise with P or Q or both in order to contribute to the fully synchronous transitions required by SCCS*. The other transitions are valid in the SCCS* interpretation because all three sub-agents are involved.

Exercise 3.10

One solution is to allocate D a resource of six es which it will use to keep track of the numbers of as, bs and cs performed. The other three agents must be forced to perform an $\bar{e}$ everytime they perform an a, b or c. In addition, the agent D must never be allowed to idle except, perhaps, when waiting for the action *start* from the environment.

$$D \stackrel{\text{def}}{=} 1:D + [d,d,d,\overline{start}]:D1$$
$$D1 \stackrel{\text{def}}{=} [e]:D2 + [e,e]:D3 + [e,e,e]:D4$$
$$D2 \stackrel{\text{def}}{=} [e]:D3 + [e,e]:D4 + [e,e,e]:D5$$
$$D3 \stackrel{\text{def}}{=} [e]:D4 + [e,e]:D5 + [e,e,e]:D6$$
$$D4 \stackrel{\text{def}}{=} [e]:D5 + [e,e]:D6 + [e,e,e]:D$$
$$D5 \stackrel{\text{def}}{=} [e]:D6 + [e,e]:D$$
$$D6 \stackrel{\text{def}}{=} [e]:D$$

We will only define the agent C as the other two agents are very similar:

$$C1 \stackrel{\text{def}}{=} 1:C1 + [\overline{d}]:C2$$
$$C2 \stackrel{\text{def}}{=} 1:C2 + [c,\overline{e}]:C1$$

A.3 Chapter 4

Exercise 4.1
Discussed in next section (4.4).

Exercise 4.2
Given $B \stackrel{\text{def}}{=} a.b.c.B$ we can define the four sub-agents required by systematically relabelling the actions. The action b will be relabelled b_i for agent B_i, while the actions a and b will be used to ensure that all the agents $B_1, \ldots, B_4$ fire in the correct order.

$$B \stackrel{\text{def}}{=} a.b.c.B$$
$$B_i \stackrel{\text{def}}{=} B[m_{i-1}/a, \overline{b_i}/b, \overline{m_{imod4}}/c] \quad (i \in \{1,\ldots,4\})$$

This is fine except for the fact that when we come to compose all the B_i in parallel we see that they are all offering the action m_{i-1} and the whole system is deadlocked. The simple way round this is to prefix the agent B_4 with the action $\overline{m_0}$, $4 \bmod 4 = 0$ of course, in the system's initial state. This gives us the following definition for the whole system:

$$System \stackrel{\text{def}}{=} (B_1 \mid B_2 \mid B_3 \mid \overline{m_0}.B4)\backslash\{m_0, \ldots, m_4\}$$

Exercise 4.3
A single set of points is a sort of bi-directional switch which takes a train on its input track and places it on one of its two output tracks but can also, of course, be used in the opposite direction to merge two tracks. There must also be actions available to change the setting of the points. In fact, we can

use a generic definition to capture the abstract notion of a point's states and then use relabelling to build up the actual definitions required:

$$PointState \stackrel{\text{def}}{=} enter.\overline{exit}.PointState + switch.PointState$$

$$PointLeft \stackrel{\text{def}}{=} PointState[exitLeft/exit, switchRight/switch]$$

$$PointRight \stackrel{\text{def}}{=} PointState[exitRight/exit, switchLeft/switch]$$

The task now is to use these definitions to build up the six points needed to build the sidings as laid out in the diagram. We will assume that all points use $PointLeft$ for their initial state.

$$P1 \stackrel{\text{def}}{=} PointLeft[\overline{p1el}/exitLeft, \overline{p1er}/exitRight,$$
$$sp1r/switchRight, sp1l/switchLeft]$$

$$P2 \stackrel{\text{def}}{=} PointLeft[p1er/enter, \overline{p2el}/exitLeft, \overline{p2er}/exitRight,$$
$$sp2r/switchRight, sp2l/switchLeft]$$

$$P3 \stackrel{\text{def}}{=} PointLeft[p2er/enter, \overline{p3el}/exitLeft, \overline{p3er}/exitRight,$$
$$sp3r/switchRight, sp3l/switchLeft]$$

$$P4 \stackrel{\text{def}}{=} PointLeft[p3er/\overline{exitLeft}, p3el/\overline{exitRight}, \overline{p4e}/enter,$$
$$sp4l/switchLeft, sp4r/switchRight]$$

$$P5 \stackrel{\text{def}}{=} PointLeft[p2el/\overline{exitLeft}, p1el/\overline{exitRight}, \overline{p5e}/enter,$$
$$sp5l/switchLeft, sp5r/switchRight]$$

$$P6 \stackrel{\text{def}}{=} PointLeft[p4e/\overline{exitLeft}, p5e/\overline{exitRight}, \overline{exit}/enter,$$
$$sp6l/switchLeft, sp6r/switchRight]$$

$$Siding \stackrel{\text{def}}{=} (P1 \mid \ldots \mid P6)\backslash\{p1e, \ldots\}$$

Exercise 4.4

To output a three-bit pattern in reverse order we have to read the bits from $DataMan$ but store the first two so that we can output the last first etc. To so this we can make use of the variables $A1$ and $A2$, which we defined earlier in chapter 4:

$$Rev \stackrel{\text{def}}{=} (RW \mid A1 \mid A2)\backslash\{rd0A_i, rd1A_i, \ldots\}$$

$$RW \stackrel{\text{def}}{=} rev.\overline{reqout}.RW0$$

$$RW0 \stackrel{\text{def}}{=} out0.\overline{rd0A1}.RW1 + out1.\overline{rd1A1}.RW1$$

$$RW1 \stackrel{\text{def}}{=} out0.\overline{rd0A2}.RW2 + out1.\overline{rd1A2}.RW2$$

$$RW2 \stackrel{\text{def}}{=} out0.\overline{revout0}.RW3 + out1.\overline{revout1}.RW3$$

$$RW3 \stackrel{\text{def}}{=} wrt0A2.\overline{revout0}.RW4 + wrt1A2.\overline{revout1}.RW4$$

$$RW4 \stackrel{\text{def}}{=} wrt0A1.\overline{revout0}.RW + wrt1A1.\overline{revout1}.RW$$

$LogicOr$ and $LogicAnd$ are quite similar to each other and need little explanation:

$$LogicOr \overset{\text{def}}{=} reqOr.\overline{reqout}.LogicOr1$$
$$LogicOr1 \overset{\text{def}}{=} out0.LogicOr2 + out1.\overline{true}.\overline{end}.LogicOr$$
$$LogicOr2 \overset{\text{def}}{=} out0.LogicOr3 + out1.\overline{true}.\overline{end}.LogicOr$$
$$LogicOr1 \overset{\text{def}}{=} out0.\overline{false}.LogicOr + out1.\overline{true}.LogicOr$$

$$LogicAnd \overset{\text{def}}{=} reqAnd.\overline{reqout}.LogicAnd1$$
$$LogicAnd1 \overset{\text{def}}{=} out1.LogicAnd2 + out0.\overline{false}.\overline{end}.LogicAnd$$
$$LogicAnd2 \overset{\text{def}}{=} out1.LogicAnd3 + out1.\overline{false}.\overline{end}.LogicAnd$$
$$LogicAnd3 \overset{\text{def}}{=} out1.\overline{true}.LogicAnd + out0.\overline{false}.LogicAnd$$

Exercise 4.5

The only difference between $Conv$ and $LogicOr$ is that the former returns $\overline{odd}$ or $\overline{even}$ depending on when it encounters a 1 while the latter always returns $\overline{true}$ if it reads a 1. The results for three 0s are $\overline{zero}$ and $\overline{false}$ respectively. Having defined $LogicOr$ we can define $LogicAnd$ by a further relabelling:

$$LogicOr \overset{\text{def}}{=} Conv[reqOr/req, true/odd, true/even, false/zero]$$
$$LogicAnd \overset{\text{def}}{=} LogicOr[reqAnd/reqOr, true/false, false/true,$$
$$out1/out0, out0/out1]$$

A.4 Chapter 5

Exercise 5.1

1. The conditional statement had to be introduced because in basic CCS, where there is no concept of data or values, actions with value parameters are treated as just actions and we can use agent choice to differentiate behaviours based on values. In value-passing CCS the separation of actions and values means that agent choice applies to actions only irrespective of value parameters and we therefore need the conditional statement in order to make behavioural choices based on data.

2. We will only define the one-armed conditional because the two-armed conditional can be introduced as a derived operator in the following manner:

$$if\ b\ then\ E\ else\ F \overset{\text{def}}{=} (if\ b\ then\ E) + (if\ \neg b\ then\ F)$$

Exercise 5.2

1. Respecifying the buffer to hold natural numbers instead of bits is relatively straightforward and you can use either of the patterns introduced above. For instance:

$$
\begin{aligned}
Cell &\overset{\text{def}}{=} in(x).\overline{out}(x).\dot{C}ell \\
Cell_1 &\overset{\text{def}}{=} Cell[m_1/out] \\
Cell_2 &\overset{\text{def}}{=} Cell[m_1/in, m_2/out] \\
Cell_3 &\overset{\text{def}}{=} Cell[m_2/in, m_3/out] \\
Cell_4 &\overset{\text{def}}{=} Cell[m_3/in] \\
Buff_N^4 &\overset{\text{def}}{=} (Cell_1 \mid Cell_2 \mid Cell_3 \mid Cell_4)\backslash\{m_1, m_2, m_3\}
\end{aligned}
$$

Notice that relabelling applies only to action names and not parameters. A problem arises when we come to respecify C and D because we do not now have separate actions $out1$ or $out2$ etc. to determine which of the two agents receives the next value. One solution is to introduce a filter, to interface between the buffer and C and D, which performs this task:

$$
\begin{aligned}
Filter &\overset{\text{def}}{=} out(x).if\ odd(x)\ then\ \overline{c}(x).Filter\ else\ \overline{d}(x).Filter \\
CVal &\overset{\text{def}}{=} c(x).c(y).c(z).\overline{mod3}(mean(x,y,z)).CVal \\
DVal &\overset{\text{def}}{=} d(w).d(x).d(y).d(z).\overline{mod4}(min(w,x,y,z)).DVal
\end{aligned}
$$

There are other solutions for $CVal$ and $DVal$ which use parameterised agents and allow the minimum value, for instance, to be computed after each input:

$$
\begin{aligned}
InitDVal &\overset{\text{def}}{=} DVal(0,0) \\
DVal(m,n) &\overset{\text{def}}{=} if\ n < 3\ then\ d(x).DVal(min(m,x),n+1) \\
&\qquad else\ d(x).\overline{mod4}(min(m,x)).DVal(0,0)
\end{aligned}
$$

2. The problem with generating natural numbers, in the manner of A and B above, is that we do not allow definitions of the form $Random \overset{\text{def}}{=} \overline{in}(x).Random$ because the parameter x is not bound to a particular value. We will see how to get around this problem later in the chapter.

Exercise 5.3

We can either introduce a semaphore, as we have done in previous examples, or make $Filter$ behave as a semaphore in addition to its existing role. The latter is an interesting exercise.

$$
\begin{aligned}
Filter^{+} &\overset{\text{def}}{=} getc.FilterC + getd.FilterD \\
FilterC &\overset{\text{def}}{=} s.FilterCVal + putc.Filter^{+} \\
FilterCVal &\overset{\text{def}}{=} out(x).if\ odd(x)\ then\ \overline{c}(x).FilterC\ else\ FilterCVal \\
FilterD &\overset{\text{def}}{=} \ldots
\end{aligned}
$$

The definition for $FilterD$ is very similar to $FilterC$. $Filter^{+}$ does not count how many acceptable values it passes and only looks for another after a synchronisation on s. $CVal$ and $DVal$ will need to be amended slightly to accommodate this.

Exercise 5.4

$$
\begin{aligned}
Buff_N^n(s) \overset{\text{def}}{=}\ &if\ length(s) > 0\ then\ \overline{out}(head(s)).Buff_N^n(tail(s)) \\
&+\ if\ length(s) < n\ then\ in(x).Buff_N^n(x::s)
\end{aligned}
$$

The two-armed conditional $if\ b\ then\ E\ else\ F$ was not used in this solution because the boolean conditions do not partition the set $\{0,\ldots,n\}$ and we wish to allow both input and output for values $0 < length(s) < n$. We will see in the semantics to follow that this is not a problem.

Exercise 5.5

1. The deadlocked agent **0** can be viewed as the agent which has a choice of doing nothing, and this can be represented by indexing over the empty set:

$$
\mathbf{0} \overset{\text{def}}{=} \sum_{v \in \{\}} E_v
$$

2. Binary choice can be defined by simply setting the indexing set to $\{1,2\}$

$$
E_1 + E_2 \overset{\text{def}}{=} \sum_{i \in \{1,2\}} E_i
$$

Exercise 5.6

Using an indexed sum over the natural numbers N in conjunction with τ actions effectively gives us a random number generator:

$$
Random \overset{\text{def}}{=} \sum_{v \in \mathrm{N}} \overline{out}(v).Random
$$

When composed with $Buff_N^4$ the resulting system would exhibit unbounded non-determinism in that not only do we have a non-deterministic choice of τ actions but there is also an infinite number of them.

Exercise 5.7

Applying the translation to the definition

$$VarVal(x) \stackrel{\text{def}}{=} \overline{wrt}(x).VarVal(x) + rd(y).VarVal(y)$$

gives us two basic CCS definitions to translate: one for 0 and one for 1. We will just translate the former:

$$VarVal(0) \stackrel{\text{def}}{=} \parallel \overline{wrt}(x).VarVal(x) + rd(y).VarVal(y)\{0/x\} \parallel$$

This requires the following translation:

$$
\begin{aligned}
&\parallel \overline{wrt}(0).VarVal(0) + rd(y).VarVal(y) \parallel \\
= \quad &\parallel \overline{wrt}(0).VarVal(0) \parallel + \parallel rd(y).VarVal(y) \parallel \\
= \quad &\overline{wrt}_0. \parallel VarVal(0) \parallel + rd_0. \parallel VarVal(0) \parallel + rd_1. \parallel VarVal(1) \parallel \\
= \quad &\overline{wrt}_0.VarVal_0 + rd_0.VarVal_0 + rd_1.VarVal_1
\end{aligned}
$$

The application of the substitutions is not shown.

Exercise 5.8

We approach the translation top-down. All agent constants are without parameters and so we concentrate on their defining expressions:

$$
\begin{aligned}
&\parallel (T \mid M \mid R) \backslash \{ok, s, r\} \parallel \\
= \quad &\parallel (T \mid M \mid R) \parallel \backslash \{l_v \mid l \in \{s, r\} \wedge v \in ASCII\} \cup \{ok\} \\
= \quad &(\parallel T \parallel\parallel M \parallel\parallel R \parallel) \backslash \{l_v \mid l \in \{s, r\} \wedge v \in ASCII\} \cup \{ok\} \\
= \quad &(T \mid M \mid R) \backslash \{l_v \mid l \in \{s, r\} \wedge v \in ASCII\} \cup \{ok\}
\end{aligned}
$$

T, M and R are mostly fairly straightforward. Some care is required for R because $receive(x)$ is an input and not an output as might be expected. This means that the parameter x of $receive$ is not bound by $r(x)$ – a mistake in the specification perhaps but to be translated as seen. The translation of M only is given:

$$
\begin{aligned}
&\parallel \overline{ok}.s(x).(\overline{r}(x).M + \tau.M) \parallel \\
&\overline{ok}. \parallel s(x).(\overline{r}(x).M + \tau.M) \parallel \\
&\overline{ok}. \textstyle\sum_{v \in ASCII} s_v. \parallel (\overline{r}(x).M + \tau.M)\{v/x\} \parallel \\
&\overline{ok}. \textstyle\sum_{v \in ASCII} s_v.(\parallel \overline{r}(v).M \parallel + \parallel \tau.M \parallel) \\
&\overline{ok}. \textstyle\sum_{v \in ASCII} s_v.(\overline{r_v}. \parallel M \parallel + \tau. \parallel M \parallel) \\
&\overline{ok}. \textstyle\sum_{v \in ASCII} s_v.(\overline{r_v}.M + \tau.M)
\end{aligned}
$$

Exercise 5.9

It is necessary to identify the constants required and then to make the necessary label definitions that depend on them.

The only constant is N the set of natural numbers. The following label definitions are required:

$$Label \quad in(N), out(N), req, reqout, odd, even, zero, end$$

It still remains to add typing information to all agent constants with parameters, eg.

$$DMVal(x : \mathrm{N}, y : \mathrm{N}, z : \mathrm{N}) \stackrel{\text{def}}{=} \ldots$$

Exercise 5.10

The translation should hold no surprises now and you should have generated the following basic CCS definitions:

$$
\begin{aligned}
Queue &\stackrel{\text{def}}{=} (Q1 \mid Q2) \backslash \{m_t, m_f\} \\
Q1 &\stackrel{\text{def}}{=} in_t.Q1'_t + in_f.Q1'_f \\
Q1'_t &\stackrel{\text{def}}{=} \overline{m_t}.Q1 \\
Q1'_f &\stackrel{\text{def}}{=} \overline{m_f}.Q1 \\
Q2 &\stackrel{\text{def}}{=} m_t.Q2'_t + m_f.Q2'_f + \overline{novalue}.Q2 \\
Q2'_t &\stackrel{\text{def}}{=} \overline{out_t}.Q2 \\
Q2'_f &\stackrel{\text{def}}{=} \overline{out_f}.Q2
\end{aligned}
$$

Exercise 5.11

You will need to define $Const\ B^+ = \{t, f, u\}$ and use this to construct the set of labels. The agents themselves can be defined as below:

$$
\begin{aligned}
Logic &\stackrel{\text{def}}{=} and.LogicAnd + or.LogicOr \\
LogicAnd &\stackrel{\text{def}}{=} out(x).LogicAnd(x) + novalue.LogicAnd(u) \\
LogicAnd(x\!:\!B^+) &\stackrel{\text{def}}{=} out(y).\overline{return}(and3(x,y)).Logic + \\
&\qquad novalue.\overline{return}(and3(x,u)).Logic \\
LogicOr &\stackrel{\text{def}}{=} out(x).LogicOr(x) + novalue.LogicOr(u) \\
LogicOr(x\!:\!B^+) &\stackrel{\text{def}}{=} out(y).\overline{return}(or3(x,y)).Logic + \\
&\qquad novalue.\overline{return}(or3(x,u)).Logic
\end{aligned}
$$

Exercise 5.12

The composition of the two systems will obviously give us:

$$LogSys \stackrel{\text{def}}{=} (Queue \mid Logic) \backslash \{out, novalue\}$$

which translates to

$$LogSys \stackrel{\text{def}}{=} (Queue \mid Logic) \backslash \{out_t, out_f, novalue\}$$

The translation of *Logic* will generate:

$$Logic \quad \overset{\text{def}}{=} \quad and.LogicAnd + or.LogicOr$$

$$LogicAnd \quad \overset{\text{def}}{=} \quad out_t.LogicAnd_t + out_f.LogicAnd_f + \\ novalue.LogicAnd_u$$

$$LogicAnd_t \quad \overset{\text{def}}{=} \quad out_t.\overline{return}_t.Logic + \\ out_f.\overline{return}_f.Logic + \\ novalue.\overline{return}_u.Logic$$

$$LogicAnd_f \quad \overset{\text{def}}{=} \quad out_t.\overline{return}_f.Logic + out_f.\overline{return}_f.Logic + \\ novalue.\overline{return}_f.Logic$$

$$LogicAnd_u \quad \overset{\text{def}}{=} \quad out_t.\overline{return}_u.Logic + out_f.\overline{return}_f.Logic + \\ novalue.\overline{return}_u.Logic$$

$$LogicOr \quad \overset{\text{def}}{=} \quad out_t.LogicOr_t + out_f.LogicOr_f + \\ novalue.LogicOr_u$$

$$LogicOr_t \quad \overset{\text{def}}{=} \quad out_t.\overline{return}_t.Logic + out_f.\overline{return}_t.Logic + \\ novalue.\overline{return}_t.Logic$$

$$LogicOr_f \quad \overset{\text{def}}{=} \quad out_t.\overline{return}_t.Logic + out_f.\overline{return}_f.Logic + \\ novalue.\overline{return}_u.Logic$$

$$LogicOr_u \quad \overset{\text{def}}{=} \quad out_t.\overline{return}_t.Logic + out_f.\overline{return}_u.Logic + \\ novalue.\overline{return}_u.Logic$$

A.5 Chapter 6

Exercise 6.1

Solutions discussed in section 6.4.

Exercise 6.2

Solutions discussed in section 6.5.

Exercise 6.3

The sensible place to turn the system off is when both sets of lights are on red. This occurs at the end of a minor lights sequence when a synchronisation on *mi* occurs. We can force the major lights to check the state of a switch before returning to green.

$$MajorWait \stackrel{\text{def}}{=} mi.(setOff.MajorOff + seton.MajorContinue$$
$$MajorContinue \stackrel{\text{def}}{=} maA_{on}.maA_{off}.maG_{on}.Major$$
$$MajorOff \stackrel{\text{def}}{=} setOn.MajorContinue$$
$$SwitchOn \stackrel{\text{def}}{=} \overline{setOn}.SwitchOn+$$
$$off.(maR_{off} \ddagger miR_off).SwitchOff$$
$$SwitchOff \stackrel{\text{def}}{=} on.(maR_{on} \ddagger miR_{on}).SwitchOn+$$
$$\overline{setOff}.SwitchOff$$

This might be regarded as only a partial solution because we can only turn the system off after the minor lights have become active. Perhaps the best way to turn the system off when the major lights are on green and the minor lights are on red is to disable the sensor and then turn the lights off.

In any such solution we have to be sure that non-determinism does not prevent the guarantee of system shutdown.

Exercise 6.4

$$MinorPL \stackrel{\text{def}}{=} (MinRon \mid MinG \mid MinA1)\backslash\{c1, c2, c3, c4, c5\}$$
$$MinG \stackrel{\text{def}}{=} c3.miG_{on}.miG_{off}.\overline{c4}.MinG$$
$$MinA1 \stackrel{\text{def}}{=} ok1.miA_{on}.\overline{c1}.MinA2$$
$$MinA2 \stackrel{\text{def}}{=} minAoff.c2.\overline{c3}.MinA3$$
$$MinA3 \stackrel{\text{def}}{=} c4.miA_{on}.miA_{off}.\overline{c5}.MinA1$$
$$MinRon \stackrel{\text{def}}{=} c1.miR_{off}.\overline{c2}.MinRoff$$
$$MinRoff \stackrel{\text{def}}{=} c5.(miR_{on} \ddagger \overline{resetS}).\overline{ok2}.MinRon$$

Exercise 6.5

1. The transition graph for $Junction1$ with the new versions of $MajorWait$ and $Minor1$ is much the same as for the previous version except that every time a synchronisation between $done$ and $\overline{done}$ occurs the null agent is composed in parallel with the other, active, agents. The first instance of this is

$$(MajorWait \mid Minor2 \mid \mathbf{0} \mid resetS.Sensor)\backslash L$$

which means that our new system has an infinite state space whereas the earlier version had a finite state space.

2. Behaviourally, the two specifications are the same in that an observer could not tell the difference in observable behaviour despite the extra τ-actions and the dramatic difference in state space.

Exercise 6.7

1. We can use SCCS to model a timed version of the lights by using the synchronous nature of the language to enable lights to be on or off for specific intervals. We use 1, the empty bag, to model a tick of the clock and model the minor green lights in the following manner:

$$Minor2 \stackrel{\text{def}}{=} [miG_{on}] \colon 1 \colon 1 \colon 1 \colon [miG_{off}] \colon \ldots$$

Using SCCS we can also model the concurrent switching off of the major red and amber lights: for instance, by the single action $[maR_{off}, maA_{off}]$.

2. The relationship between actions and time in SCCS is that all actions take exactly one unit of time which is why we had a delay of 3 between the switching on and off of the minor green lights.

A.6 Chapter 7

Exercise 7.1

1. Soft delays have the following form:

$$(t).\underline{\alpha}.P$$

These agents have to wait t units of time before the action α becomes available but will then be willing to wait as long as necessary before performing that action.

2. The general pattern for an agent that will be active for t units of time and then deadlock in terms of time is

$$P \mid (t).\mathbf{0}$$

In other words, after t units of time have elapsed actions will be possible but no further time will be able to pass. Thus any other agents composed in parallel with it will also be in temporal deadlock after t units of time.

3. $Timeout_t(P, \mathbf{0})$ is the agent which is forced to behave as P after a maximum delay of t.

Exercise 7.2

1. We use strong choice to model $TimeOut1$:

$$TimeOut1_t \stackrel{\text{def}}{=} \underline{\alpha}.P + (t).Q$$

This agent allows $\alpha.P$ to begin execution at the expense of Q as long as α occurs within t time units, otherwise an action will be forced either from $\alpha.P$ or Q, assuming of course that Q does not have a delay immediately available.

2. Using a combination of strong and weak choice we can specify $TimeOut2$:

$$TimeOut2_t \overset{\text{def}}{=} (t+1).Q + \!\!+ \underline{\alpha}.P + (t).0$$

This agent allows the action α to enable P to become active at the expense of P as long as it does so within t units of time, after which Q will be forced if a further delay of 1 time unit occurs. Strong choice binds more tightly than weak choice and so no parentheses are necessary in this case.

Exercise 7.3

1. Transition graph for $A1 \mid A2$

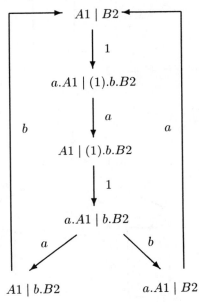

2. Not shown.

3. Transition graph for $A1 + B2$

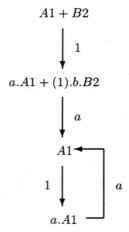

4. Transition graph for $A1 +\!\!+ B2$

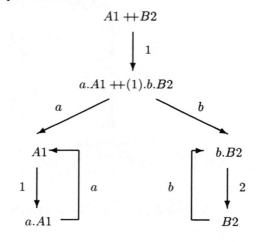

5. Transition graph for $\underline{a}.A1 + (2).b.B2$

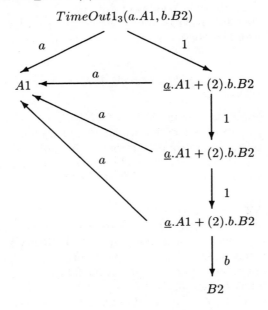

$$TimeOut1_3(a.A1, b.B2)$$

Exercise 7.4

1. Poof of $A1 \mid B2 \overset{1}{\leadsto} A1 \mid (1).b.B2$

$$
\cfrac{
  Time_1 \cfrac{\rule{5cm}{0.4pt}}{TCon_1 \cfrac{(1).a.A1 \overset{1}{\leadsto} a.A1}{A1 \overset{1}{\leadsto} a.A1}} \qquad
  Time_2 \cfrac{\rule{5cm}{0.4pt}}{TCon_1 \cfrac{(2).b.B2 \overset{1}{\leadsto} (1).b.B2}{B2 \overset{1}{\leadsto} (1).b.B2}}
}{
  TCom \qquad A1 \mid B2 \overset{1}{\leadsto} a.A1 \mid (1).b.B2
}
$$

2. Similar to the example in section 7.3.

A.7 Chapter 9

Exercise 9.1

First a strong bisimulation to establish $Buff_2 \sim B0'$:

$$
\begin{aligned}
\{ &(Buff_2 &,& \quad B0'), \\
&((\overline{m}.C_1 \mid C_2)\backslash &,& \quad B1'), \\
&((C_1 \mid \overline{out}.C_2)\backslash\{m\} &,& \quad in.B0' + \overline{out}.B2'), \\
&((\overline{m}.C_1 \mid \overline{out}.C_2)\backslash\{m\} &,& \quad B2')\}
\end{aligned}
$$

You should also find that $B0 \sim C \mid C$ even though the former preserves the order of inputs while the latter does not.

None of the other pairings can be related by strong bisimulation, $Buff_2 \not\sim C' \mid C' \not\sim B0$. For $Buff_2 \not\sim B0$ we observe the following:

$$\{(Buff_2 \quad , \quad B0),$$
$$((\overline{m}.C_1 \mid C_2)\backslash\{m\} \quad , \quad B1),$$
$$\cdots$$

$Buff_2 \sim B0$ is true iff $(\overline{m}.C_1 \mid C_2)\backslash\{m\} \sim B1$ is true but $(\overline{m}.C_1 \mid C_2)\backslash\{m\}$ can only do a τ action whilst $B0$ can do both in or $\overline{out}$ but not τ, and we therefore cannot build a strong bisimulation for these two agents.

Notice that $C' \mid C'$ is not strongly equivalent to any of the other agents in this exercise.

Exercise 9.2

You should find that D_0 is not strongly equivalent to any of the other three agents, which are all strongly equivalent. However, there is a problem in that G is not image-finite, ie. it does not have a finite state space, and thus we cannot build finite strong bisimulations to relate it to E_1 or F. Draw the transition graph for E_1, for instance, and then start to draw the transition graph for G. You should find that the behaviour patterns match up even though the numbers of states do not.

Exercise 9.3

9.1 You should now find that all agents are observationally equivalent. In particular you should have that $Buff_2 \approx B0$ and, perhaps surprisingly, $B0 \approx C' \mid C'$. The weak bisimulation for the latter is given below:

$$\{(B0 \quad , \quad C' \mid C'),$$
$$(B1 \quad , \quad C' \mid \tau.\overline{out}.C'),$$
$$(B1 \quad , \quad \tau.\overline{out}.C' \mid C'),$$
$$(B1 \quad , \quad C' \mid \overline{out}.C'),$$
$$(B1 \quad , \quad \overline{out}.C' \mid C'),$$
$$(B2 \quad , \quad \tau.\overline{out}.C' \mid \tau.\overline{out}.C'),$$
$$(B2 \quad , \quad \tau.\overline{out}.C' \mid \overline{out}.C'),$$
$$(B2 \quad , \quad \overline{out}.C' \mid \tau.\overline{out}.C'),$$
$$(B2 \quad , \quad \overline{out}.C' \mid \overline{out}.C')\}$$

9.2 You should now find that all these agents are also observationally equivalent. For instance:

$$\{(D_0 \quad , \quad E_1),$$
$$(D_1 \quad , \quad E_1),$$
$$(D_2 \quad , \quad E_2)\}$$

Be careful in the above not to add the pair (D_1, E_2) which are not observationally equivalent even though they arise as a result of τ-actions from the pair (D_0, E_1).

Exercise 9.4

1. $Mx \sim Spec_3$

2. $Mx \approx Spec_2 \approx Spec_3$

3. All strong equivalences are also observational equivalences. The former is a subset of the latter.

Exercise 9.5

Most of the observational equivalences established in the earlier exercises are also congruences because initial τ-actions can be matched by at least one initial τ action by other observationally equivalent agents. A particular exception arises from the set of agents D_0, E_1, F and G which are all observationally equivalent. However, D_0 is not congruent to the other three because although it can match initial τ-actions the resulting states are not observationally equivalent, eg. (D_1, E_2). The observational equivalence only worked by allowing D_0 an empty initial sequence of τ-actions which, of course, violates parts 2 and 3 of the definition of observational congruence.

Exercise 9.6

By substituting $in(e_1)$ for $in(x)$ etc. you can build up a simple bisimulation to prove that the two agents are observationally equivalent and in fact congruent. This only works because the two agents are data-independent, which means that data is only stored and does not affect behaviour. If conditional statements were included in their definitions then this simple extension to equivalences would not work.

A.8 Chapter 10

Exercise 10.1

1.

$$
\begin{array}{ll}
& \alpha.(P + \underline{\tau.\tau.P}) \quad \text{(PRE1)} \\
\approx^c & \alpha.\underline{(P + \tau.P)} \quad \text{(PRE2)} \\
\approx^c & \underline{\alpha.\tau.P} \quad \text{(PRE1)} \\
\approx^c & \alpha.P
\end{array}
$$

2.

$$
\begin{array}{ll}
\quad P + \underline{S} & \text{(CON1)} \\
\approx^c \quad P + \tau.(P + Q) & \text{(PRE2)} \\
\approx^c \quad P + \overline{((P + Q) + \tau.(P + Q))} & \text{(CH2)} \\
\approx^c \quad \overline{(P + (P + Q)) + \tau.(P + Q)} & \text{(CH2)} \\
\approx^c \quad \overline{((P + P) + Q)) + \tau.(P + Q)} & \text{(CH3)} \\
\approx^c \quad \overline{\tau.(P + Q)} & \text{(CON1)} \\
\approx^c \quad S &
\end{array}
$$

3.

$$
\begin{array}{ll}
\quad \overline{\tau.(P + T)} & \text{(PRE1)} \\
\approx^c \quad \overline{(P + \underline{T}) + \tau.(P + T)} & \text{(CON1)} \\
\approx^c \quad (P + \alpha.(Q + \tau.R)) + \tau.(P + T) & \text{(PRE3)} \\
\approx^c \quad (P + \overline{\alpha.(Q + \tau.R) + \alpha.R}) + \tau.(P + T) & \text{(CH2)} \\
\approx^c \quad \overline{((P + \alpha.(Q + \tau.R)) + \alpha.R) + \tau.(P + T)} & \text{(CH1)} \\
\approx^c \quad \overline{(\alpha.R + (P + \alpha.(Q + \tau.R))) + \tau.(P + T)} & \text{(CH2)} \\
\approx^c \quad \alpha.R + \overline{((P + \alpha.(Q + \tau.R)) + \tau.(P + T))} & \text{(CON1)} \\
\approx^c \quad \alpha.R + ((P + \overline{T}) + \tau.(P + T)) & \text{(PRE2)} \\
\approx^c \quad \alpha.R + \overline{\tau.(P + T)} & \text{(CH1)} \\
\approx^c \quad \tau.(P + T) + \alpha.R &
\end{array}
$$

Exercise 10.2

$$
\begin{array}{ll}
\quad G & \text{(CON1)} \\
\approx^c \quad (G_1 \mid G_2) \backslash \{c, l\} & \text{(CON1)} \times 2 \\
\approx^c \quad (a.G_1 + \bar{c}.0 \mid c.b.G_3) \backslash \{c, l\} & \text{(EX)} \\
\approx^c \quad a.(G_1 \mid c.b.G_3) \backslash \{c, l\} + \tau.(0 \mid b.G_3) \backslash \{c, l\} & \text{(CON1)} \\
\approx^c \quad a.(G_1 \mid G_2) \backslash \{c, l\} + \tau.(0 \mid b.G_3) \backslash \{c, l\} & \text{(CON1)} \\
\approx^c \quad a.G + \tau.(0 \mid b.G_3) \backslash \{c, l\} & \text{CH1, (CH4)} \\
\approx^c \quad a.G + \tau.b.G_3 \backslash \{c, l\} & \text{(CON1)} \\
\approx^c \quad a.G + \tau.b.(G_1 \mid G_2) \backslash \{c, l\} & \text{(CON1)} \\
\approx^c \quad a.G + \tau.b.G &
\end{array}
$$

Exercise 10.3

If you did exercise 10.2 then you have more or less solved this problem already. Using the first constant law it is easy to show that $E_1 \approx^c a.E_1 + \tau.b.E_1$ and we can use this pattern for our equation, $X \approx^c a.X + \tau.b.X$. In exercise 10.2 we already proved that G has this pattern and by the second constant law we can therefore duduce that E_1 and G are congruent.

We cannot prove $D_0 \approx^c G$ because they do not match up on initial τ-actions. The equational laws preserve observational congruence.

Exercise 10.4

The problem should be familiar by now. You need to find some equations that characterise the behaviour pattern involved. Using $Spec_1$ etc. you identify this pattern, which amounts to three equations if you take the definitions for $Spec_i$ as they stand or two if you simplify them a little:

$$X \stackrel{\text{def}}{=} \tau.\overline{send}.Y$$
$$Y \stackrel{\text{def}}{=} receive.X + \tau.Z$$
$$Z \stackrel{\text{def}}{=} receive.\overline{send}.Y + \overline{send}.receive.Y$$

$Spec$ should satisfy these equations easily.

You then need to apply the expansion law etc. to $System$ to find expressions to substitute for X, Y and Z in your set of equations.

Exercise 10.6

No answer, but two hints instead:

1. Simplify the right hand side of the definition for $Proc2$.

2. It will help if you can prove the following:

$$Proc1 \approx^c (A \mid \overline{n}.b.B \mid m.C)\backslash\{m, n\}$$

A.9 Chapter 11

Exercise 11.1

1. It is difficult to be precise in English but we might identify the following statements about each of the agents:

   (a) D is the only agent which can do an a and then have the choice of both b and c.

   (b) E is the only agent that can start with an a and then do b but not c or c but not b. In addition, E cannot do a d as its second action.

   (c) F is the only agent which can do an e but not an a as its first action.

   (d) G is the only agent that can do both an e and an a as its first action.

2. Several properties spring to mind:

   (a) All agents can do an e or an a as their first action. This is assuming we mean 'or' in the logical sense of at least one of the two actions and possibly both.

   (b) All agents can do a b or a c as their second action, again taking 'or' in the logical sense.

Exercise 11.2

1. $\langle a \rangle tt \wedge [a](\langle b \rangle tt \wedge \langle c \rangle)tt$

2. $\langle a \rangle tt \wedge [a]((\langle b \rangle tt \wedge [c]ff) \vee ([b]ff \wedge \langle c \rangle tt) \wedge [d]ff)$
3. $[a]ff \wedge \langle e \rangle tt$
4. $\langle a \rangle tt \wedge \langle e \rangle tt$

Exercise 11.3

1. $\langle forward \rangle tt \wedge [forward]\langle forward \rangle tt$
2. $\langle forward \rangle tt \wedge [forward](\langle right \rangle tt \wedge [right](\langle left \rangle tt \wedge [back]ff))$
3. The only way to express this at present is to say that *forward* is possible and every other action in the transition system is impossible:

$$\langle forward \rangle tt \wedge [back]ff \wedge \ldots$$

4. Similar problem to 3 above, except this time there are more permutations. We will come back to this problem later in the chapter.

Exercise 11.4

1. $[-forward]ff$
2. $[-][-][forward]ff$

Exercise 11.5

1. $[inleft][inright][-]ff \wedge [inright][inleft]ff$

   Notice that $[inleft, inright][inleft, inright][-]$ does not express this property because it could mean that *inleft* followed by *inleft* could lead to a deadlock, which is not the case for the CCS model in question.

2. This is difficult for several reasons. First, we can only specify finite-length properties and secondly we have to express a property which captures the idea that the buffer must be empty before direction is changed. We will come back to this in the next chapter. The property $[inleft][\tau]\langle - \rangle tt$ expresses the idea that as long as an *inleft* is followed by a τ then no deadlock will occur goes some way towards an answer.

A.10 Chapter 12

Exercise 12.1

1. It is always true that after an a both b and c are possible. You could also say that it is always true that a, b and c are possible.
2. It is always true that a is possible or b and not c or c and not b.
3. It is always true that only e is possible or after any action only e will be possible.
4. It is always possible to perform d sometime in the future.

Exercise 12.2

1. $\mathbf{AG}[a](\langle b \rangle tt \wedge \langle c \rangle tt)$
2. $\mathbf{AG}(\langle a \rangle tt \vee (\langle b \rangle tt \wedge [c]ff) \vee (\langle c \rangle tt \wedge [b]ff))$
3. $\mathbf{AG}[-e]ff \vee (\langle - \rangle tt \wedge [-][-e]ff)$
4. $\mathbf{AG}\,\mathbf{EF}\langle d \rangle tt$

Exercise 12.4

1. $\mathbf{EF}\langle back \rangle tt$
2. $\mathbf{AGEF}\langle forward \rangle tt$
3. $\mathbf{AG}\neg(\langle left \rangle tt \wedge \langle right \rangle tt)$
4. $\mathbf{AF}\langle right \rangle tt$
5. $\mathbf{AG}[left]([left]ff\,\mathcal{U}\,\langle right \rangle tt)$

   Similarly for $right$. This is in fact a very common form for properties of real-time systems.
6. $AF[right, left, back]ff$ As with many of these properties expressed in English, there are other possible interpretations.

Exercise 12.5

It is best to check these on the Concurrency Workbench but we can make some observations.

1. This is true for $start$ because there is a trace from the initial state which leads to $back$ being possible.
2. This is false because if the action $stop$ is ever performed then no actions at all including $forward$ would be possible. Remember, this is a combination of $Always$ and $Sometime$, not just $Sometime$.
3. This is true, there is no state in which both actions are possible.

4. Not true as for 2.

5. This is true although we might also wish to add that after a *left* the action *right* might never occur. Which version of U is this?

6. This is true for the property we have expressed because performing the action *stop* immediately leads to a deadlock, which means none of the actions in question has occurred, or will ever occur. Remember finite traces which lead to deadlocked states are valid computations and deadlocked states can satisfy negative properties.

B

Reference Manual

In section B.1 we collect together the syntactic and semantic definitions for all the languages we have studied in Part I of the book. In the second section the reader will find all the basic definitions used in Part II where we considered formal reasoning about specifications. Milner's book, *Communication and Concurrency* [Mil89], is generally regarded as the de facto standard for the CCS family of languages and any deviations from this or other such standards are noted at the end of the appropriate sections.

B.1 Naming conventions

We start by listing the principal naming conventions adopted throughout this book and which, wherever possible, also follow those of Milner:

$\mathcal{A}$ An infinite set of names $a, b, c, \ldots$ range over $\mathcal{A}$; and in, get, put, etc. are examples of names.

$\overline{\mathcal{A}}$ An infinite set of co-names $\bar{a}, \bar{b}, \bar{c}, \ldots$ range over $\overline{\mathcal{A}}$; and $\overline{get}, \overline{put}, \overline{out}, \overline{mod3}$ are examples of co-names.

$\mathcal{L}$ The set of labels $\mathcal{A} \cup \overline{\mathcal{A}}$, $l, l', \ldots$ range over $\mathcal{L}$. We will use K and L to stand for subsets of $\mathcal{L}$.

Act The set of all possible actions $\mathcal{L} \cup \{\tau\}$: α and β range over **Act**.

$\mathcal{K}$ The set of agent constants $A, B \ldots$, range over $\mathcal{K}$; and $Mx, Buff_2, B0$, etc. are examples of agent constants.

$\mathcal{X}$ The set of agent variables $X, Y, Z, \ldots$ range over $\mathcal{X}$.

$\mathcal{E}$ The set of basic CCS agent expressions $E, F, G, \ldots$ range over $\mathcal{E}$.

$\mathcal{E}^+$ The set of value-passing CCS agent expressions $E, F, G, \ldots$ were also used to range over $\mathcal{E}^+$.

$\mathcal{E}^T$ The set of TCCS agent expressions $E, F, G, \ldots$ were also used to range over $\mathcal{E}^T$.

B.2 Syntax and semantics

B.2.1 Basic CCS

The complete syntax for basic CCS is given below. Notice that the relabelling operator from chapter 4 is included.

$$
\begin{aligned}
\mathcal{E} \quad ::= \quad & \mathbf{0} \\
\mid \quad & A \\
\mid \quad & \mathcal{E}\backslash K \\
\mid \quad & \mathcal{E}[f] \\
\mid \quad & (\mathcal{E}) \\
\mid \quad & \alpha.\mathcal{E} \\
\mid \quad & \mathcal{E} \mid \mathcal{E} \\
\mid \quad & \mathcal{E} + \mathcal{E}
\end{aligned}
$$

The operators are given the following semantics:

$$\mathbf{Pref} \ \dfrac{}{\alpha.E \xrightarrow{\alpha} E}$$

$$\mathbf{Sum_1} \ \dfrac{E \xrightarrow{\alpha} E'}{E + F \xrightarrow{\alpha} E'} \qquad \mathbf{Sum_2} \ \dfrac{F \xrightarrow{\alpha} F'}{E + F \xrightarrow{\alpha} F'}$$

$$\mathbf{Com_1} \ \dfrac{E \xrightarrow{\alpha} E'}{E \mid F \xrightarrow{\alpha} E' \mid F} \qquad \mathbf{Com_2} \ \dfrac{F \xrightarrow{\alpha} F'}{E \mid F \xrightarrow{\alpha} E \mid F'}$$

$$\mathbf{Com_3} \ \dfrac{E \xrightarrow{l} E' \ F \xrightarrow{\bar{l}} F'}{E \mid F \xrightarrow{\tau} E' \mid F'}$$

$$\mathbf{Res} \ \dfrac{E \xrightarrow{\alpha} E'}{E\backslash L \xrightarrow{\alpha} E'\backslash L} \ (\alpha, \bar{\alpha} \notin L) \quad \mathbf{Rel} \ \dfrac{E \xrightarrow{l} E'}{E[f] \xrightarrow{f(l)} E'[f]}$$

$$\mathbf{Con_1} \ \dfrac{E \xrightarrow{\alpha} E'}{A \xrightarrow{\alpha} E'} \ (A \overset{\text{def}}{=} E) \quad \mathbf{Con_2} \ \dfrac{E \xrightarrow{\alpha} E'}{E \xrightarrow{\alpha} A} \ (A \overset{\text{def}}{=} E')$$

$$\mathbf{Brac_1} \ \dfrac{E \xrightarrow{\alpha} E'}{(E) \xrightarrow{\alpha} E'} \ (E \equiv E_1 + E_2) \ \mathbf{Brac_2} \ \dfrac{E \xrightarrow{\alpha} E'}{(E) \xrightarrow{\alpha} (E')} \ (E \equiv E_1 \mid E_2)$$

$$\mathbf{Rec} \ \dfrac{E\{rec(X,E)/X\} \xrightarrow{\alpha} E'}{rec(X,E) \xrightarrow{\alpha} E'}$$

The *full* definition of relabelling is

$$\mathbf{RealRel} \ \dfrac{E \xrightarrow{l} E'}{E[f] \xrightarrow{[f](l)} E'[f]} \quad [f] = Id_{Act} \oplus f \oplus \bar{f}$$

Milner defines the following operators for basic CCS:

$$\mathcal{E} \quad ::= \quad E \backslash R \quad (R \subseteq \mathbf{L})$$
$$\mid \quad E[f]$$
$$\mid \quad \alpha.E$$
$$\mid \quad E \mid F$$
$$\mid \quad \sum_{i \in I} E_i$$

In terms of semantics, Milner gives a single rule for constants, $\mathbf{Con_1}$, and no rules for brackets. Binary choice is replaced by a generalised form, indexed choice, the definition for which is:

$$\mathbf{Sum_j} \quad \frac{E_j \xrightarrow{\alpha} E_j'}{\sum_{i \in I} E_i \xrightarrow{\alpha} E_j} \quad (j \in I)$$

This definition of choice allows not only the binary choice rules given above but also the deadlocked agent 0 to be derived. In the former case the indexed set is simply $\{1,2\}$, while in the latter case 0 has the following definition:

$$0 \stackrel{\text{def}}{=} \sum_{i \in \{\}} E_i$$

Notice that if we are to translate value-passing CCS into basic CCS then the indexed choice operator, introduced in chapter 5 of this book, must form part of basic CCS.

The definitions for the interrupt operator, which does not form part of basic CCS, are given here for convenience. The associated timed rule is given in the TCCS section.

$$\mathbf{Int_1} \quad \frac{E \xrightarrow{\alpha} E'}{E \uparrow F \xrightarrow{\alpha} E' \uparrow F} \qquad \mathbf{Int_2} \quad \frac{F \xrightarrow{\alpha} F'}{E \uparrow F \xrightarrow{\alpha} F'}$$

B.2.2 CCS^+, CCS^* and $SCCS^*$

The syntax of CCS^+ is as for CCS because it is the semantic interpretation of the expressions that has changed:

$$\mathbf{PreP} \frac{}{\alpha.E \xrightarrow{[\alpha]} E}$$

$$\mathbf{PreP^*} \frac{}{\sigma.E \xrightarrow{\sigma} E}$$

$$\mathbf{SumP_1} \frac{E \xrightarrow{\sigma} E'}{E + F \xrightarrow{\sigma} E'} \qquad \mathbf{SumP_2} \frac{F \xrightarrow{\sigma} F'}{E + F \xrightarrow{\sigma} F'}$$

$$\mathbf{ComP_1} \frac{E \xrightarrow{\sigma} E'}{E \mid F \xrightarrow{\sigma} E' \mid F} \qquad \mathbf{ComP_2} \frac{F \xrightarrow{\sigma} F'}{E \mid F \xrightarrow{\sigma} E \mid F'}$$

$$\textbf{ComP}_3 \ \frac{E \xrightarrow{\sigma_1} E' \ F \xrightarrow{\sigma_2} F'}{E \mid F \xrightarrow{T(\sigma_1,\sigma_2)} E' \mid F'}$$

$$\textbf{ResP} \ \frac{E \xrightarrow{\sigma} E'}{E \backslash L \xrightarrow{\sigma} E' \backslash L} \ (dom \ \sigma \cap (L \cup \overline{L}) = \{\}$$

$$\textbf{ConP} \ \frac{E \xrightarrow{\sigma} E'}{P \xrightarrow{\sigma} E'} \ (P \overset{\text{def}}{=} E)$$

$$\textbf{BracP}_1 \ \frac{E \xrightarrow{\sigma} E'}{(E) \xrightarrow{\sigma} E'} \ (E \equiv E_1 + E_2) \quad \textbf{BracP}_2 \ \frac{E \xrightarrow{\sigma} E'}{(E) \xrightarrow{\sigma} (E')} \ (E \equiv E_1 \mid E_2)$$

$$\textbf{RecP} \ \frac{E\{rec(X,E)/X\} \xrightarrow{\sigma} E'}{rec(X,E) \xrightarrow{\sigma} E'}$$

$$
\begin{aligned}
T \quad &: \quad bag \ \mathbf{L} \times bag \ \mathbf{L} \to bag \ \mathbf{L} \\
T(x,y) \quad &= \quad let \ z = x \cap_+ \overline{y} \ in \\
&\qquad (x \backslash_+ z) \ \cup_+ \ (y \backslash_+ \overline{z})
\end{aligned}
$$

The syntax of CCS* is as for CCS$^+$ except that all prefixes and transitions are given in terms of bags of actions instead of atomic actions. The prefix expression $\alpha.E$ for the latter is replaced by $\sigma.E$. Of course, this has the effect of replacing atomic action prefixes by bags of atomic actions wherever they occur in all other expressions.

Semantics of CCS* is as for CCS$^+$ except that **PreP** is replaced by the following rule:

$$\textbf{PreP}^* \ \frac{}{\sigma.E \xrightarrow{\sigma} E}$$

to accomodate the syntactic changes. The other change is that the restriction operator '\' is replaced by '/' which means permission instead. This is done because the function T effectively forces synchronisations.

In the syntax for SCCS*, the prefix operator '.' is replaced by ':' ; Milner demonstrates that the former can be defined in terms of the latter.

The semantics for SCCS* is arrived at by simply deleting the rules **Comp$_1$** and **Comp$_2$** and thus achieving a synchronous calculus.

Neither CCS$^+$ nor CCS* is defined by Milner but they were developed by the author, along with SCCS*, for teaching purposes. Milner does, however, define a language called the Synchronous Calculus of Communicating Systems (SCCS), to which the author's SCCS* corresponds. The main difference is that Milner defines concurrent actions in terms of a commutative group rather than bags. As stated in the body of the text, any work with truly concurrent systems should be undertaken in SCCS, not in SCCS* which is just a teaching language.

B.2.3 Value-passing CCS

$$\mathcal{E}^+ \quad ::= \quad \mathbf{0}$$
$$| \quad E \backslash R$$
$$| \quad \mathcal{E}^+[f]$$
$$| \quad l(x).\mathcal{E}^+$$
$$| \quad \bar{l}(x).\mathcal{E}^+$$
$$| \quad \alpha.\mathcal{E}^+$$
$$| \quad \mathcal{E}^+ \mid \mathcal{E}^+$$
$$| \quad \mathcal{E}^+ + \mathcal{E}^+$$
$$| \quad if\ b\ then\ \mathcal{E}^+$$

$\|\text{-}\| \ \mathcal{E}^+ \rightarrow Exp$

$$
\begin{aligned}
\|l(x).E\| &= \textstyle\sum_{v \in V} l_v.\|E\{v/x\}\| \\
\|\bar{l}(e).E\| &= \bar{l}_e.\|E\| \\
\|\alpha.E\| &= \alpha.\|E\| \\
\|E + F\| &= \|E\| + \|F\| \\
\|E \mid F\| &= \|E\| \mid \|F\| \\
\|E \backslash R\| &= \|E\| \backslash \{l_v \mid l \in R \wedge v \in V\} \\
\|E[f]\| &= \|E\|[\widehat{f}] \ \ (\widehat{f}(l_v) = f(l)_v) \\
\|if\ b\ then\ E\| &= \left\{ \begin{array}{l} \|E\| \ \ \text{if } b = true \\ \mathbf{0} \ \ \text{otherwise} \end{array} \right. \\
\|P(e_1, \dots, e_n)\| &= P_{e_1, \dots, e_n}
\end{aligned}
$$

The presentation of both the syntax and semantics for value-passing CCS is to all intents and purposes that of Milner.

B.2.4 Timed CCS (TCCS)

The syntax of the strong version of TCCS differs from that of CCS in a number of ways. Expressions of the forms $(t).E$ and $\underline{\alpha}.E$ stand for the agent E delayed by t units of time and idle respectively. In addition, there are both weak and strong forms of binary choice.

$$\mathcal{E}^T \quad ::= \quad \mathbf{0}$$
$$| \quad \underline{\mathbf{0}}$$
$$| \quad A$$
$$| \quad \mathcal{E}^T[f]$$
$$| \quad \mathcal{E}^T \backslash R$$
$$| \quad \alpha.\mathcal{E}^T$$
$$| \quad (t).\mathcal{E}^T$$
$$| \quad \underline{\alpha}.\mathcal{E}^T$$
$$| \quad \mathcal{E}^T \mid \mathcal{E}^T$$
$$| \quad \mathcal{E}^T + \mathcal{E}^T$$
$$| \quad \mathcal{E}^T \mathbin{+\!\!+} \mathcal{E}^T$$

The semantics for TCCS consists of the rules for CCS with the addition of the following rules for timed expressions. We start by defining action rules for the new choice operators and agents which are idle:

$$\textbf{Sum}_1\textbf{op}\quad \frac{E \overset{\alpha}{\to} E'}{EopF \overset{\alpha}{\to} E'} \qquad \textbf{Sum}_2\textbf{op}\quad \frac{F \overset{\alpha}{\to}'}{EopF \overset{\alpha}{\to} F'} \qquad op \in \{+, +\!\!+\}$$

$$\textbf{Idle}_1\quad \frac{}{\alpha.E \overset{\alpha}{\to} E}$$

The timing rules now follow:

$$\textbf{Idle}_2\quad \frac{}{\underline{0} \overset{t}{\rightsquigarrow} \underline{0}} \qquad \textbf{Idle}_3\quad \frac{}{\alpha.E \overset{t}{\rightsquigarrow} \alpha.E}$$

$$\textbf{Time}_1\quad \frac{}{(t).E \overset{t}{\rightsquigarrow} E} \qquad \textbf{Time}_2\,\frac{}{(s+t).E \overset{s}{\rightsquigarrow} (t).E}$$

$$\textbf{Time}_3\quad \frac{E \overset{s}{\rightsquigarrow} E'}{(t).E \overset{s+t}{\rightsquigarrow} E'}$$

$$\textbf{TWSum}_1\quad \frac{E \overset{t}{\rightsquigarrow} E',\ F \nearrow t}{E + F \overset{t}{\rightsquigarrow} E'}$$

$$\textbf{TWSum}_2\quad \frac{F \overset{t}{\rightsquigarrow} F',\ E \nearrow t}{E + F \overset{t}{\rightsquigarrow} F'}$$

$$\textbf{TWSum}_3\quad \frac{E \overset{t}{\rightsquigarrow} E'\quad F \overset{t}{\rightsquigarrow} F'}{E + F \overset{t}{\rightsquigarrow} E' + F'}$$

$$\textbf{TSSum}\quad \frac{E \overset{t}{\rightsquigarrow} E'\quad F \overset{t}{\rightsquigarrow} F'}{E +\!\!+ F \overset{t}{\rightsquigarrow} E' + F'}$$

$$\textbf{TCom}\quad \frac{E \overset{t}{\rightsquigarrow} E'\quad F \overset{t}{\rightsquigarrow} F'}{E \mid F \overset{t}{\rightsquigarrow} E' \mid F'}$$

$$\textbf{TRes}\quad \frac{E \overset{t}{\rightsquigarrow} E'}{E\backslash L \overset{t}{\rightsquigarrow} E'\backslash L}$$

$$\textbf{TRel}\quad \frac{E \overset{t}{\rightsquigarrow} E'}{E[S] \overset{t}{\rightsquigarrow} E'[S]}$$

$$\textbf{TCon}\quad \frac{E \overset{t}{\rightsquigarrow} E'}{P \overset{t}{\rightsquigarrow} E'}(P \overset{\text{def}}{=} E)$$

The following rules allow proofs to be constructed whether or not an agent is capable of a given delay.

$$\frac{}{\underline{0} \uparrow t} \qquad \frac{}{\alpha.E \uparrow t}$$

$$\frac{}{(t).P \uparrow s} \ (s \le t) \qquad \frac{P \uparrow t_0}{(t).E \uparrow s} \ (s \le t_0 + t)$$

$$\frac{P \uparrow t}{P + Q \uparrow t} \qquad \frac{Q \uparrow t}{P + Q \uparrow t}$$

$$\frac{P \uparrow t, \ Q \uparrow t}{P +\!\!+ Q \uparrow t} \qquad \frac{P \uparrow t, \ Q \uparrow t}{P \mid Q \uparrow t}$$

$$\frac{P \uparrow t}{P \backslash R \uparrow t} \qquad \frac{P \uparrow t}{P[f] \uparrow t}$$

$$\frac{E \uparrow t}{P \uparrow t} \ (P \stackrel{\text{def}}{=} E)$$

B.3 Formal reasoning

B.3.1 Equivalences

In this section we collect together the various definitions for equivalence together, but start with some of the supporting definitions. Everything in this section is derived directly from Milner's book.

Definition 9.8 A binary relation $\mathbf{R}$ over some set Λ is an equivalence relation when the following hold:

1. $(E, E) \in \mathbf{R} \ \forall E \in \Lambda$

2. $(E, F) \in \mathbf{R}$ and $(F, G) \in \mathbf{R}$ implies $(E, G) \in \mathbf{R}$

3. $(E, F) \in \mathbf{R}$ implies $(F, E) \in \mathbf{R}$

Definition 9.9 A relation $\mathbf{R}$ over some set Λ is a congruence relation when the following hold:

1. $\mathbf{R}$ is an equivalence relation.

2. If $E \in \Lambda$ and E' is a subexpression of E and $E' \approx^c F'$ then $E \approx^c F$ where F is E with F' substituted for E'.

Definition 9.1 A binary relation, $\mathbf{R} \subseteq \mathcal{E} \times \mathcal{E}$, is a bisimulation if, whenever $(E, F) \in \mathbf{R}$, then for all actions $\alpha \in$ the following is true :

$$1) \ E \stackrel{\alpha}{\to} E' \text{ implies } \exists F' \bullet F \stackrel{\alpha}{\to} F' \wedge (E', F') \in \mathbf{R}$$

$$2) \ F \stackrel{\alpha}{\to} F' \text{ implies } \exists E' \bullet E \stackrel{\alpha}{\to} E' \wedge (E', F') \in \mathbf{R}$$

Definition 9.2 $E \sim F$ (E and F are strongly equivalent) exactly when there is a strong bisimulation $\mathbf{R}$ with $(E, F) \in \mathbf{R}$.

Definition 9.3 $\sim = \bigcup \{\mathbf{R} : \mathbf{R} \text{ is a strong bisimulation}\}$

$$E \stackrel{a}{\Rightarrow} E' \quad \text{means} \quad \begin{array}{l} E \stackrel{\epsilon}{\Rightarrow} E_1, \\ E_1 \stackrel{a}{\rightarrow} E_2, \\ E_2 \stackrel{\epsilon}{\Rightarrow} E' \end{array}$$

Definition 9.4 An observable counterpart, $E \stackrel{\hat{a}}{\Rightarrow} E'$, is defined to be a if $a \neq \tau$ else ϵ.

Definition 9.5 A binary relation, $\mathbf{S} \subseteq \mathcal{E} \times \mathcal{E}$, over agents is a weak bisimulation if, whenever $(E, F) \in \mathbf{S}$, then for all $\alpha \in \text{Act}$ the following is true:

1. $E \stackrel{\alpha}{\rightarrow} E'$ implies $\exists F' \bullet F \stackrel{\hat{\alpha}}{\Rightarrow} F' \wedge (E', F') \in \mathbf{S}$

2. $F \stackrel{\alpha}{\rightarrow} F'$ implies $\exists E' \bullet E \stackrel{\hat{\alpha}}{\Rightarrow} E' \wedge (E', F') \in \mathbf{S}$

Definition 9.6 $E \approx F$ are weakly bisimilar if there is a weak bisimulation $\mathbf{S}$ such that $(E, F) \in \mathbf{S}$.

Definition 9.7 $\approx = \bigcup \{\mathbf{S} : \mathbf{S} \text{ is a weak bisimulation}\}$

Definition 9.10 $E \approx^c F$ exactly when the following hold:
1. $E \approx F$
2. If C is a CCS expression involving E and D is the CCS expression obtained by substituting E for F, then $C \approx D$.

Definition 9.11 A binary relation, $\mathbf{R} \subseteq \mathcal{E}^{\mathcal{R}} \times \mathcal{E}^{\mathcal{T}}$, is a timed bisimulation if, whenever $(E, F) \in \mathbf{R}$, then for all actions α and delays t the following are true:

1) $E \stackrel{\alpha}{\rightarrow} E'$ implies $\exists F' \bullet F \stackrel{\alpha}{\rightarrow} F' \wedge E' \mathbf{R} F'$

2) $F \stackrel{\alpha}{\rightarrow} F'$ implies $\exists E' \bullet E \stackrel{\alpha}{\rightarrow} E' \wedge E' \mathbf{R} F'$

3) $E \stackrel{t}{\leadsto} E'$ implies $\exists F' \bullet F \stackrel{t}{\leadsto} F' \wedge E' \mathbf{R} F'$

4) $F \stackrel{t}{\leadsto} F'$ implies $\exists E' \bullet E \stackrel{t}{\leadsto} E' \wedge E' \mathbf{R} F'$

B.3.2 Equational laws

Milner defines a larger set of equational laws than were introduced in chapter 10. However, the set of laws collected in this section includes most of those in Milner's book and the reader will thus find some unfamiliar ones.

Laws for choice

CH1 $E + F \approx^c F + E$

CH2 $E + (F + G) \approx^c (E + F) + G$

CH3 $E + E \approx^c E$

CH4 $E + 0 \approx^c E$

Laws for prefix

PRE1 $\alpha.\tau.E \approx^c \alpha.E$

PRE2 $E + \tau.E \approx^c \tau.E$

PRE3 $\alpha.(E + \tau.F) + \alpha.F \approx^c \alpha.(E + \tau.F)$

Laws for constants

We extend agent expressions to include agent variables and use X, Y, Z as elements of this set. Thus we would now allow agent definitions of the form

$$X \stackrel{\text{def}}{=} a.X + \tau.b.X$$

Definition 10.2 Let E be any agent expression.

1. An agent variable X is *sequential* in E if it only occurs within prefix or choice operators in E.

2. An agent variable X is *guarded* in E if each occurrence of X in E is within some subexpression of the form $l.F$ of E.

The first law for constants say that constants are congruent with their definitions. The second law states that definitions containing variables may be used to prove the observational congruence of agents, providing that certain conditions are met.

CON1 If $A \stackrel{\text{def}}{=} E$ then $A \approx^c E$.

CON2 If

$$\begin{aligned}
\widetilde{P} &\equiv P_1, \ldots, P_n \\
\widetilde{Q} &\equiv Q_1, \ldots, Q_n \\
\widetilde{X} &\equiv X_1, \ldots, X_n
\end{aligned}$$

and if $\widetilde{P} = \widetilde{E}\{\widetilde{P}/\widetilde{X}\}$ and $\widetilde{Q} = \widetilde{E}\{\widetilde{Q}/\widetilde{X}\}$ then $\widetilde{P} \approx^c \widetilde{Q}$, where $\widetilde{X}$ is guarded and sequential in $\widetilde{E}$.

Laws for composition

COM1 $E \mid F \approx^c F \mid E$

COM2 $E \mid (F \mid G) \approx^c (E \mid F) \mid G$

COM3 $E \mid 0 \approx^c E$

Laws for restriction
Definition 10.1

$$
\begin{aligned}
sort(\mathbf{0}) &= \{\} \\
sort(l.E) &= \{l\} \cup sort(E) \\
sort(\tau.E) &= sort(E) \\
sort(E + F) &= sort(E) \cup sort(F) \\
sort(E \mid F) &= sort(E) \cup sort(F) \\
sort(E\backslash L) &= sort(E)\backslash(L \cup \overline{L})
\end{aligned}
$$

RES1 $E\backslash L \approx^c E$ if $sort(E) \cap (L \cup \overline{L}) = \{\}$

RES2 $E\backslash K\backslash L \approx^c E\backslash(K \cup L)$

RES3 $(E \mid F)\backslash L \approx^c E\backslash L \mid F\backslash L$ if $sort(E) \cap \overline{sort(F)} \cap (L \cup \overline{L}) = \{\}$

RES4 $E[f]\backslash L \approx^c E\backslash f^{-1}(L)[f]$

Relabelling laws
NB. The relabelling laws were not used at all in the text.

REL1 $E[id] \approx^c E$

REL2 $E[f] \approx^c E[f']$ if $f\rceil sort(E) = f'\rceil sort(E)$

REL3 $E[f][f'] \approx^c E[f' \circ f]$

REL4 $(E \mid F)[f] \approx^c E[f] \mid F[f]$ if $f\rceil(L \cup \overline{L})$ is one to one, where $L = sort(E \mid F)$ and $f\rceil L$ means f domain restricted to L.

The expansion law
The expansion law provides a means of relating certain types of agents defined in terms of parallel composition with observationally congruent agents defined in terms of sequence and choice:

EX

$$
\begin{aligned}
\text{If} \quad P &\equiv \prod_{i \in I} E_i\backslash L \\
\text{then} \quad P &\approx^c \sum\{\alpha.(E_1 \mid \ldots \mid E_i' \mid \ldots \mid E_n)\backslash L : E_i \xrightarrow{\alpha} E_i', \alpha \notin L \cup \overline{L}\} \\
&\quad + \\
&\quad \sum\{\tau.(E_1 \mid \ldots \mid E_i' \mid \ldots \mid E_j' \mid \ldots \mid E_n)\backslash L : \\
&\qquad E_i \xrightarrow{l} E_i', \ E_j \xrightarrow{\overline{l}} E_j', i < j\}
\end{aligned}
$$

The expansion law can be extended to include relabelling.
Corollary to the expansion law

CX1 $(\alpha.E)\backslash L \approx^c \begin{cases} 0 \text{ if } \alpha \in (L \cup \overline{L}) \\ \alpha.E\backslash L \text{ otherwise} \end{cases}$

CX2 $(\alpha.E)[f] \approx^c f(\alpha).E[f]$

CX3 $(E + F)\backslash L \approx^c E\backslash L + F\backslash L$

CX4 $(E + F)[f] \approx^c E[f] + F[f]$

B.3.3 Temporal logic

HML

The definitions for HML follow those of Stirling [Sti91].

$$P ::= tt \mid \neg P \mid P \wedge P \mid [a]P$$

$$
\begin{aligned}
&E \models tt \\
&E \models \neg A &&\text{iff } E \not\models A \\
&E \models A \wedge B &&\text{iff } E \models A \text{ and } E \models B \\
&E \models [a]A &&\text{iff } \forall E' \in S \bullet E \xrightarrow{a} E' \text{ implies } E' \models A
\end{aligned}
$$

E satisfies A, $E \models A$, iff $E \in \|A\|$ where $\|A\| \colon P \to \mathbf{P}S$ has the following definition:

$$
\begin{aligned}
\|tt\| &= S \\
\|\neg A\| &= S \setminus \|A\| \\
\|A \wedge B\| &= \|A\| \cap \|B\| \\
\|[a]A\| &= \{E \in S \mid \forall E' \in S \bullet E \xrightarrow{a} E' \text{ implies } E' \in \|A\|\}
\end{aligned}
$$

$$
\begin{aligned}
ff &\stackrel{\text{def}}{=} \neg tt \\
\langle a \rangle A &\stackrel{\text{def}}{=} \neg[a]\neg A
\end{aligned}
$$

$$\|\neg tt\| = S \setminus \|tt\| = S \setminus S = \{\}$$

$$\|\langle a \rangle A\| = \{E \in S \mid \exists E' \bullet E \xrightarrow{a} E' \wedge E' \in \|A\|\}$$

HML$^+$

Note that the use of the term HML$^+$ is non-standard and both logics are usually referred to as HML.

$$E \models [K]A \text{ iff } \forall E' \in S \bullet \forall a \in K \bullet E \xrightarrow{a} E' \; \textit{implies} \; E' \models A$$

$$[a_1, \ldots, a_n] \equiv [\{a_1, \ldots, a_n\}]$$

$$[-K] \equiv [T - K]$$

$$[-] \equiv [T]$$

The following rule extends HML to include timed properties:

$$
\begin{aligned}
E \; \models \; \{t\}A \text{ iff } &E \models A \; \vee \\
&(\exists E' \in S, t' \in \; \mathcal{T} \bullet E \xrightarrow{t'} E' \wedge t' \leq t \wedge E' \models A)
\end{aligned}
$$

Linear-time temporal logic

NB: The linear and branching time temporal logics were developed for teaching purposes and are not standard for CCS. Consult Stirling [Sti91] for the standard introduction to temporal logic for CCS; the linear and branching time logics defined here are a subset of that defined by Stirling.

$$P ::= \ tt \mid \neg P \mid P \wedge P \mid \ [K]P \mid \{t\}P \mid \mathbf{G}P \mid P\,\mathcal{U}P$$

$$\mathbf{F} \stackrel{\text{def}}{=} \neg \mathbf{G} \neg$$

The empty trace is represented by $\langle \rangle$ and concatenation of traces by st for all s and t in T^*, where T^* is the set of all traces (strings) over some action set T. We define a prefix ordering on strings in the following manner:

$$\forall s, s' \in T^* \bullet s \leq s' \ iff \ \exists s'' \in T^* \bullet ss'' = s'$$

With this new notation we can extend the satisfaction relation as required:

$$
\begin{aligned}
E \ &\models \ \mathbf{G}A \ \ iff \ \forall s \in T^*, E' \in S \bullet E \xrightarrow{s} E' \ \text{implies} \ E' \models A \\
E \ &\models \ A\,\mathcal{U}B \ \ iff \ \exists s \in T^*, E' \in S \bullet (E \xrightarrow{s} E' \wedge E' \models B) \\
&\wedge \ \ \forall s' \in T^*, E'' \in S \bullet (s' \leq s \wedge E \xrightarrow{s'} E'' \ \text{implies} \ E'' \models A)
\end{aligned}
$$

$$E \models \ \mathbf{F}A \ \ iff \ \exists s \in T^*, E' \in S \bullet E \xrightarrow{s} E' \wedge E' \models A$$

$$\bigcirc A \stackrel{\text{def}}{=} \langle - \rangle tt \wedge [-]A$$

Branching-time temporal logic

$$P ::= \ tt \mid \neg P \mid P \wedge P \mid \ [K]P \mid \{t\}P \mid \mathbf{G}P \mid P\,\mathcal{U}P \mid \mathbf{A}P$$

Assuming T^F to be the set of all finite traces,

$$
\begin{aligned}
T^\omega \ &= \ T^* \setminus T^F \\
T^\bullet \ &= \ \{s \in T^F \mid \exists E \in S \bullet \forall s' \in T \bullet \xrightarrow{s} E \wedge \neg E \xrightarrow{s'}\} \\
T^{max} \ &= \ T^\omega \cup T^\bullet
\end{aligned}
$$

$$
\begin{aligned}
E \ &\models \ \mathbf{AG}P \ \ iff \ \forall s \in T^*, E' \in S \bullet E \xrightarrow{s} E' \ \text{implies} \ E' \models P \\
E \ &\models \ \mathbf{EG}P \ \ iff \ \exists s \in T^{max}, \forall s' \in T^*, E' \in S \bullet (E \xrightarrow{s'} E' \wedge s' \leq s) \\
&\quad \text{implies} \ E' \models P
\end{aligned}
$$

$$
\begin{aligned}
\mathbf{AF}P \ &= \ \neg \mathbf{E}\neg \mathbf{G}P \\
\mathbf{EF}P \ &= \ \neg \mathbf{A}\neg \mathbf{G}P
\end{aligned}
$$

References

[Bai91] J. Baillie. A CCS case study: a safety-critical system. *Software Engineering Journal*, July 1991.

[Bar86] H. Barringer. Program logics – a short survey. Technical Report UMCS-86-11-1, Department of Computer Science, University of Manchester, 1986.

[Boe91] B. Boehm. Software risk management: Principles and practices. *IEEE Software*, 8(1):32–41, 1991.

[Bru91] G. Bruns. A language for value-passing CCS. Technical Report ECS-LFCS-91-175, Laboratory for the Foundations of Computer Science, Edinburgh University, 1991.

[BW90] A. Burns and A. Wellings. *Real-Time Systems and their Programming Languages*. Addison-Wesley, London, 1990.

[CK93] editor C. Kronlof. *Method Integration – Concepts and Case Studies*. John Wiley and Sons, 1993.

[Dil94] A. Diller. *Z: An Introduction to Formal Methods (2nd Edition)*. John Wiley and Sons, 1994.

[FC92] F. Moller and C. Tofts An overview of TCCS. In *Proceedings of Euromicro '92*, Athens, 1992.

[FH94] P. C. Fencott and B. Hebbron. The application of HAZOP studies to integrated requirements models for control systems. In *Safecomp '94*. Instrument Society of America, 1994.

[Gar86] S. J. Garland. *Introduction to Computer Science with Applications in Pascal*. Addison-Wesley, 1986.

[Hen88] M. Hennessy. *Algebraic Theory of Processes*. The MIT Press, Cambridge, Mass., 1988.

[HL94] M. Hennessy and H. Lin. Symbolic bisimulations. Technical Report, Computer Science, University of Sussex, 1994.

[Hoa85] C. A. R. Hoare. *Communicating Sequential Processes*. Prentice-Hall, Hemel Hempstead, 1985.

[Jon90] C. B. Jones. *Systematic Software Development Using VDM (2nd Edition)*. Prentice-Hall, 1990.

[LG89] M. Locker and G. Griffiths. Alsett : Towards an educational ipse. *Software Engineering Journal*, July 1989. Alsett was the original name for Ascent.

[Mil89] R. Milner. *Communication and Concurrency*. Prentice-Hall, Hemel Hempstead, 1989.

[Mol92] F. Moller. The Edinburgh concurrency workbench (version 6.1). Technical Report User Manual, Laboratory for the Foundations of Computer Science, University of Edinburgh, 1992.

[Mor90] C. Morgan. *Programming from Specifications*. Prentice-Hall, 1990.

[MT89] F. Moller and C. Tofts. A temporal calculus of communicating systems. Technical Report ECS-LFCS-89-104, Laboratory for the Foundations of Computer Science, Edinburgh University, 1989.

[Par87] J. Parrow. Submodule construction as equation solving in CCS. In *Proceedings of Software Technology and Theoretical Computer Science*, Lecture Notes in Computer Science, Oxford, 1987. Springer-Verlag.

[PCFP94] M. Lockyer, S. J. O'Brien, P. C. Fencott, A. J. Galloway and S. Pearson. Formalising the semantics of Ward/Mellor essential models using a process algebra. In *Formal Methods Europe '94*, Lecture Notes in Computer Science, Oxford, 1994. Springer-Verlag.

[PCFT92] M. Lockyer, P. C. Fencott and P. Taylor. The integration of structured and formal notations for real time systems specification. In *Methods for Information Systems Design*. Pergamon Press, 1992.

[Plo81] G. D. Plotkin. A structured approach to operational sematics. Technical Report DAIMI-FN-19, Aarhus University, 1981.

[RB92a] D. Simpson, R. Bosworth and S. English. Concurrency clichés. Technical Report UBC 92/5, Department of Computer Science, Univeristy of Brighton, 1992.

[RB92b] D. Simpson, R. Bosworth and S. English. The dining philosophers. Technical Report BPC 92/3, Department of Computer Science, University of Brighton, 1992.

[RCS89] J. Parrow R, Cleaveland and B. Steffen. The concurrency workbench: A semantics based tool for the verification of concurrent systems. Technical Report ECS-LFCS-89-83, Laboratory for the Foundations of Computer Science, Edinburgh University, 1989.

[Sch93] Z. Schreiber. Implementing process calculi in C. Technical Report DoC 93/5, Department of Computer Science, Imperial College, 1993.

[Sem91] L. Semmens. Using Yourdon and Z: An approach to formal specification. In J. Nichols, editor, *Proceedings of the Fifth Annual Z User Group Meeting*, Workshops in Computer Science, Oxford, 1991. Springer-Verlag.

[Sti91] C. Stirling. An introduction to modal and temporal logics for CCS. *Lecture Notes In Computer Science*, (491):2–20, 1991.

[Tof89] C. Tofts. Timing concurrent processes. Technical Report ECS-LFCS-89-103, Laboratory for the Foundations of Computer Science, Edinburgh University, 1989.

[Wal89] D. J. Walker. Automated analysis of mutual exclusion algorithms using CCS. *Formal Aspects of Computing*, 1, 1989.

[WM85] P. T. Ward and S. J. Mellor. *Structured Development For Real-Time Systems*. Prentice-Hall, Hemel Hempstead, 1985.

[You89] E. Yourdon. *Modern Structured Analysis*. Prentice-Hall, 1989.

Index